THE PANORAMA OF MODERN LITERATURE

THE
PANORAMA
OF
MODERN LITERATURE

CONTRIBUTED BY THIRTY-ONE
GREAT MODERN WRITERS

With an Introduction by
CHRISTOPHER MORLEY

Garden City   New York

DOUBLEDAY, DORAN & COMPANY, INC.

MCMXXXIV

PRINTED AT THE *Country Life Press*, GARDEN CITY, N. Y., U. S. A.

Acknowledgments

THANKS are due the following firms and individuals for permission to use material mentioned:

Pearl S. Buck, and the *Woman's Home Companion* for "The Frill," copyright, 1933, by Pearl S. Buck.

Doubleday, Doran & Company, Inc., and the authors or their representatives for "American Names" from *Ballads and Poems* by Stephen Vincent Benét, copyright, 1927, by Stephen Vincent Benét; "The Night Visitor" from *The Night Visitor and Other Stories* by Arnold Bennett, copyright, 1929, by Doubleday, Doran & Company, Inc.; "Night on the Great Beach" from *The Outermost House* by Henry Beston, copyright, 1928, by Doubleday, Doran & Company, Inc.; *Typhoon* by Joseph Conrad, copyright, 1902, by Jessie Conrad; "Mild Oats" from *Collected Sketches and Lyrics* by Noel Coward, copyright, 1931, 1932, by Noel Coward; "The Horror of the Heights" from *The Black Doctor and Other Tales of Terror and Mystery*, by A. Conan Doyle, copyright, 1913, by Lady Jean Conan Doyle; "Fräulein" from *They Brought Their Women*, by Edna Ferber, copyright, 1932, by Edna Ferber; "The Shadowy Third" from *The Shadowy Third and Other Stories* by Ellen Glasgow, copyright, 1916, by Ellen Glasgow; "The Palio at Siena" from *Along the Road* by Aldous Huxley, copyright, 1925, by Doubleday, Doran & Company, Inc.; "The Old Trouper" from *Archy and Mehitabel* by Don Marquis, copyright, 1927, by Doubleday, Doran & Company, Inc.; "On a Balcony" from *Harbours of Memory* by William McFee, copyright, 1919, by William McFee; "Off the Deep End" by Christopher Morley, copyright, 1928, by Christopher Morley; "The Vicar of Lynch" from *Trivia* by Logan Pearsall Smith, copyright, 1917, by Doubleday, Doran & Company,

Inc.; "The Fascinating Stranger" from *The Fascinating Stranger and Other Stories* by Booth Tarkington, copyright, 1922, by Booth Tarkington; "The Man with the Red Beard" from *The Ringer Returns* by Edgar Wallace; "The Silver Mask" from *All Souls' Night* by Hugh Walpole, copyright, 1933, by Doubleday, Doran & Company, Inc.; "The Flowering of the Strange Orchid" from *The Short Stories of H. G. Wells;* "The Smile That Wins" from *Mulliner Nights* by P. G. Wodehouse, copyright, 1931, by Pelham Granville Wodehouse.

Harper & Brothers for "Sonnets" from *Fatal Interview* by Edna St. Vincent Millay, copyright, 1931, by Edna St. Vincent Millay.

Henry Holt & Co. for "The Home Town of the Army Ants" from *The Edge of the Jungle* by William Beebe, copyright, 1921, by Henry Holt & Co.

Sinclair Lewis for "Dollar Chasers," copyright, 1931, by Sinclair Lewis.

The Macmillan Company for "Flammonde" from *Collected Poems* by Edwin Arlington Robinson, and "The Seekers" from *Poems*, 1929 edition, by John Masefield.

The *New Yorker* and the authors for "The Garter" by Dorothy Parker (also by permission of The Viking Press); "The Vanderbilt Convention" by Frank Sullivan; "Interview with Daisy" by E. B. White; "The Greatest Man in the World" by James Thurber, and "It's All Wrong" by Ogden Nash.

T. S. Stribling for "The Mating of Pompalone," copyright, 1925, by T. S. Stribling.

The Viking Press, Inc., for *Amok* by Stefan Zweig, copyright, 1931, by The Viking Press, Inc.

Contents

viii   Contents

Introduction

"HERE is offered, Benign Reader" (so the Elizabethan preface-writers used to begin) "matter of sundry sorts and to content divers humors. I hasten to participate them to your judicial views; and stand ever your Lordship's most dutiful and desirous to please you."

In some such manner, like a waiter letting off the champagne-cork with a resounding pop, stewards in the literary dining saloons of the 16th or 17th century, introduced their great platters of meat and mirth. I wish the modern spokesman had available such concisely pungent rhetoric. Like the gateway or porter's lodge of a Tudor mansion, the ornamental preface led the way inward. You'd find Miss Clara Gebert's anthology of *Elizabethan Dedications and Prefaces* a delightful work if you're interested in literary manners. (University of Pennsylvania Press.) And the book business then wasn't very different from now: e.g. Lyly's preface to *Euphues* (1579) which remarks, "We commonly see the booke that at Christmas lyeth bound on the Stacioners stall, at Easter to be broken in the Haberdasshers shop." The haberdasher, evidently, took the part of the modern drugstore.

All this has little to do with the volume in hand, except that it was in my mind that from the days of Caxton to now the Omnibus volume has been a favorite resource for the publisher and a thrifty pleasure for the reader. It plays the same excellent rôle in literature that the delicatessen shop does in housekeeping. How tempting a miscellany of neatly packaged provenders, ready for urgent appetite or freakish taste. Perhaps omnibus is not quite a romantic enough word. I like to think of a book of this sort as a sort of excursion steamer or Fall River Line boat. You see it pulling out from the pier towards dusk, brilliant with lights and crowded with the most unexpected passengers. Those cheerful vessels are famous, or notorious, for casual and agreeable encounter. So here likewise you will find all sorts of human various. From Dorothy Parker's garter or Don Marquis's trouping cat to the deplorable neurosis of the Vicar of Lynch; from Conrad's Typhoon to Mr. Wodehouse's comedy, there is no mood that will not find its requirement in print. I speak without full acquaintance, for I have seen only the publisher's tentative list of contents, and have had nothing whatever to do with his choices. And I am embarrassed also, for I note in the prospectus a small relic of my own. But I hope I need not therefore seem disinterested toward so generous an assortment. Like Doctor Watson, who seemed to Miss Mary Morstan "cold and distant in the cab" when he drove her home on a famous occasion, I can be honorably frigid toward that one passenger without discrediting the romance of hansom cabs in general.

The Omnibus or Excursion Steamer volume serves the difficult economics of the printer's trade by giving a great deal of pleasure at incredibly low cost. The reader, I sometimes think, has the same peculiar privilege as the customs inspector who goes down the bay in a revenue cutter to board the incoming liner. The whole great company of travellers pass before him in file with their baggage declarations; he can mark what he will for detailed examination and he obtains a most surprising synopsis of mortal doings. Here, like a great ship crowded with goods and personalities, lies the book at anchor before you.

The best sort of introducer is the one who does not remain on the stage to weave his fingers while better men are speaking. After his brief words he is wise to retire into the body of the hall and join the audience. That sagacious publisher, the late Frank Doubleday, when his printing plant was being built, discovered that the architects were scheming an ornamental portico which he thought would detract from the simplicity of the building. Without saying anything to anyone he removed the blue-prints from the workroom and hid them. So here: if there were any plans for a more elaborate preface, they've been lost. Famous vintage does not need a fancy label.

CHRISTOPHER MORLEY.

THE PANORAMA OF MODERN LITERATURE

Sinclair Lewis

DOLLAR CHASERS

"THERE must be some quite decent people in America. You know—people who were born in England," said Lionel Trudgeon.

Adrian Smallways complained, "Quite! But after all, why discuss it? Doubtless, America does exist. So do tripe and the collected works of Anatole France. But need one disturb one's digestion by mentioning them at dinner?"

"Because I think I shall go there."

"My dear fellow," Adrian whimpered, "I know you have courage. Otherwise you couldn't have faced the world at Lady Sibyl's teas after having written a novel like *Hop Scotch*. But why, to speak seriously, waste courage on America, where they shoot down people on Fifth Avenue every hour? I give you my word, an American acquaintance of mine told me that he had been shot himself, and many of his friends were often shot."

"Nonsense!" began George Fountain, but Lionel interrupted him:

"I must go. I must increase my sales. *Hop Scotch* is my best novel, and yet the miserable Americans have bought only thirty-five thousand of it. And even in Great Britain it has done seven thousand! Quite my best book. I am sure that if I go over there and lecture, I can— oh, I'm not so naïve as to suppose I can make the dollar chasers appreciate my book, but I can create so much personal interest that they will at least buy a hundred thousand or so."

"Have you ever lectured, anywhere—ever spoken in public?" asked George Fountain.

He was in Parliament, though Parliament was scarcely conscious of it as yet, and his speeches on the coördination of home spinning and electrification were celebrated throughout the constituency of Upper Twitching.

"I speak? Publicly? Certainly not! I am, I trust, a gentleman!" said Lionel, perhaps too trustingly.

"Then how——"

"My dear fellow, all one has to do is to stand up and raise one's voice! I don't like to have to go over and inspire the beastly Americans. For all I care they may rot—or is it stew?—yes, of course it is—they may stew in their own juice. But as to being able to do it—why, my dear fellow, I'm not dumb, am I? I'm able to speak a bright word or two in postprandial chat, am I not? I have been heard to hold forth a bit at the club on occasion, n'est-ce pas?"

"You have!" groaned Fountain.

"Then that's what I shall do publicly."

"Lionel is quite right," pronounced Adrian Smallways, with the authority of chief book reviewer for the *New Olympus*, and author of *Lyrics of Lesbos* and *A Brief Suggestion for the Assertion of a British Protectorate over Poland and Russia*. He quavered: "Doubtless, Lionel's hosts, or his lecture agent, or whatever they call the beastly fellow, will be able to protect him from the gunmen and press men and what not. Priestley and Chesterton have come home safe, and if they escaped, why not Lionel? Its an admirable notion, after all. And one must think of one's duty, mustn't one? Here's this vast country, America, with no art, no universities you could call universities, no scholarship, no manners; all this illiterate horde longing for the enlightenment that Lionel can bring them. He ought not to be deaf to a call like that. And before I forget it, Lionel, insist that they pay you at least a thousand dollars a lecture; they're quite able to, and it's a virtue to spoil the Egyptians."

"Oh, Lord, I suppose you'll go," sighed Fountain. "Whenever you see a Briton with a wistful Rossetti look in his eyes, he's going either to have his tea or lecture in America. But if you do, my dear fellow, don't be too instructive. I see chaps—Americans—about the House. Some of them are rather informed. Been in Russia—that sort of thing, you know."

"Nonsense! Of course the Americans are sensitive to the slightest bit of criticism. They wail over it like children. But they long for it," Smallways gave judgment. "They wouldn't respect you if you didn't treat them firmly. They simply slaver with delight over some chap strong enough to tell them what dollar chasers they are."

"I'm not entirely sure," said Fountain. "I say, how would the English like it if some American came here lecturing and told us that in all our Indian policy we have been guinea chasers?"

"Like it? My good worthy Fountain, in the first place, can you imagine the English being such fools as to gather in large, gaudy numbers in a stuffy hall to listen to any American author lecturing about anything? Even if they liked his books, which is manifestly improbable, can you imagine more than two curates and one imbecile child caring a hang how the fellow looked, how he wore his nose, or how he expressed his opinions about bobbed hair and the government?"

"No, that is the one entirely obvious superiority of the British to the Americans," Fountain admitted.

"And second," snarled Smallways, "if any such wandering mountebank of a foreigner dared publicly to express his disapprobation of our policy in India or elsewhere, we should merely politely hand him his visa and kick him out in five hours. If he should dare! The mere thought of any Yankee criticizing us makes me indignant! But we wouldn't be sensitive. No, thank God, no Englishman ever minds it in the least if you criticize him or his country. We're too superior, to speak frankly. We're not puerile, like the Americans. But this is beside the point.

"The point is that the Americans love the rod that chastises them. See how much they endure from their own writers, men like Morton Norton, who, for all his crude and boisterous journalese, does at least refuse to boost, does knock the Americans about. And, Lionel, if you really are so courageous as to dare risk being shot down in the middle of a lecture, you must not fail to interest them, to make yourself popular, by giving them a thoroughly good insulting.

"But don't commit the error of merely continuing the old and familiar insults. By now everyone knows the truths—and of course they are truths—that no American male animal, unless he has lived in England for years, thinks of anything save making money. That he talks of nothing else. That he is no sportsman and, though he sometimes manages to win from us at golf and tennis and polo, he cares for nothing but the winning. That though we saved their country from invasion by the Germans, they have not been willing to contribute even money—and heaven knows they contributed nothing else. That they speak a comic imitation of moorland Yorkshire——"

"They do rather, don't they?" bubbled Lionel. "A perfectly moldy English. I say, did you see that perfectly priceless bit in *Comedy* last week? Two professors, from Yale or Harvard or one of those schools, are excavating in Assyria. One bright laddie—they were both too simply too, with their vast spectacles under their sun helmets—one stout fellow murmurs to the other, 'Say, bo, if this yere kink what we're yanking out of this old hick cemeterry could shoot his face off, I just reckon to bet he would cer'nly talk awful queer English that eddicated guys like you and me couldn't hardly savvy!' Too quaint!"

"Quite," continued Adrian. "But that obvious hideousness of American life has been adequately emphasized—not that we have been able to impress them, but we have done our duty. No, you must have a new message, such as Bernard Shaw's splendid theory that the trouble with Americans is that they're all villagers."

Fountain protested, "But it isn't true. It's the English who are villagers. Every Englishman believes that everything is completely right in his own village—which may be Piccadilly or Sub-Fribble on the Esk—and that everything outside it, everything foreign, is utterly wrong. The real trouble with the Americans is that they are too far from the soil, too urban——"

"The trouble with the Americans is that they review books by English authors in so flippant and familiar a manner," said Lionel.

"The trouble with America is that it is ridden by evangelicism instead of obeying the Church of England," said Mrs. Fountain, who up to this time had not——

"The trouble with America is that the children are so dreadful—so noisy, so raucous, so disrespectful to their parents," said Mrs. Trudgeon, who hadn't either.

"The real trouble with America is that they have no history, no tradition. I am informed that there isn't in the entire land a building erected before 1820," said Mrs. Smallways.

"But as I was saying," shrieked Adrian Smallways, snatching again at the whirling wheel of the conversation, "you must—— What the deuce does it matter whether the Americans really are villagers or not? What does that mean, anyhow? Nothing! We're not talking of a reasonable and scholarly criticism, such as one would deliver in England. We're finding something that will stir up the American animals."

"I'll stir them!" beamed Lionel Trudgeon. "They'll remember me!"

II

Lionel Trudgeon, novelist, was born in Cumberland, just below the border of Scotland. It is one of the few unquestioned discoveries of scholarship that all countries start with grim, sturdy, hard-minded men in the north and proceed through amiable but mediocre people, like farmers and sculptors and grocers, to the southern border, along which the citizens are invariably gay, melodious, witty and very indolent. It is doubtless this fact which enabled the Lord to fix national boundaries in the beginning of history and caused Him to command us to keep them forever just as they are.

In the north of Sweden, therefore, the folk are hardy, silent and fond of swimming after seals; while in the south they are gentle and given to literature and the manufacture of matches, entirely on behalf of brightness. Cross a few miles of Baltic Sea, and these fascinating phenomena are repeated. It is known to every amateur ethnologist that all Northern Germans are stern and oppressive while the Southern Germans, especially the Bavarians, are fond of drinking beer and dancing in short leather pants, and in wartime slay the enemy only in the spirit of pleasantry. Again cross one inch of border and you come instantly on the Northern French, a stalwart race entirely in contrast to the short, round and jolly people of Provence.

Cross from Provence into Italy, and immediately you are among that tall, severe, typically northern folk, the Lombards, so different from the trifling but kindly Italians of the south. Regarding Africa, in turn, I cannot say, as my atlas is up in Vermont, that Northern state so different from—well imagine a Coolidge in Mississippi!

Thus had Lionel Trudgeon been born a few miles to the north, he would have been born a Southern Scotsman, very genial, but as he was born in most northern England, in Cumberland, he was grim, he was a very man of granite, though you might not have guessed it from his aspect, since he was a dark little man, rather thin, with bilious eyes and a mouth with such depressed lines beside it that it resembled a bracket wearily lying on its side.

His being reet Coomberland explained everything. If a chirping London hostess was offended by his blatting, "You don't know what you're talking about," he explained that it was his Cumberland forthrightness. If a man at the club seemed insulted, it was Lionel's Cumberland humor, which no soft and witless Southern Englishman could understand. If he delayed in paying a bill, it was his Cumberland sturdiness, which kept him from being done by tradesmen.

Indeed, Lionel's boyhood had been hard. If he had not gone on, to the age of forty-one, being heroic about it, one would have felt sympathy for those parched years of studying in a flinty schoolhouse under a drunken master, of writing little stories for blurry little magazines to make his way through the two years he had at the University of Birmingham before he staggered hungrily to London and Fleet Street.

Because of his early poverty, he hated Oxford men and Cambridge men and Sandhurst men, he hated Mayfair and pretty women in shining frocks and men who wore evening clothes as though they were not evening clothes and people who laughed without waiting to hurt some one. He was anti-English—except when he was with Frenchmen or Americans or Tibetans or such like inferiors, when he became more acidly English than a Duke or even a naturalized Polish Jew. Because he hated London, and because he enjoyed hating, he rarely left it. And because he was sour and dour and suspicious, he wrote novels that were full of gamboling and buttercups and quaintness and sly good humor, of adventurousness and loud-singing companions on the highway and quantities of beer and limericks on benches under jolly inn-signs.

He was the author of *Maypole, Buns and Barley Water, 'Twas Brillig, Bonnie Bonnets, The Celestial Rucksack, The Best Butter*, the new novel, *Hop Scotch*, and a smaller volume, *How the Capsule Thought Method Made a Novelist of Me*. This last has had a circulation of 1,237,000 copies and has been commended by Lieut. General Sir Tipley Strobe, by the Administrator-General for the island of M'Gomba, and by the King of South Arabia, and may be obtained free (enclose 1½d. for postage) from C.T.M., Ltd., The Strand, London.

So great is Lionel's influence that his publishers estimate that, as a result of reading *The Celestial Rucksack*, no fewer than 16,722 persons have been inspired to take walking tours averaging 6.21 days each. Lionel's own and only walking trips have been two, the longer of which, studiously undertaken to obtain material for his book, lasted from six A.M. to four P.M., when it began to rain. Ordinarily, except for two weeks at Floating Nautilus

Terrace, Littlehampton, every summer, he spent all his nights and laborious days in his house in St. John's Wood, London, a tall, thin, tarry house with a little mussy grass, seven delphiniums, and a monkey-puzzle tree in the garden.

None of his books were historical novels, not even *Bonnie Bonnets,* for all its misleading title. That opus concerned a jolly bunch of boys and girls, with a jolly daddy and mammy, living in a jolly glade in Cumberland, who used to play at being Bonny Prince Charlie and followers. Indeed, Lionel was very strong against historical novels. He wrote mean things about them in the *New Olympus.* There was enough romance today, he said, without going back to the past.

Besides going back to the past would have required his sitting in the British Museum and researching, which meant dressing and Lionel did like huddling in slippers and bathrobe.

He had a philosophy. Very definite. The trouble with today was that we had let slip from life the color that his misguided rivals tried to supply with silly historical romances. That wasn't the way to do it at all. We must restore. Restore maypole dancing on the green. Restore silk tights and cloaks and the Charles I version of ten-gallon hats, plus feathers. Wear swords and be zealous to protect our honor.

Not that Lionel in private life would have been quite sure which end of a sword to use.

And drink lots of beer and be happy, no matter how much it hurt.

Lionel was eager to let the Americans in on his philosophy, though he doubted whether they could understand it, like the citizenry of such bright traditional places as Leeds and the Durham mining towns and the slums of London.

His books had all done well in America. He was neither rich nor poor, though he was decidedly the former in conversation at literary parties, and the latter with his publishers. In England, aside from the vogue of *The*

Celestial Rucksack among earnest young people given to morning calisthenics and playing harmonicas all over the landscape, he was unknown, so unknown that he was gruffly meek even before Adrian Smallways.

Young ladies from America who came over, on an average of seven a day, to interview the literary celebrities of Great Britain for the home newspapers yearned to English acquaintances, "And now tell me! Where can I reach Lionel Trudgeon? Where is his house? I just know he lives in a darling thatched cottage on some darling village green."

"Trudgeon? Trudgeon? Oh, is he the bloke that writes the Diddle Diddle Dumpling novels? I didn't even know he had a house. Shall we have a spot of tea?"

III

Young Mr. Pete Carr, Editor and author-snatcher for the firm of Grimsby and Horn, New York, was innocent. He had been merely a crime and police reporter for the newspapers and he knew little of the dangerous rackets of authorships. He had, in a year with Grimsby and Horn, found that American authors are hard-boiled; that all they wanted, besides front-page reviews, entirely laudatory, was large advances, enormous royalties, and having their hands held whenever they quarreled with their wives or lost their shirts on the stock market.

But he was certain that English authors were different. That Oxford-cloister, dreaming-downs, soft-footfalls-of-the-ghost-of-Hardy atmosphere—oh, they had tradition and gentleness, those boys, thought Pete, and he came rejoicing on his first trip to London, to look about and steal joyously what authors he could from other firms.

It did not occur to his innocence that he might have difficulty in keeping his own.

He was so green that he went to the Royal Grand Imperial Hotel, which is fully as modern as a hotel in

Kalamazoo. The walls of its black and silver barroom are all in triangles and zigzags, and the bartender, formerly of the Nineteenth Hole Club, New York, is the inventor of Our Lindy cocktail. Pete, who had eyeglasses but could box, had a suite with a satinwood bed and ninety towels in the bathroom. It was swell.

Now older American author-snatchers when they go to London avoid the Royal Grand Imperial. They go to one of the good old family hotels, like Smith's or Jones' or Robinson's, where you bathe in tin tubs, if at all, and where the room waiter is likely to be found curled under the round table with the ink-spotted turkey-red cover in the living-room, dreaming of his younger days in the Crimean War. That is in order to impress English authors with the poverty of the firm. A suite at the Royal Grand Imperial has been known to inspire the author of a book on dahlias to demand £10,000 advance on his next book—on The Tall Beardless Iris.

Settled in his suite, realizing that though the cocktails were dearer than in a New York speakeasy and not quite so good, yet you could order them anytime, Pete looked forward to many happy, long, long hours discussing Proust with the English authors.

The first visitor announced from below was Mr. Lionel Trudgeon, a Grimsby and Horn author who was known at the Firm as a "regulation thirty-six, ready-made and safe to order in small quantities." But Pete had no such commercialized notions. He was thrilled. Golly! Perhaps Mr. Trudgeon would go on a walking trip with him! Pete saw them sitting together in a taproom of blackened oak, while Mr. Trudgeon smilingly told him legends of the strange peasant folk. He was at the door, hand effusively out, when Mr. Trudgeon knocked.

"This is a great pleasure!" Pete caroled.

Lionel looked at Pete's hand as though it were an obscene postcard offered by a vendor in Paris; he took it and dropped it, as though it weren't funny enough or dirty enough.

"Oh. Thanks so much. How much had *Hop Scotch* sold in America on the day you left?"

"Why, I don't know, exactly."

"You don't know? Really! I thought you Yankee publisher chaps kept track of every copy and every penny!"

"We try to, but—— I should think it'd sold about 23,000."

"Is that all? Um. Very curious. Don't quite understand it, I must say. I was told that Grimsby and Horn were so enterprising and that sort of thing. At least we ought to be able to expect that of them, now oughtn't we! Well, will it go 30,000?"

"Why, I hope so. We're doing our best."

"But really! Really! One doesn't have an American publisher merely to do his best, now does one! You can scarcely expect to have English authors, you know, I mean pukka English authors, if you merely do your best, as you would with an American author, now can you! Will it go 25,000?"

"Oh, I'm almost sure——"

"You don't mind if I sit down, do you, Carr?"

"I was just about to ask you——"

"Oh, it's quite all right, quite all right, my dear fellow. We all expect to be informal and get rid of our idiotic English propriety with Americans, you know, and make them feel at home. Now, Carr, I have an idea, and I think I'll have you arrange the details. I shall go to America and lecture. Particularly on American authors. Tell your good people what they are really like. I shall want a thousand dollars a lecture, but do you think I ought to demand expenses also?"

"Whee! That's a lot of money, Mr. Trudgeon."

"A thousand? in America? Come, come, my dear fellow, don't be commercial! After all, we are supporting you by our war loan payments, you know, and if a chap is to endure the boredom of going to your country, the least you can do is to express your appreciation, don't you think? Come, come! I understand a lot of your countrymen read nothing but the magazines, and such drivel as Morton Norton, instead of the classics and Walpole and Priestley and Maugham and myself. I'll jolly soon put an end to that! So you think I ought to demand expenses, also?"

"Listen, Mr. Trudgeon, honestly—— Would you like a drink?"

"At this time a day? Really! I'm afraid I don't enjoy getting drunk daily, like you Americans! And expenses?"

"Listen, Mr. Trudgeon. I wonder if you realize that America has had quite a lot of lecturers lately? They haven't all gotten away with it."

" 'Gotten away with it'! What a jolly expression! So carefree. You know—like buffaloes. My word, I often think it a pity that our English tradition of scholarship makes it impossible for us to depart from the rigidity of correct speech. I don't at all mind the American jargon. I rather enjoy it. You were saying?"

"Well, I want a drink, anyway. I need one!" As Pete rang, he fretted, "Now please get this!"

" 'Get this'! Oh, delightful!"

"There's been a lot of lecturers over lately who came on their own, without getting asked very hot, and a lot of 'em have been flops."

" 'Flops'! I must remember that."

"And a lot of the visiting firemen have had to do regular vaudeville stunts to get over. They go back home and tell the home folks what wows they were in the sticks——"

"Really, Carr, would you mind translating?"

"Waiter! Two highballs—whisky and sodas, I mean. Make mine a triple, and hustle it. . . . Mr. Trudgeon, I've never told you about the time I took part in the Cicero raid, have I? Curious, I don't really think that hop-head looked like you."

"Carr, if you don't mind my saying so, I'm quite at sea."

"I understand. So sorry, Mr. Trudgeon. Just talking

to myself. Bad habit I've had ever since I took to the use
of heroin, at the age of six."

"How terrible!"

"Yes. Isn't it! And I thought I was cured. But there's
something about the London climate that seems to make
me want to go back to the habit—or something. But as I
was saying, being translated: A great many of the distinguished gentry who lecture in America return to their
homes and give the impression that they have been giving
the heathen the low-down—the higher messages about
Beowulf and the Atharva Veda and——"

"Ah! You know something of literature? Really!"

"No. I don't. Probably I did when I took my Ph.D.
But then I went democratic, and now all I know is four-
alarm fires."

"Oh yes, yes, yes, I see. Quite!"

"And as I was saying: As a matter of fact, the only
way some of these magnificos got over in the States was
by persuading Clarence Darrow to debate with them on
the evils of short skirts—one flop, sudden death, winner
to choose his side of the debate."

"But really——!"

"No, it's no longer a pipe. But of course, if you want
to go, I'm at your service. Mr. Grimsby told me to give
you his particular regards. I can get in touch with
Charley Beaseley, the lecture agent. But I wish you'd
think it over."

"Quite. Tell this Beaseley that I can't consider less
than a thousand, no matter how much he urges. He's not
to try to do me in, you know! You're a Yankee, too; you'll
know how to handle him. Oh, thanks. A little more soda,
please."

"I am going to America. Though why this beastly firm
can't sell my books over there without urging me to come
over and help them——!" said Mr. Lionel Trudgeon to
Mrs. Lionel Trudgeon.

"Shall I be with you, dear?" asked Mrs. Trudgeon.

"You shall not be with me, dear!" said Mr. Trudgeon.

Pete Carr said nothing about it until he dined with
George Fountain, three nights later.

"I know how you feel about our Lionel, Mr. Carr,"
said Fountain. "But you take him more seriously than
most of us do. He is no more typical of the English than
the man who shouts 'We won the war' in the Savoy Grill
is typical of America. But there are just enough Lionels
to make it hard for the rest of us. I wish some novelist
would do him."

"No decent novelist would touch so nasty a subject,"
said Pete, morosely.

"When my voice is heard in Parliament," sighed Fountain, "which will probably be three general elections after
the Millennium, I shall ask the Governor a question, to
wit: why does Downing Street go to the trouble of sending
a wise and tactful ambassador to Washington, and then
—when poison is so cheap—permit all our good will to be
ruined by some itching volunteer like Lionel? But really,
that's the proof that you Americans are provincial—that
you take the Trudgeons seriously! The same?

IV

It is the new rule and the new mystery. A Russian
countess escapes from Russia two jumps ahead of the
bayonets and comes to America to lecture. A German admiral who defeated a British admiral comes to lecture
about defeating the British admiral, who is simultaneously
lecturing about defeating the German admiral, and their
orbits cross at Terre Haute, and they have a drink of
gin together, with their feet up on a hotel bed, and
secretly snicker.

A Hindu gets in wrong with the British authorities
and comes to lecture about it, and on the program next
Thursday—three P.M., Gold Ballroom of the Golightly

Hotel, tickets at the Dauphin Piano Company—he will
be followed by a British authority who will explain that
all Hindus are crazy.

A Czech who speaks no language save Berber and
North Malaysian lectures on Eskimo art, in both his
languages, and a Cuban pelota player addresses three
thousand cheering members of the Omaha Athletic Club.
An Irish poet lady, whose last volume had two reviews—
"Pleasant Verse," Cork *Examiner;* and "8vo., 126 pages,
5/6, privately printed," Belfast *Post*—lectures to three
hundred and seventy assemblies, winding up in Carnegie
Hall, New York, with Mayor Walker, Stephen Wise,
Edna St. Vincent Millay, and Bishop Manning on the
platform.

And all the while there is an adequate native mass
production of lectures by baseball players, anti-prohibi-
tionists, authors, Rotarians, Admiral Bryd, champion
fly-casters, advocates of cremation, gentlemen who talked
last night with the ghost of Cicero, the only dentist living
West of Denver who has flown the Atlantic backwards
while playing solitaire, and modern educators who believe
that teachers, books, schools, and children should all be
abolished in the interest of free expression of the ego.

The mystery is not why the lecturers come, but why
the audiences come.

A probable explanation—which I shall present in a
lecture tonight before a joint meeting of the Stamford
Amateur Firemen's Sodality and the Parent-Teacher
Association—is that all Americans, but particularly
American women, are the greatest believers in the world.
Now if you believe anything long enough and hard
enough, you get tired of it, and want something new,
preferably something utterly contradictory, and the
gaudiest new messages and new thoughts and new gram-
mar are to be found in lectures.

The really nice, normal, wholesome woman listens in
turn to a Socialist, a Communist, who explains that the
only scoundrel worse than the capitalist is the wishy-
washy Socialist, a labor union official, who makes it clear

that all politics is idiotic and that what we need is more unions, the president of the birdcage trust, who confesses that he is in business only to benefit his employees, and finally a liberal clergyman who reveals that all these economic struggles would be immediately settled if we only loved one another more. After each of these illuminations she goes home to her husband and explains that she was fooled the time before, but now she understands it all.

To supply the retail trade in this edification and inspiration business, there exists a class of jobbers known as "lecture agents."

A lecture agent is a combination of insurance salesman and wet nurse.

For a year or so he sends out gaudy circulars, picturing potential lecturers wearing dress suits, Greek uniforms, or polar expedition parkas. He sells the goods—usually long. He swears that each lecturer is witty, possessed of melodious and far-reaching voice, and guaranteed to keep sober during lecture hours. He hopes that he is betting right on two out of three of these specifications. He rarely is.

When the lecturer arrives, the agent meets him at the dock, persuades him to be interviewed, persuades the reporters to interview him, rushes him off to a hotel, gives him the address of a bootlegger, lends him fifty dollars, puts him to bed to sober up, then returns to the office to figure out by what route he can send the lecturer from Mankato, to Yankton, South Dakota, to Columbia, Missouri, all in three days, and still work in a stop at Bangor, Maine.

He charges twenty-five per cent. commission.

Insurance companies decline to insure him at any rate.

The lecture agent to whom Grimsby and Horn turned over all their troubles—which is the trade name for authors—was Charles Beaseley. He was a tall, thin man, as melancholy as a preacher's dog. His hobby was mushrooms, because mushroom cellars were so cool and quiet and free of celebrities.

To Mr. Beaseley came Pete Carr, of Grimsby and Horn, just returned from England, and he said bitterly, "I have another author for you to tout."

"Well, I hope he's better than your Greek countess who eloped with the night clerk just before the one big lecture date I had for her!"

"You didn't get stung with her any worse than we did! We found out she wasn't a Greek countess—she was a Polish forger, and helped her father manufacture black horse-hair watch-chains—she wrote that book *The Grecian Art of Dancing* by taking the encyclopedia articles on Greece, art and dancing, and combining them. No, this bird is the real thing—Trudgeon, that wrote *Hop Scotch*."

"Book any good?"

"How would I know! I'm too busy writing ads for our books to read 'em."

"I've seen favorable reviews."

"Oh, the reviewers haven't read it either. They don't keep it long enough. They get a pint of gin for every unsoiled two dollar and a half review copy. Still, I do know some reviewers that are so scrupulous that when they're reviewing a book, they're careful to drink only the gin that came from that particular book. But *Hop Scotch* must be all right. Ernest Boyd roasted it."

"Can Trudgeon talk?"

"And how!"

"Well, I'll see what I can do."

"Say, Charley, when an Englishman highhats you for your inferior culture and manners and shoes, what do you do?"

"Why, I look at him soulfully, with all my American provincialism and naïveté in my boyish face, and I say the Americans and Britishers are cousins, ain't we, and he nods regretfully, like one author hearing another praised. Then I ramble on:

" 'But of course a stronger bond between the two coun-

tries than even our common language is our newness.
England has been civilized for only a thousand years—
since the Scandinavian Normans invaded you and took
charge of the real Britons and taught them to bathe—
and America, even along the Atlantic seaboard, has been
civilized for only four hundred, whereas, of course, Italy
has been civilized for more than two thousand years,
Greece, five thousand, Egypt, perhaps ten thousand.
Those wise old nations, how they must laugh at the rawness of the British and Americans, and of couse that
makes your simple and homey folks and us long to stick
together, doesn't it!"

"You'd be surprised, Pete. These few friendly words
make an Englishman choke up with rage so he can almost
never explain that he doesn't long to do any sticking-
together whatever!"

Upon the announcement that Lionel Trudgeon was
coming to America to lecture, the sale of *Hop Scotch*
went up to forty-two thousand, and with murder in his
heart, Pete Carr prepared advertisements informing the
rejoicing public that at last they would be able in person
to see the sunny face and hear the rollicking voice of him
whose sprightly romance and joyous optimism had—
especially in these days of sordid realism—lifted the
burden from so many heavily laden spirits and shown
them the flower-starred path back to happy childhood.

Pete actually wrote that way.

Every one at the speakeasy commented on his bad
temper these days.

V

There were not many celebrities on the R.M.S. *Corybantic* this time—only eighteen sons of dukes who were
hoping to get jobs on Wall Street, a few ex-kings of
Greece, an explorer who had the novel notion of writing
a book about the trip he had made to the Arctic before
he had made it, and Lionel Trudgeon. There wasn't a

single senator to tell the boys that he had been all over
Europe and found it full of conditions and tendencies.
In this vulgar company, Lionel stood out, and it was for
him that the ship news reporters headed when they raced
aboard at Quarantine, at eight-thirty in the morning.

Since six o'clock he had been waiting for them, in the
Etruscan Lounge, in a large Hawaiian chair under the
portraits of Walter Raleigh and Lord Beaverbrook.

All the way over he had been composing and learning
by heart an interview which, he earnestly hoped, would
satisfy the appetite for insults of even the Americans.

As the reporters came up to him, Lionel looked at them
like a wounded doe, and said, "Yaas?"

"Is this Mr. Trudgeon?"

"It is."

"We're from the newspapers."

"I'm afraid you must blame that on yourselves, not on
me!" He laughed. That was a funny one. But it didn't
really seem to go so well with the reporters, whose leader
said blankly:

"May we ask you a few questions?"

"You mean you wish to interview me?"

"It's often called that."

"But why should any one wish to interview me?"

"We don't! The city editor told us to."

"Oh!"

This interview wasn't going at all the way he had
planned it. The reporters didn't know their parts. And
they looked slightly irritated. He hastened to stand, wave
them to chairs, and say with playful tactfulness:

"Really, I'm just a humble, unknown scribbler, like
yourselves, but if I can raise you in the esteem of your
superiors, and if I can—I know the great American
public craves for inspiration and instruction, and if I
can give you any helpful messages, I shall be glad."

He thought they looked a little glassy-eyed, rather
drowned and soggy, but one of them spoke briskly
enough:

"What do you think of the present-day flapper, Mr. Trudgeon?"

Lionel perched gracefully on a chair-arm and spoke with all the lightness of a lecturer on taxation, shaking his cigarette holder at them:

"The trouble with your query is that it is shallow. The flapper, even your American flappers who get drunk every night, cannot be explained without understanding that she does not stand alone. She is the endproduct of a wider condition, of the fact that in America there is, of course, no longer any family life whatsoever. While I have never been so fortunate as to be here in the States before, I have been authoritatively informed that the most interesting fact about the Americans is not their lawlessness, their universal violence, their constant drunkenness, but the fact that the love of parents for their children has now almost completely disappeared.

"Mind you, I am not criticizing. This fact, in which I am sure all you gentlemen will concur, may be for the best. Doubtless in the past there has been too much family tyranny. I shall merely say that in England, with our old-fashioned domesticity, we simply should not care for that sort of thing.

"It's because of this that you have your gin-crazed young girls, your innumerable young man of good family and university training who become what you call gunmen, and these dreadful American children who scream and fight and never obey their parents. Again, however, let me hasten to repeat that I am not criticizing—I just want the Americans to understand their own civilization —because it is of course, one kind of civilization.

"And quite akin to the disappearance of domesticity is the fact that Americans do not—I won't say they can not but certainly they do not—care at all for flowers and gardens. I believe that a few of your great millionaires are able to create gardens by importing English gardeners, but over there, of course, even those of us who are not wealthy make and love our own wee plots. I wish you could see mine! It's doubless just old-fashioned lack of what you call pep, but personally I prefer working in my garden on my—my delphiniums, for example, to guzzling spirits.

"Have I made myself clear, gentlemen? Do you see this need of a deeper, more fundamental criticism? Is it clear?"

The *Trumpet* reporter remarked, "Oh, quite clear!" with what seemed to Lionel a gratifying enthusiasm.

"What do you think of American writers and readers, Mr. Trudgeon?" asked the Coagulated Press reporter. He was such an innocent young man, with fine flaxen hair. Lionel looked at him pityingly as he pontificated:

"American writers? There aren't any! I mean, worth serious critical consideration. I shall explain that in my lecture this afternoon. Will you gentlemen be present?"

"Oh, sure!" gurgled the innocent C. P. man. "We ship news reporters always go to afternoon lectures."

"I shall be pleased. Doubtless you will find tickets at the door, but I should advise you to get them early this morning, as I understand there will be a large attendance. And about American readers now. I should be the last to condemn them. They have been very kind to my own poor efforts. . . . I don't know whether you will find this an interesting item of news, but if you care to know, I have been informed by wireless that my *Hop Scotch* has now passed 50,000 in sales. . . . But American readers——

"Well really, if you will pardon my English forth-rightness, I'm afraid I shan't be able to emulate your unctious American politicians in flattering the press, and the trouble, you know, with American readers is that they don't read! They buy books, but only so that they may leave them about to impress the neighbors. I am credibly informed that not one in ten of the books you find in any American home has ever had the pages cut!"

"One in ten?" said the C. P. man.

"Yes, one in ten."

"That's very interesting," murmured the *Evening Falcon* reporter.

"Yes, isn't it. And you can see its significance. I'm sure

we shall all be glad to play up to it heavily," beamed the
Chronicle man.

"I'm very pleased!"

Poor Lionel!

Let it not be thought that the impartial heart of his
historian is altogether sympathetic toward the young
gentlemen of the press, and as a rock, a chill and granite
rock, toward the bright idiocies of Lionel. Though a man
invite himself into a den of smiling catamounts when he
might have stayed home and taken his catamount cries
over the radio, yet can one but be sorry for him as the
swift beasts, still smiling and purring, take their leap.
It is a world of grief and misinformation, and though it is
to be suspected that only by sin and ignorance does any
man ever get into a position where he must endure being
interviewed, yet one must pity him.

In the days when fiction was still fiction and not merely
a footnote to the Census Report, the authors used properly to end a chapter, "Little did our hero think that
before night came down, he would encounter the most surprising and distressing adventures."

Well, little did Lionel think either.

Poor Lionel!

Lionel did not see the skyscrapers from his steamer, for
the interview lasted till the *Corybantic* was tucked into
her dock. The reporters continued to be gratifyingly
interested in all opinions. It was the first time in his life
that any one had been particularly interested in any of
his opinions, and Lionel, pleased by these polite though
necessarily American and uneducated young men, was
delighted to help them by giving them all his wisdom.

He explained that all American women boss their husbands in a manner which no Englishman would endure.
That Prohibition had not been altogether a success. That
Canada was just north of the United States and contained Montreal and other cities. That much of American slang is different from the lecture-room speech of an

Oxonian philologist. That cricket is considered sport. That all Americans hustle—that the citizen of Dakota as he leaps into the subway after a day in his office on the sixtieth story is thinking only of night clubs, and not of the serener and more cultured things of life.

But he allowed the Americans some democracy and a good deal of willingness to learn from Europe, and he accepted a cigar, which the Coagulated Press man gave him with more gratitude and enthusiasm than seemed necessary.

"No," said the *Trumpet* reporter to the younger C. P. man in the subway, "you are wrong. You haven't been doing the ship run as long as I have. Trudgeon isn't worse than most of the visiting English author-lecturers. He's just about average. It started with Dickens and Matthew Arnold. They were four times as unpleasant as this little man; Dickens because he had so much more imagination, and Mat because he had actually a book.

"And don't, please don't, forget the golden-hearted Continentals. No Englishman ever exposed our cannibalism and idol-worship more richly than that jolly old Russo-German, Count Keyserling, and no Scotsman ever tried to vend so little oratorical ability for such large fees as the profound Franco-Belgian, Monsieur Maeterlinck. No, Eddie, you're wrong. When you start doing ship news, you think you've encountered the world's worst cranks, society climbers, publicity grabbers, and grouches with your first Ark-load. But there's always more and worse ones. . . . I wonder if the wife would like me to bring Lionel's hide home with me, when I finish my story? It would look nice as a rug in the sun porch."

VI

Lionel was pleased, as he rode away from the steamer pier in a taxicab with Pete Carr of Grimsby and Horn, and Charles Beaseley, the lecture agent. For the quarter

of New York near the docks was as unkempt as the
mining-camp settings he had seen in movies. Rheumatic
brick houses, with graceful old doorways now greasy and
splintered, crouched like blank old men beside the cement
walls of warehouses. A freight train, unguarded, ran
through a street of mouldy laundries and groceries and
chop-suey joints above which were tenements with torn
bedding hanging on rusty fire-escapes. The streets were
fluttering with torn paper, dusty with ashes, stale air and
hopeless and cruel.

"A terrible country!" said Lionel, happily. "And where
are these notorious high buildings?"

They came up on the elevated speedway and Lionel
looked out on the Empire State Building, a tower of silver
in the morning sunlight, tall with the terrifying tallness
of a mountain. Behind it he saw the crags, like the Dolo-
mites, of the Chrysler Building and the Lincoln and the
Chanin.

"Good God!" he cried. He turned on Beasley and Pete.
He said informatively, rebukingly, "Why, they are tall!
And really rather beautiful!"

"No?" said Pete. "What do you think, Charley?"

"I suppose they really are. I hadn't looked at it that
way," mused Beasley. "By the way, Mr. Trudgeon, did
it ever occur to you that an even greater bond between
England and America than our language is our common
rawness? Now Italy with its twenty-five hundred years of
culture——"

Even in his rage at Beasley's ignorance and provincial
impertinence, Lionel continued to stare out of the taxicab. He admitted that most of the men on Fifth Avenue
were not wearing tan shoes with top hats. Many of the
shops seemed luxurious and even clean. There was no one
openly wearing a revolver or carrying a machine gun, and
many of the jaws had a stillness which would indicate that
their owners were chewing neither gum nor tobacco.

It was confusing and a little vexing. He would have to
revise parts of his lecture for that afternoon. But the
hotel suite to which they were taking him would, in its

Babylonian and vulgar luxury, undoubtedly give him new jeers with which to delight his hungry audience.

He was again disappointed and put upon. The suite to which Beaseley and Pete conducted him, and which looked down on the slightly motheaten wilderness of Central Park, had neither a gilded ceiling, a hand-painted picture of a nude, a private bar, nor any of the other quaint extravagances he had seen in cinema presentations of high life in New York. The walls were gray, the furniture was of maple, rather simple and apparently comfortable, and the only picture in all the suite was an etching.

In fact, it was too restrained.

Lionel did like the English style of having nice things about, such as a hundred or two signed photographs of acquaintances, nine or ten silver boxes, with ivory elephants and carved wooden bears and glass pussies and papier-mâché models of the Coliseum at Terra Regis and amber fish and plaster Taj Mahals and amber fish and a rack with sixteen pipes. But one couldn't have everything when he was roughing it, and he said to Pete tolerantly, "Not at all in bad taste, you know."

"Thanks," said Pete; and "Can you endure some more interviews? The literary young ladies will be after you."

"Personally, my dear Carr, I detest publicity. I am not opinionated. I do not venture to fling out sensational statements, nor indeed any statements except in regard to such few things as I know authoritatively and completely, such as how to write novels and plays and essays. And poetry, of course. But as you are my host, I shall bow to your wishes, no matter how unreasonable they may seem to me privately, and try to get what publicity I can for your publishing house, and by the way, it seems to me a bit strange, you know, that your managing director, your Mr. Grimsby—well, on my first visit to your dratted country, he might have met me at the dock!"

"Terribly sorry, Mr. Trudgeon, but he had a conference with Morton Norton this morning."

"But my dear fellow, this Norton person is merely another American author!"

"I know, Mr. Trudgeon, but he's an awful sympathy-grabber and dollar chaser. After all, how can you expect him to have the restraint and unselfishness and culture of an English author?"

"That's true, of course."

"And Mr. Grimsby will be calling on you this morning. And I trust that you will care to come to my apartment —the most important critics in New York will be there— for dinner and a small party this evening."

"Oh Lord, why must you advertising chaps exhibit me like a pet bear? I begin to understand my friends who have yielded to the Yankee urging and lectured in America—I understand their saying that there is always, everywhere, here, a simply too intolerable intrusion on one's privacy. But as you have already arranged this affair, of course I'll do what I can to help you."

Through all this conversation, Charles Beaseley had been answering the telephone and one would add, were it not a tautology, doing Lionel's lying for him.

No, Mr. Trudgeon could not address the Dry Fly Casting Association of Harlem, tomorrow, because he was going to California.

No, Mr. Trudgeon could not deliver even a few remarks to the Higher Light Brotherhood of Los Angeles, because it was improbable that his lecture trip would ever take him to California.

Yes, Mr. Trudgeon would be tickled to death to be interviewed by the literary editor of the Metuchen *Recorder*.

No, Mr. Trudgeon would be unable to spend the week-end with Dr. and Mrs. Sylvester Cowen of Redding Ridge, even though their daughter, Gladys, did write poetry.

Yes, Mr. Trudgeon had all the insurance he wanted and, no, he was not interested in being handed twenty-seven per cent. a year on a guaranteed investment.

No, Mr. Trudgeon was not related to the Trunjons of Arkansas, despite the similarity of names. Mr. Trudgeon

was of an old French family and the name was originally
spelled Tresor. No, his hero, Peter Smiling, was entirely
fictitious, and not modeled on Paul Smelly of the South
Bend Baseball Team. Not at all. Delighted to give you
any information I can. Why, this is the secretary—Mr.
Trudgeon himself is in conference with his publisher,
Mr. Grimsby. So Sorry. Not at all. Good day.

Yes, Mr. Trudgeon would like one case of Scotch, one
case of gin, two bottles each of French and Italian. Charge
that to my account—Beaseley, West Thirty-seventh.

No, Mr. Trudgeon would not care for any insurance
and anyway, he has raging encarditis.

No, he's gone out for the day.

At first Lionel listened to Beaseley on the telephone
with amusement befitting an English gentleman noting
the quaint customs of the native tribesman. Then he became irritated.

"I say," he drawled——

He didn't really drawl it. "I say" is hard to drawl. You
can do better with "Oh!" But in the epic story about himself which constantly, every waking second and a good
many sleeping ones, Lionel Trudgeon was telling himself
about himself, he narrated now, " 'I say,' drawled the
quietly humorous author, amused by the antics of his 'lecture agent,' and realizing that he, i.e. the author, was the
heir of Dickens not only in his art but also in his experience among American bounders."

"I say, Beaseley, it's awfully kind of you to take charge
of the telephone for me, but really, you might occasionally ask me about these giddy decisions I'm supposed to
be making!"

For the first time, Charles Beaseley did not sound respectful:

"Trudgeon, if I'm to continue your lecture trip—which
is by no means stated in the Constitution—you must permit me to handle it, and to protect you from pests. For
some reason that is not at all clear to me, there are a great
many people who wish to meet you. They would exhaust

you, and make it impossible for you to continue lecturing. I happen to know my game. At least, Grimsby and Horn and a few other publishers seem to think so. Now do you wish me to go on handling you, or don't you?"

"Why, my dear fellow, of course! And for the life of me, I don't see why you should be so irritated. And just landed—— Oh, do what you will! Good God, I'm not human! I have no privacy! I shall not be permitted to say anything I really think! Do what you like!"

Lionel was rather on the wailing side, while to himself he was thinking, "Why these American beggars should be so touchy is something I simply cannot conceive! We let them into the War beside us, didn't we? And why they cannot speak to a chap like a gentleman would—is something that, I suppose, will always be beyond the ken of an English University man. Well, *courage, mon brave!* After all, my Uncle Percy lived out those last sad years among the Zulus!"

Poor Lionel!

Lionel was, while Pete and Beaseley disappeared into the bedroom, from which came tantalizing sounds of a call to Room Service and then of a cork, interviewed by a gurgling but not very juvenile lady reporter.

She asked him whether he didn't think that cooking wasn't as important as poetry—at least lots of times, you know how I mean, of course leaving out Edna Millay and, oh you know—that many males prefered flappers with pretty but vapid faces to women with more character and learning, that the farmhouses of Nebraska were sometimes less charming than those of Essex—Lionel had never been in Essex—that Joseph Conrad was quite a good writer, that Rome fell because the Roman gals wore one-piece bathing-suits, and that his, Lionel's, books carried the moral that the eternal human spirit was more important than automobiles.

Lionel agreed, in each case.

Then the news-reel photographers and sound magicians arrived.

For one minute Lionel told the 67,800,000 persons of his potential American audience (and that would make a lot of money, even at fifteen per cent. royalty) that he liked their country, and that all Englishmen and Yankees were brothers under the skin, and that New York had a large population.

He also gave interviews to the editor of the *International Jewish News*, the editor of the *Anglo-Catholic Harbinger*, the American correspondent of the Praha *Wassistdann*, and six special writers of whom one would get his copy into the Sunday papers.

He was tired after it and very happy.

Lionel Trudgeon had sense enough to know that poor little rich America was yearning for the culture that only such persons as he could bring. He was sorry for the Americans. Really. He was willing to do almost anything for them, even to invite select representatives of them to dinner in London, providing he need not live in their ghastly land. (But just to dinner once, you understand; cordial and all that sort of thing, as one would invite a Hindu or an acrobat, but not involving one's self, you see how I mean.) He saw that he, almost alone, had come here understanding the really rather pathetic Americanos. Yet until now he had been modest. He had—he continued in "The Romantic Story of a Cumberland Boy," as told, night and day, by Lionel Trudgeon to the admiring fancy of Lionel Trudgeon—he had, until now, supposed that British lecturers so popular as Hugh Walpole and John Cowper Powys had rather cornered the Yankee market. But, moment by moment, he saw that it was he alone whom the natives needed. . . . You know; sort of Kipling and Yeats-Brown thing; natives turning to the pukka District Magistrate for succor.

And why had he been chosen by their charmingly childish minds as almost a god?

It was because Walpole and Powys, or so he had been told, seemed almost to accept many Americans as being of their own caste. They did not insult? What idiots! How, then, could the natives accept them as proper superiors? It was he, Lionel Trudgeon, who had discovered, all by himself, that the Americans doted on being insulted, and so already, three hours after his arrival, he was the King George, the Lindbergh, the Al Capone of American culture!

Superb!

So, wearied though he was by his sacrifices to America, Lionel glowed as he sat down to luncheon with Simeon Grimsby, president of Grimsby and Horn, publishers, at the De Peyster Club.

Mr. Grimsby was not quite like any of the Americans of whom Lionel had formed so perfect a picture. These ideal and standardized Americans were of three sorts: old and chin-whiskered and funny; middle-aged and plump and horn-spectacled and funnier; and young and noisy and completely obnoxious. True, neither Pete Carr nor Charles Beaseley nor any of the people whom he had met on the steamer or at his hotel had completely fitted into the pigeon-holes of this theory but, Lionel thought wittily, it's the exceptions that prove the rule.

But he was bothered by Mr. Simeon Grimsby.

Mr. Grimsby was tall and slim, with a little white mustache. He looked like a retired British General—not that Lionel knew so many British generals so very intimately. He neither said, "Waal, I swan, I'm really tickled to see you," as rustic Americans always did, nor yet "Say, gee, kiddo we're cern'ly putting over the old novel for you," in the manner of the even more comic modern Yankee. He said, in fact, "Do you mind a sherry and bitters instead of a cocktail?"

It was quite the best sherry Lionel had ever tasted. Sherry. Yes. That was a splendid notion. Quite British. He would get in some sherry when he got home.

Then, quietly, with all that St. John's Wood manner which no American can ever imitate, Lionel purred:

"It seems to me perfectly beastly to bring in these business matters at a gentleman's luncheon, but I have to go out on this perfectly beastly lecture jaunt and I shall be so little in New York and—— The fact is, sir, that I should like to talk to you about my next book."

He really did say "sir" to Grimsby, American though the man was. He hoped Grimsby appreciated it, but he was never quite sure for Grimsby seemed scarcely flattered as he droned:

"I should be very happy to. . . . Do you like the clam chowder?"

"That's what it is? A bit strange, don't you think? Oh, but admirable, admirable, I'm sure! . . . Frightful ordeal with the reporters this morning. Thank Heaven, one escapes that sort of thing in London. . . . And as I was saying, I should like to discuss my new book."

"What is it to be, Mr. Trudgeon, if I may ask?"

"A book about America. 'Babylon,' I am calling it."

"That's very interesting. But didn't you land only three hours ago?

"Quite. But I have ten thousand words of it done. On the steamer. And the title—that I had six years ago."

"I am sure it will be very interesting. But isn't it a bit early to discuss it?"

"No, because—— Mr. Grimsby, let us be frank! I realize that in business no Englishman, however clever, is the match for any American, however vulgar. Let us admit that, at the beginning, and save such a very great deal, shall I say, of hypocrisy and that financial fencing which is so distasteful to an Englishman! I mean to say, the kind of unappetizing bickering you must have with a man like Morton Norton. So shall we just say that on this next book I am to have an advance of £10,000— $50,000, I believe you call it, in your country—with twenty per cent. royalty from the beginning, and $35,000 advertising guarantee?"

Mr. Grimsby ate his clam chowder slowly.

Lionel was disappointed. It seemed to him that Grimsby lost, spoonful by spoonful, his resemblance to an English general; indeed it seemed to him that when Grimsby spoke, after an intolerable pause, he showed a levity unworthy of a serious literary discussion:

"Mr. Trudgeon, I realize, of course, that we need to know what you think of us, of America. I realize that the very best thing for America would be to import Stanley Baldwin or Lloyd George or MacDonald, after their brilliant solution of all British difficulties, and have them show us how to run this country. But, you see, we are commercialists. I, for example, would like to see my firm pay its stockholders and its employees. I am afraid I have no real literary sense. I realize that the works of Lionel Trudgeon, with their enticing picture of English highroads, are needed to save America from its crassness. Yet so commercial am I that really, I do not see how we can afford to lose more than a hundred thousand a year, even on your books. May I suggest that you see some other and more authentically literary publisher?"

And it is a fact that so viciously commercial did Grimsby continue to be that in the end Lionel was able to get only a beggarly $10,000 advance, fifteen per cent. to fifty thousand, and no advertising guarantee.

It was with a sour mental stomach, as well as the accumulated weariness of his services this day to American letters, that he arrived at the Bach and Schützenverein Hall for his lecture, at three in the afternoon.

VII

Lionel had landed so late in the morning, he had been so pestered by people ever since, that he had no chance to see the afternoon papers before he appeared for his first lecture.

He was sorry, too.

He had never seen an American newspaper, but they must be very amusing, with their news about gunmen and their advertisements of chewing gum and their too utterly quaint notions of what was happening in Europe.

But duty called, and no Englishman has ever yet shirked his duty.

So, with that quietness of Essex Gardens, Lionel

climbed into a taxicab with Pete Carr and Beaseley and, a bit bothered as to what he was to say for an hour, but certain that whatever he said would be of value to his audience, he permitted himself to be taken to the hall.

Suddenly he was a bit afraid.

There might be two hundred people there. His fee was a thousand dollars, and even Americans would scarcely pay more than five dollars—a guinea!—apiece, even to hear an English novelist. But how could he talk to two hundred people? He had never in his life talked to more than twelve, and most of the twelve had interrupted him and insisted on doing their own talking. Good Heavens! He had not quite realized that a lecture tour included lecturing!

They left the taxi at a small door on Thirty-eighth Street.

An elderly woman, gray and beautiful—really, if she hadn't been an American she might have been a lady—was standing at the small door. It was raining, and she held an umbrella over her.

She dashed out to the taxicab and, as Lionel wriggled out—leaving his helpers to pay the fare—she said, "Is this Mr. Trudgeon? I was sure it was! I am the chairman for this afternoon."

Lionel let her hold the umbrella over him.

She led him down a bleak hallway to the room where lecturers wait—the Condemned Cell, Beaseley called it. The room was tastefully furnished with a pitcher of water, a glass, and one chair. Lionel took the chair.

The lady chairman introduced him to a type of American new to him, and very refreshing—the kind who adequately appreciated England. She was of a Cook's Tour age; she used a lorgnon; and her voice was like the water that comes down at Lodore.

"Oh, please keep your seat, Mr. Trudgeon. It's such an honor to meet you. When I heard you were going to lecture, I said to my husband, 'Oh, I do hope I'm going to have a chance to meet him.' But he doesn't appreciate lectures, or literature either. He's crazy about his golf.

I often say I'm a golf widow! But he does love England as I do. I just love England. We've been there a great deal. We often go there in summer. We stay at the Royal Grand Imperial in London. It's such a lovely hotel, don't you think?"

"Oh, admirable!"

"But as I often say, people—don't you detest these tourists who just see the surface of the country and all —and as I often say, people that only know London don't know England at all. My husband and I get out and motor all over—in England, I mean. We often stayed at the Crown and Anchor in Rye. Of course you know Rye."

"Rather," said Lionel, who didn't.

"Do you by any chance know Mrs. Essington-Blatt there?"

"I'm afraid I don't."

"She's such a lovely person—so talented. Oh! You must know St. Vincent Orelay, who writes for the *New Politician*."

Lionel did. Mr. Orelay had roasted all of his books. He said with all the joy of a toothache, "Oh yes, quite!"

"He's a great friend of ours. It was so curious, our meeting him. We were on a train, it was a smoking compartment, an English train, I mean, and there was such a nice-looking gentleman opposite us, I thought to myself, 'My, I would like to meet him,' but of course I'm so accustomed to England, I didn't do what a lot of crude Americans that haven't traveled would do, I didn't speak to him, and pretty soon he said to my husband, 'Have you a match?' and so we got to talking, and come to find out, he was St. Vincent Orelay, and so he became a great friend of ours—he came to have dinner with us in London, and I said to him, 'Mr. Orelay, I hope you won't think I'm one of these gushing Americans, but it is a great privilege to have you for dinner!'"

"Yes, rather!" said Lionel.

"I do hope you're going to enjoy your American tour. But I'm afraid you're going to find us pretty crude, Mr. Trudgeon. Not like England. Why, the trouble I have getting my husband to dress for dinner evenings when we haven't guests——! But I mustn't keep you. I just wanted to tell you how splendid we all think it is of you to take the trouble and come here, and I just do hope you'll rebuke this awful American dollar chasing!"

"Thanks so much," said Lionel, as one who talks in his sleep.

And then he was led out on the platform, and went quietly crazy.

He was facing not two hundred but two thousand persons, some of them male.

He felt naked.

But Englishmen get used to anything, even curry, and after five minutes, during which the lady chairman was whispering to the audience that Mr. Lionel Trudgeon combined the quaintness of Dickens with the learning of Philo Vance and the oratorical powers of William Jennings Bryan, he had recovered his nerve so completely as to be able to look up at the balcony, which was flowery with the adoring eyes of literary ladies. And he arose and began the first of those lectures which were to make history:

"Since I landed in America, I have been asked my opinion of American writers so many times that, in all humility, I venture to give you a brief view of how they appear to us in our doubtless dusty isolation in England.

"I have been astonished, ever since I was first privileged to gaze upon the magnificence of your geat buildings from New York Bay, by the number of enterprising journalists who have asked me what I thought of the style of So-and-so or of This-and-that. Now if I may say so without being impolite, none of your writers, not one —and I speak from many years of laborious experience as a poor, driven book-reviewer——I mean to say:

"Your writers have many bounteous gifts. They have vigor, a charming though rather rustic humor, cleverness in what you call 'plots.' They are so fortunate as not to be cursed with the complexities of our older civilization. They are simple. They are blessed—and I say this in praise, not in disparagement—in not even suspecting that there are deep, subtle, distressing aspects of life beyond money-making, lassoo-throwing, and what you call 'cuddling.'

"Why should they not be satisfied with these gifts of the gods and not demand also qualities denied them by your lack of tradition?

"Style? What do I think of their style? The style of American writers? why, my dear friends, what do I think of the egg of the Unicorn—a mythological monster. What do I think of tax rates in Ultima Thule? What do I think of the pet poodle of Jack the Giant Killer? 'Style,' my dear friends, is a quality which can come only from a long tradition, like that of England. It mirrors castes and kings, wars and lamentations, high honor and indurated misery such as you, my friends, are fortunate enough not to have experienced.

"The style of Ernest Hemingway, forsooth!

"Mr. Hemingway is a very bright young man. Had he stayed home in Idaho or Menominee or whatever raw virile state he had for the scene of his birth, he might have written something surprisingly like real literature—of a sort; something I might have admired. But this young man, crude and beautifully strong, actually dares try to present the old and languorous passions of Paris and of Spain. Also Italy, or so I am told. It is as though a bookish and perhaps too effetely English bookman like myself were so bold as to try to express your American prowess—in novels, I mean.

"And the others? Hergesheimer? Michael Arlen imitating Conrad! Cabell? An incompetent Hewlett. Tarkington? Oh, his 'Penrod' stories are amusing enough, but when he tries to be serious as in 'Ethan Frome,' he becomes heavy. He should leave that to the English. Dreiser? A Bavarian peasant in dinner clothes. Lewis? a mere propagandist; a shrill and humorless scold who thinks to reform the world by nagging. Miss Cather? Admirable only so long as she sticks to her native Swedes of Montana."

What he said then about the other writers cannot be printed in these chaste pages, for Lionel became more and more exhilarated and instructive as he saw that people, and so many people, were really going to listen to him for an hour without once interrupting him to snap "Nonsense!" He forgot to be cautious. He said what he really thought, which, like being hanged, is interesting even when it is scarcely safe.

He noted that the young gentlemen and ladies below him at the press table were making notes with passion and speed.

He was a success! He was as great in lecturing as in writing. By tomorrow he would be a sensation throughout America.

He was.

Lionel was encouraged to turn from artistic inspiration to more fundamental helps to the American people, to a correction of their shaky philosophy of life:

"There is a great deal of nonsense talked about democracy. My American friends naïvely tell me that they are democratic because they regard themselves as no better than their chauffeurs. But I, being an Englishman, simply do not trouble to think, ever, whether I am better or worse than my chauffeur. The undemocracy lies in being so self-conscious as to set the chauffeur outside one's self and stand off and look at him coldly and consider whether he is better or worse or anything else. Until you Americans are as easy with your chauffeurs as I am with mine, you will not even begin to understand that most traditional and well-bred of all attitudes—authentic democracy."

Not that Lionel had ever had a chauffeur.

But he hoped to have one immediately after this lecture trip.

When he had been eloquent for fifty-seven minutes, which is a thousand dollars' worth, in the best markets, he wanted to escape, for had he not done his distasteful chore? But he had yet to learn the lecturer's worst task: shaking hands with the people who came up to him afterward. Eight out of any given ten admirers, in any city, said, "I just wanted to tell you how much I have enjoyed your books," and to this statement no reasonable response has yet been devised. Upon hearing it, most lecturers feel like babies to whom spinsters gurgle, "Izzums dearums littlems kittlums?" A baby in such a case desires to say, "Like hell I am!" So does a lecturer.

But one out of each ten demanded, "Mr. Trudgeon, what did you mean to prove when you made Timothy Tinker in *'Twas Brillig* say to Effie McGoun, 'For the heart of a man, 'tis the heart of an oak, but the heart of woman is its shimmering bough'?"

Now Lionel didn't remember that he had made Tim say anything so damned silly, and what it meant, if anything, he had no idea. So he murmured, "That—oh, that was symbolic."

It seemed to satisfy them.

And one out of ten, in every town, was certain to be a broad, meaty male, who chuckled at him and shook his hand very painfully and roared, "Well, Brother Trudgeon, I'm going to say something I bet you've never heard before! I don't like your books!"

What the answer to that one was, Lionel did learn, though later his American colleagues advised, "Go jump in the lake!" a retort which seemed to him singularly meaningless.

And so, feeling that he had this day done something for his American cousins which they would never forget, Lionel departed for his hotel, and in the lobby got all the evening papers.

He was on the front page of the *Evening Day Book* and the story began:

"Now that Priestley and Chesterton have returned to civilization, America has worried about how it would carry on without an official governess to tell us when to wash our little faces. We need not have worried. We have a new one, and its name is Lionel—Lionel Trudgeon, the author of *Hot Scotch*.

"Lionel says we are all wrong. Here are some of his rebukes, spiritedly delivered on the *Corybantic* when she arrived from the land of wit and steak and kidney pudding this morning:

"All American flappers get drunk every evening.

"Their fathers never see them except when they bring home the family gin.

"At this year's Westchester Flower Show, there were only two entries, both potted palms. The judges were potted, also."

"Why!" wailed Lionel, "I never said anything of the kind!"

He turned sadly to the other newspapers.

They were not quite so kind as the *Day Book*.

And next morning—after an evening at Pete Carr's, of which he afterward remembered nothing beyond the fourth gin and ginger ale—he rang for all the morning papers and they were much worse than the evening papers.

"Why, I wonder if the Americans really do like hearing the truth about their loathsome country?" fretted Lionel.

The worst of the morning papers was the *Dispatch-Chronicle-Star-Item-Register*, which had recently absorbed the *Standard and Tidings*. The editor of that journal had caused to be interviewed one Morton Norton, an American writer and editor. Now Norton had acquired three Rolls-Royces, a castle in Jugoslavia, and a dachshund by writing novels and articles kidding his native America. His best-known novels were *Maple Avenue*, and *The Follies of Trout Fishing*, and he edited a magazine bound in green in which he monthly stated that all senators were in the pay of the power trust, that Walter Damrosch had no idea of how to conduct the Missa Solemnis, and that George Washington's real name was Wasinski. Lionel did not like Norton's books, but he had always boosted them, because he felt that they were anti-American.

Yet in the interview in the *Dispatch-Chronicle-Star-Item-Register*, this Norton, this embosomed viper, was quoted as saying, "I am glad that Dr. Trudgeon has, my spies tell me, started lecturing. He must be able to lecture, since he certainly cannot write. I shall be glad to help him. I hope he will come to my house. I'll give him a good meal, which is something no Englishman has ever had. I hope to meet him because England is my favorite country, aside from the food, the climate, and the people."

Lionel said aloud, "Trying to be a card! The Americans are really quite at their worst when they try to be humorous."

And, less aloud, "I wonder if dear old G. B. S. was right? I wonder if they really do appreciate being insulted? But I must attack something in America. Oh! By Jove! Neat! I'll attack Morton Norton!"

VIII

If Lionel knew anything whatever about the difference between the English and the Americans—I said "if"—he knew that no Englishman ever addresses strangers on trains, and no American ever fails to. He was glad of this. For the enrichment of *Babylon*, his coming book on America, it might be useful to talk with several ordinary Americans and thus check up on what he had already planned to write about them. Where better than on trains? He would then not waste any of the time which he ought to give to lecturing, being interviewed, autographing books in shops, and other really practical activities.

When he sailed into the club car on the Western Reserve Limited, bound for the broad, free, primitive plains of Ohio, and his second lecture, Lionel was sniffy. He tipped the porter, who had lugged his hat box, writing case, and four solid leather suitcases into the sleeper, brought him a drink of water, and led him to the club car, a dime, then stared about him, with a paragraph of copy from each second of stare. The car—and how comic to shorten "Carriage" to "car"! seemed comfortable enough, and there were free magazines. Lionel noted that; it would save him money. But there was no privacy.

In a proper British compartment, you could touch knees with an archdeacon, and stare him down. Thus to rise above physical proximity, you learned to develop an inner and spiritual privacy. But here there was plenty of leg room, and so many strangers in a row that you could not pick out any one of them to hate. So you had almost no chance to snub any particular person, and no chance to develop that inner privacy.

It was disconcerting.

Still, when they began to talk to him, to tell him about their motors, children, investments, and golf, as all American travelers always do, then he'd be able to snub them right enough!

The person to the right of him, in the row of arm chairs in the club car, was a quivering little fox terrier of a man, evidently filled with mean curiosity. Inwardly, Lionel could hear him blatting. "English, ain't you? First trip to God's country?" and himself answering as befitted a countryman of the late Lord Curzon, "Oh, quite!"

Then the objectionable native would squeak, "I'm in the undertaking game, brother. What's your line?"

And what Lionel would do to him! This was going to be good! Here was a whole chapter for the book.

The above is translated into American from Lionel's own more classically English thoughts, which ran: "Rather! Too poisonous! Mouldy! I say! Sick-making! I shall write about him in my book: 'With that shyness which is the misfortune of every Englishman, I am afraid I was unable to enter quite completely into the friendliness of my rather recent acquaintance, the undertaker, thus romantically encountered *sulla ferrovia*. It is a part of our quaint, old-fashioned English insularity that we respect our neighbor's probably vicious disinclination to hear our troubles or to admire our virtues, and I am afraid that we ourselves rather desire to maintain the same stupid restraint. But I chivvied myself, *à la mode du voyage de la découverte*, to put on something of that boisterous mood which characterizes all Americans even, or especially, in public—they have doubtless acquired it from association with their joyous negro population—and I answered my new friend's query as to my "line of business" with "I'm afraid I am merely a scribbler of tales."

It's wonderful how much a trained observer and recorder can get out of one conversation, even when it has not yet occurred.

On the other side of Lionel was a man broad and ruddy and hairy—probably a coarse but competent business executive. And this one, he would talk tediously to Lionel about sales and markets and graphs, about bond issues and ribbing up the ole sales force to put a lil more pep into the ole biz.

Lionel shuddered in anticipation of his coming boredom. His tongue sucked in fascination at his mental aching tooth. He waited, bravely, not even protecting himself and the British Empire by reading. He looked at the fox terrier man invitingly. For his art he was ready to endure anything.

There was nothing to endure.

The train passed Yonkers. The two buyers up front bought ginger ale, mixed it with something from their flasks, and were heard to hum "She's my little round-the-world tour, and we've got to Lapland now." That was as it should be, for Lionel. But the rest of the passengers were silent. No one spoke to any one else. Two men were writing in order books on their knees. One smoked a cigar and scratched his chin and seemed to be thinking. The others were reading. The train swayed just enough to resemble a summer hammock, and the steady "chuck-a-chuck" of the cars was somnolent. Lionel could have gone to sleep, he realized, feeling almost secure against invasion of his privacy.

He roused himself. This wasn't at all as it should be—as it had to be, if his book was going to come out right.

He had to be bored! He had to be annoyed! He had to be invaded!

He looked resolutely at the terrier gentleman, who went on reading. Lionel saw that the book was a detective story by E. Phillips Wallace. It was either *The Purple Poison* or *The Midnight Mob* or *The Vanished Viper*. Just the sort of thing a common Yankee trader would read! And Lionel knew, because he had read all the works of Wallace and tried to imitate them.

The fox terrier lowered the book to light a cigarette, and Lionel looked encouraging. The terrier stared at him, and went back to his book. Lionel was furious. What did the cad think he was, staring like that—an Englishman? Humph! . . . Humph is a word used in writing about Englishmen. It is pronounced "ff."

After Poughkeepsie, Lionel could not endure it. He touched the terrier's arm and hinted, "May I have a match?"

The terrier lowered his book, lifted his hand to the large box of matches on the wall between them, lighted a match, handed it over, in silence, and was about to return to his book when Lionel said with desperate joviality:

"I see you're reading a Wallace book, my friend. Very agreeable, isn't it, to escape from the hustle of business with a good peppy yarn. I do myself."

The terrier looked interested. "Do you really? Perhaps, then, you can enlighten me. I am assistant professor of psychology at the University of Chicago, and I am making a research into escapism. I have been trying to discover what it is in such a book as this that narcoticizes an extrovert—a bustling but unthinking man like yourself. Just tell me why you like to read them. Not that I am above recreation, you understand; I dearly love, after a day of real work, to escape for a few moments into Proust or William Faulkner or James Joyce. But why do men like you prefer violent and simple-minded adventure?"

"I—I—I—— Really, my dear sir, I never read such things! My favorite author is——" He couldn't remem-

ber who his favorite authors were, aside from E. Phillips
Wallace and Lionel Trudgeon. "I read only highbrow—
I mean——" He was stuck again. He couldn't think of a
fancy synonym for "highbrow." In the high literary circles in which Lionel eddied, when they meant "highbrow"
they said "highbrow."

He ended, almost diffidently, "I mean, I don't read
those sort of books, y' see? Thanks so much for the
match."

And, furiously, dismissing the boor who had thus thrust
himself upon him, Lionel opened his own book, which was
The Highgate Horror by Agatha Lowndes.

It was not till they had passed Hudson that any one
else spoke to Lionel. Then the ruddy man, the brutal captain of industry on his left, observed, as Lionel laid down
his book, "Pretty scenery along the river."

"Yes, rather!" bubbled Lionel. "Splendid place for
hoardings. I'll bet my bottom dollar, boy, they'd bring
some up-and-coming gee that opines how to shoot the
works cent. per cent. on the layout, what, by gigolo!"

"Frightfully sorry, but I'm afraid I don't understand
you. Do you by any chance come from Tasmania? That
particular dialect I don't know."

"I do not! From London!"

"Curious."

"I mean to say—I was expressing myself in American
slang, so you'd understand me. I mean one could make a
frightful lot of money renting out the Palisades for advertising."

"I hope no one will. But perhaps I don't understand
that sort of thing. I'm doubtless divorced from reality,
in my library."

"Then you're not a business man?"

"In a way, I trust! A certain business of the spirit. I
am the Episcopal bishop of Northern Winnemac."

But Lionel did meet a business man, and the business
man spoke to him first.

He was walking the platform during the halt at Albany when a man fell into step and remarked, "Good evening."

Lionel glared. Couldn't a chap go anywhere in this barbaric country without having his privacy intruded on?

"Pardon my speaking to you, but you're lecturing in my town next Tuesday, and I wonder if there's anything I can do to make your stay pleasant? I know you from your picture, of course. My name is Wendell—I'm with the Catawatomie Brass Fittings Company."

"Ah! Doubtless president of it!"

"No. I'm chairman of the board."

"Well, it's a relief to meet one American who isn't so lofty as to be a 'president'! Tell me! It is true, isn't it, that all American business men talk chiefly of stocks and bonds and golf?"

"I suppose so. Don't writers talk of royalties and sales and golf?"

"Really, my dear sir, I don't!"

"Oh, you don't!" The fellow was definitely rude, Lionel rejoiced. "What do you talk about, then?"

"Well, if you must know—though in all humility I cannot understand the universal American longing to know all the details of the uninteresting private lives of celebrities—I usually talk about painting and music."

"Oh, fine! Then maybe you can tell me. When I was in England last I tried to find out where the Portrait of Lady Alnwych by Sir Roger Holcome was. It's not in the National or the Tate or in Manchester. I asked every one. Do you know whether it's in some private collection?"

"Of course. In that of the Duke of Burnham," chillingly explained Lionel. He had never heard of Sir Roger Holcome, but he believed there really was a Duke of Burnham. And with a nod he left this intruder upon his privacies, and rushed to his seat to begin the notes for his long chapter on "That Ambivalent Amiability of Americanos."

Future historians will find golden treasure in the first-hand observations in the manners of the United Statsians in the primitive 1930's, as later set down, from his notes, by Lionel:

"It is a mere bit of British swank to say that the Americans have no conversation. True, this stalwart and sensible folk do not, like our own victims of culture, waste the long evenings in sitting by the fire, over the circling port, discussing art and music and the intricacies of political man. True, they show their delightful and unquenchable *jeunesse* by giving their evenings to bridge, poker, the cinema, and very rapid motor flights to nowhere.

"But the fact is that they do have conversation. . . . For an effete Englishman, a bit too much. . . . You mount the long and shining steel train for your first diffident journey from New York to the bounteous and innocent West. There is but one seat vacant—your own—and beside it crouches a quivering, peppy, nerve-ridden little fox terrier of a man, reading a trashy detective story. He looks in melancholy now and then at the emptiness of your seat. Is he to have no one with whom to talk, poor lad? His somewhat bilious eye—for all its uncanny and vulpine shrewdness showing the result of too many business 'conference' and cigars and cocktails—takes on a more blond glitter as he sees that you will be beside him, and give him a chance to use those conversational powers of Homo Americanus, which are unsurpassed in all the civilized, so to speak, world. That *Pax mundi ist Pause des Mundes* the blessed soul neither knows nor cares.

"You seat yourself. The insolent darky who has carried your light hand-luggage demands and receives an enormous *pourboire*. Your uninvited friend instantly opens fire:

"Well, brother, j'uh get hit bad in the stock market today? Say, I swan, things is pretty fierce. Why, say, I guess you're a limey, ain't you? What's your line of biz?"

Dear Lionel!

IX

Lionel Trudgeon was four weeks out of New York, which is much like saying, in a sea story, that the S. S. *Ramadingo*, 3672 tons burthen, Master J. Squilp, was six months out of Liverpool, with her plates buckled, her stack sheathed with rime, her drinking water foul, and her skipper just entering the D. T.'s. Lionel was four weeks out, and he was no longer an excited novice but a veteran lecturer, and damned sick of it. America was to him now merely a steady hiccup of towns and lecture halls and trains and gin.

He wrote home weekly that he had not had one single portable tin tub, decent skipper, or potable cup of tea all this time, and every one said "lab-OR-a-tory" and "Mil-i-tary" instead of "labtry" and "miltry." But to complete this narrative of martyrdom, it is necessary to give a typical day in the edifying life of a lecturer, of a buck-and-wing dancer in the literary vaudeville.

Lionel's train was due in the city of Zenith at 7:17 A. M. He lay in his berth, dreaming that he was riding up Ben Nevis on a New Mexican burro, playing "The Afternoon of a Faun" on an anvil, when the porter twitched at his sheet. That quiet twitching is the loudest, the most alarming noise in the world. Lionel snorted, turned over, and dug into his folded pillow as though he were trying to eat it.

The porter twitched again. Lionel sat up in terrified rage, muttering, "What is it, what is it?"

"Zenith in twenty minutes, mister."

But in Lionel's *Babylon* this porter was to say, "Ah obsquatulates to paraphrase dot dis ole choo-choo stops hisself at dis ole Zenith in jes' one thoid of a' hour, boss gemmun, yessah, she shu' do."

"Oh, dam Zenith!" wailed Lionel, and he recklessly threw himself on the pillow again. He slept for ten seconds. But he was a trained lecturer, now, and it had become his life to make certain that he arrived in towns to which he did not wish to go, to be present on time at halls which he hated, and to be brightly inspiring to people in regard to whom the best he hoped was that they would all die of wood alcohol.

He yawned, groaned, scratched and peeled himself out of his wrinkled pajamas—lecturers four weeks out get new notions as to what constitutes a clean garment, the standard being that a clean one is not likely to be commented on by the reporters.

Four weeks ago he had never exposed himself to view in a Pullman aisle in anything less than full clothes with spats and a stick. Now, in undershirt, trousers, and slippers, his hair like an untrimmed hedge, he wavered, still scratching, into the dressing-room and glared morosely at the fat traveling man who, as always, was ahead of him, bending over a washbowl, his suspenders hanging loose and swaying with the train.

Ugh! And the dressing-room smelled of toothpaste!

Lionel let it go with splashing his face, combing his hair, and smoking a cigarette.

Teeth? Nails? Don't be silly! Did the second engineer of the S. S. *Ramadingo*, six months out, dress for dinner? Lionel would get these refinements in sometime before the lecture that——

O Lord! he agonized. Was it possible that in just thirteen and a half hours he would again be saying quaint things, the same horrible, quaint, instructive things as last evening, to another omelet of upturned faces?

But as the train came into the Zenith Union Station, Lionel was in the vestibule, looking celebrated in a new overcoat, the collar turned up to frame his clever face, his stick hooked carelessly on his arm, smoking a cigarette in an amber holder which he detested and used only to impress the Committee.

The Committee, the dread O. G. P. U. ruling all his life now, were waiting, their gray and coffeeless early-morning look turning to sickening cordiality as they recognized him. There was Mrs. A. S. Baxter, wife of the well-known eye, ear, nose, throat, lung and heart specialist, and president of the Lyre and Quill Club, Miss Adeline Swenson, president of the Zenith Chapter of the International Sisterhood of Scribes, and the Reverend T. Candlebury Benner. Dr. Benner was the popular pastor of the First Baptist Church, and president of the Book Browsers' Club. He was plump and very cordial.

"Did you have a good trip from Indianapolis, Brother Trutton?" he beamed.

"Oh, splendid, thanks, sir."

"Did you really? Did you sleep well?" fretted Mrs. Baxter.

"Oh, splendid, thanks."

"I'm so glad," said Miss Swenson. "The last lecturer we had came in on this same train just a week ago—isn't that curious!—and he hadn't slept very well, and honestly —well, of course there are lots of people that do admire Professor Choucroute, and I don't suppose I ought to comment, but honestly, I thought his lecture was just punk, and you know, Mr. Trudgeon, how horrible it is to sit and have to listen to a lecturer that doesn't know his job real good but—— But I'm sure you'll be much better!"

Mrs. Baxter murmured, "I just want to take this opportunity of telling you how much my husband and I have enjoyed your books, I think we've read every word you've ever written."

Four weeks before, Lionel would secretly have reflected, "I hope not! The book I ghosted for the Nudist Society! My ads for Esprit du Printemps Soap!" But now the old hardboiled Professional said mechanically, "So kindo-you. I'm so gladtopleasedyou."

"Now I know you're tired and want to get right up to your hotel and rest, so we won't keep you one moment," whinnied Mrs. Baxter, "but if I may detain you just for one teeney-weeney second, do you prefer an amplifier in the hall tonight, it's such a lovely hall, the D. A. R. Temple, or would you rather not?"

"I really don't mind a bit."

"But just tell us what you want."

"Really, I'm quite agreeable to either."

"Oh, but you mustn't be so generous, Mr. Trudgeon. Just tell us which you prefer."

"Why, honestly, either one."

"But you must——"

Miss Swenson charged in: "I'm sure he'd rather not have one."

"Yes, perhaps it would be better not to have one," droned Lionel; while within he was vowing, "The next female that says amplifier—punctually at eight-thirty—your chairman will be Mrs. —— prefer a glass of water on the reading stand—just meet a few intimate friends who are interested in books and reading, or any of the other trade terms of this calamitous business, I'm going to sock her on the jaw, and I know that's good American, by thunder!"

But even as he thus wearily bristled up at Fate, Dr. Benner was purring, "Tell me, Brother Trutton, don't you feel there's too much, uh, if the ladies will pardon me, uh, dirt in so much of contemporary fiction?"

"Oh yes, rather!"

"And too much pessimism?"

"Rather!"

"Don't you feel that these degenerate forms of literature, such as satire and this so-called realism, are but too oft merely the substitutes among second-raters for the imagination required to produce really uplifting romantic literature?"

"Oh yes, quite," said Lionel, longing for a good, long, wholesome, dreary Zola novel, with just a million word chapter by Dreiser to top it off.

He was taken in Mrs. Baxter's own car to the Hotel Thornleigh. Mrs. Baxter drove. Mrs. Baxter should not have driven. In traffic she kept turning her head to explain the importance of the sights. She apologized for the Thornleigh. It was not suitable to a city like Zenith; it had only ten stories and was all of ten years old. But, she insisted, within a year they would have a really up-to-date caravanserai, twenty-eight stories high, with a radio

and free mineral water in every room. And Mr. Trudgeon
must admit that this new shop of Lewis and Onestone,
four stories entirely devoted to lingerie and silk stockings,
was equal to anything in New York.

Lionel didn't mind her driving—not more than he had
minded the Battle of the Marne. He was too busy trying
to recall the name of this city, now he was here.

Poor Lionel!

In his hotel suite, he had just removed his collar and
was looking—vainly—in his bag for a clean one when the
first reporter telephoned. Within half an hour Lionel had
sent a bellboy for a clean collar and shirt, donned them,
and he was facing six reporters from the four Zenith
newspapers, as the *Advocate-Times* had detailed not only
a reporter but also the literary and society editors.

The dean of them, and the oldest—except for the society editor, who was a lady of sixty-eight—was the
Advocate reporter. He was a disillusioned veteran of
twenty-three. He knew every speakeasy, politician, police sergeant, quack, and shyster in Zenith, and he
thought well of none of them. He was convinced, and in
all states of liquor heard to say, that all the respectable
lawyers and ministers and doctors and merchants in town
were just as bad as the convicted crooks, only they had
not yet been found out. He had also spent a week in Chicago and four days in New York. There was, in fact, no
Inside Stuff in the world that he did not know, and he had
read practically all of a Galsworthy novel.

"Now, Trudgeon," the veteran said briskly, while the
literary editor and the society editor looked pained, "I
understand you don't like this country. Flock of yaps,
eh? Well, give us a good line about it. Go the limit!"

"But I do like it! Very much! I've just had the pleasure of touring it for a month and I think I may say with
safety that it has the most beautiful women, the most
hospitable men, the most charming homes——"

"Yeah, I know all that tripe. The tallest buildings and
the best bullhead fishing. That all goes free with the blue

plate lunch. I don't want that. Now when you landed in
N. Y., you gave the gents of the press some hot stuff."

"But that was an error! You see, I'm a Cumberland
man, and our sense of humor isn't always understood."

"Yeah?"

"I was joking, you know. D' you see—joking! Actually, I felt, even before I came here, that the future safety
of the world depends on the union of the English-speak-
ing peoples——"

"Sure. I know. Hams across the sea. World safe for the
two Al's, Smith and Bania. But can't you give us something interesting? Don't you think all Americans are
vulgar and uneducated? Don't you think our gals drink
like pickerel? Don't you think our writers are punk?"

"I must, as always, firmly say 'no' to all those questions, I am afraid. If you want a good story, as you call
it, you may quote me as saying that, in my opinion,
America is only at the beginning of its great career, and
the day may come when an Englishman will actually
come here merely for pleasure!"

"Well, I'll get a line out of that. S' long!"

For another half an hour the reporters tried pitifully
to make him say something nice and disagreeable, and
departed wailing. Then spoke the society editor:

"What do you think of the Prince of Wales, Mr.
Trudgeon?"

"I've always liked him very much. Pleasant, democratic
chap, very easy to talk to. Takes as much interest in one's
books as he would in problems of state or horses or South
American exports."

It was not true that Lionel had never seen the Prince.
He had, only a few hundred yards away, at the Derby.

"And who is your closest friend among the British nobility, Mr. Trudgeon?"

"Mine? I can scarce say I have one. You must remember that I am merely a humble scribbler. I wouldn't be
much more likely to know the nobility than if I were an
American. But of course I do like running down to the
Duke of Burnham's for a week-end, you know."

The literary editor, a fetching maiden of twenty-two, interrupted to breathe reverently, "Mr. Trudgeon—there are so many earnest young literary aspirants who would like to know—what are your literary methods? Do you write in the morning or at night? Do you use white paper or yellow? Do you dictate or type or write it all out long-hand? Do you start with a plot or a character? Do you think genius is just an infinite capacity for taking pains? And what is your philosophy of life—and don't you notice there is much less poverty and crime since women got the vote?"

He told her.

In fact, within an hour and a half Lionel had given the thirsting Americans enough information and inspiration to last till the next lecturer should come along, a week later.

His day had just begun.

The newspaper photographers pictured him sitting in an arm chair reading one of his own books, leaning an elbow on a table with his forefinger against his cheek, standing on the roof of the hotel and looking across the tower of the Second National Building, and shaking hands with the president of the Boosters' Club.

He was hustled to Station WZEN and for five minutes, between the Singing Seals and the advertisement of Choom, the Gum with Vitamins, he told the world how much he loved—uh—oh yes, Zenith.

At one o'clock there was a dreadful lunch at the residence of Mrs. Baxter.

Except for the Rev. Dr. Benner, and the hostess' husband, who seemed sulky, and an artistic photographer, who wore a velvet coat, Lionel was the only male among thirty-one women, such earnestly cordial and respectable women that he dared not even say "damn," nor tell the one about the charwoman and the lodger which had been his social stock in trade at Boosters' Club dinners. There were cocktails, but they were fruit cocktails, and there was an awful salad with a chunk of cream cheese nesting on it.

Lionel sat next to Miss Adeline Swenson of the International Order of Sisters of the Quill, and the conversation with her was literary.

Four weeks ago, Lionel had enjoyed good literary conversation: panning fellow authors and finding out how much they got from editors. Now he longed to talk of stocks, bonds, golf, Amos 'n' Andy, or anything save books. But Miss Swenson was as sweet and as relentless as warm taffy candy:

"Mr. Trudgeon, what do you think of Conrad?"

"This isn't for publication, I hope? Well, just confidentially, between ourselves, poor old Conrad was merely a highbrow Marryat. He couldn't write the English language."

"What do you think of Wells?"

"Oh, he! Just a social theorist."

"And Bennett?"

"Of course I greatly admired Bennett, but he was a bit common, don't you think?"

"And Galsworthy? You must excuse my boring you with so many questions, but we ladies here do want to get our views about these things straight."

"Why, Galsworthy, like Hugh Walpole, writes very decently when he does pretty little stories, but when they try, as one might say, to paint a broader canvas, with deeper themes, they simply haven't the power."

"And Shaw?"

"Oh, no one speaks of Shaw any more."

"And what about the English critics? Which of them do you find the most helpful?"

"My dear young lady! None of them, except perhaps Adrian Smallways. The trouble with our critics is that they're destructive and not constructive. They take our little efforts and just seek for the bad side, not the fine side. Why there was an article in the *Express*—imagine a mere newspaper daring to criticize the arts!—that said my books were veal and kidney pie with whipped cream on them! Fancy that! I was so cross. That's the sort of thing one has to suffer from the envy of these uncreative critics!"

After that, the conversation wasn't so bad, for Miss Swenson encouraged him to talk of his books and his grievances. But later, Mrs. Baxter, on his other side, insisted on discussing the Zenith Little Theater. Now Lionel had already made large research into the entire subject of the American drama. He had gone to two shows in New York, and discussed the little theaters for fully fifteen minutes with a school-teacher in Nashville. His notes on the drama, for his book, were complete, and why should he waste more time on it?

He was delighted when the luncheon was over, and he could begin his lecture, at three o'clock.

The lecture itself was the easiest part of the day. He was so well rehearsed now that all he had to do was to open his mouth and let it run on automatically for an hour, while he slept. He informed his excited auditors that America had quite a nice future, that America and the British Empire together could keep the Huns, Hottentots, and Bolos in a state satisfactory to Britain, and, in a superb peroration, he gave them permission to ignore Morton Norton's criticism of American talkies, breakfast food, Channing Pollock, near-beer, and the Yosemite Valley.

After his lecture, and the hand-shaking with those who came forward with a thought for the day, he faithfully attended to his most important task: making sure that he got what some classes of his fellow workmen called "the wages," and others called "the swag," but which Lionel preferred to call his emolument—his honorarium—his stipend—his remuneration—his fee. For he was an English author, and as such hated all money, particularly all dollars, unless they were chastely presented to him in a check, in a sealed envelope, presented to him rather apologetically by the chairman of the committee.

But he made sure he got that envelope, and he instantly sneaked off back-stage to see that the amount was right.

Beaseley, the lecture agent, had told him a dreadful

story of an English author who, eight years before, had been informed by the chairman that she would mail him the check, and she had not done so. With that ghastly danger in mind, Lionel smilingly but firmly declined to leave the platform until the emolument was in his fist.

Then, worst torture of the day, came the tea and reception at the Zenith Women's Club.

With nothing but fruit punch and sugar wafers to sustain him, poor Lionel—poor Lionel!—had to shake hands with a determined line of three hundred females. It was like the wish-dream of a beef critter: three hundred intended victims each taking a jab at the lone butcher instead of being each in turn jabbed by him. Three hundred—and each of them wrung the Maestro, leered at him, told him how much better any Britisher was than any American, murmured "I just wanted to tell you how much I've enjoyed your books," and waited for a snappy and memorable answer.

All of it in the refined atmosphere of the club lounge: chintz curtains, portraits of St. Theresa and Carrie Chapman Catt, small gilt tea-tables, and a bulletin board announcing the meetings of committees to uplift the Cree Indians, victims of snuff, Croatians, Democrats, shut-ins, White Russians, Finnish asphalt miners, persons who split infinitives, and young ladies, if any, who had not learned the facts of life.

And a pervading smell of eau de cologne and fur neckpieces, and such a gentle murmurous prattle that he wanted to yell.

He was able to get in only half an hour nap before he had to dress for the dinner of the Chamber of Commerce, at which he rose and, without a blush resultant from the seven nips of rye which seven different Good Samaritans had secretly given him in the cloak-room—proclaimed that, uh, Zenith, was the most beautiful and go-ahead city he had seen in the United States.

After him, several local geographers rose and said that Zenith was the most beautiful and go-ahead city in the world, though they certainly did have to hand Mr. Trudgeon's native London a lot, providing they didn't have to live there, and this certainly was an evening of international friendship and informative discussions which would go down in their memories for many years.

It was ten o'clock before a rotund and cheery-looking man named Tracy Goldblatt leaned over Lionel's chair and whispered, "Don't you want to get away from this gab-fest? I'm going to have a few folks out at the house —some swell gals, and I'll guarantee my Scotch is the best in the state of Winnemac!"

Lionel arose with haste.

He never did learn just who Mr. Tracy Goldblatt was. Sometimes, in trains, meditating upon that evening, he fancied that Mr. Goldblatt was a department-store magnate, a popular rabbi, a chiropractor, a musical comedy librettist, an explorer, or a Ukrainian spy. Anyway, he was something like that, and his drawing-room was handsome, his cellar was excellent, and through the divine haze of Lionel's fourth highball, there swam toward him a young lady who looked like Adele Astaire.

Lionel sat with her on the stairs and, holding her hand, told her that she reminded him of his sister. He had two more drinks and told her that she reminded him of Diana Manners, Cleopatra, and the heroine of his *The Best Butter*. After the next he wept, and said that America was the lousiest country in the world, and how about the two of them starting for England, that evening?

He had been told that all American girls surrender to any Englishman instantly and with enthusiasm. But tonight, for the fifth time since his arrival, he found that there was something wrong with the system. This girl patted his hand maternally, clucked sympathetically, and chirped, "Yes, yes, dear, you'll sleep it off tonight. Mother doesn't mind. Nony, nony, mustn't try to kissum girl friend. You just stick to writing, Lionel. You do that better!"

And presently—he must have slipped down a step or two on the stairs—she didn't seem to be the girl to whom he had been proposing, but another one, more blonde, and

he wept again, and when he had recovered he was being
taken to his train in a sedan, with a hilarious group of
four or eight others.

Before the train left, the Morning *Advocate-Times* had
come out. The motor ride had sufficiently cleared his head
so that, in a pained and aching manner, he was able to
read the leading editorial:

"Old-time readers of this Palladium of Learning will
have reason to suspect that this screed is not, as usual,
written by one of the hired hands. A certain testiness and
intolerance and old-fashioned obliquity of vision in it will
lead them to guess that it is being pounded out, with two
fingers, on his aged coffee mill, by that old crab, the
Owner, himself.

"We returned that evening from some good duck-
shooting down South to some pretty poor snipe-shooting
here.

"The boys and girls in our city room have been having
cat fits over one Lionel Trudgeon, interviewing him and
mugging his not especially Grecian face and reporting a
speech in which he says we, the United States, were all
right, after all, some ways. We're letting their pieces
ride. We believe in letting them write what they like in
this Citadel of Liberty, providing they don't fool with
finance or taxes or with parties given by the Old Man's
Old Lady or something important like that.

"But we have read a book by this Lionel. We got stuck
with it on a train. We had nothing else to read but it
and our check book, and the latter hadn't much of the
reading matter left except on the lefthand side.

"We read his book. It was pretty fair. It was about a
couple of bobbed haired English, one female and one
allegedly male, who went walking and met a lot of hoboes
and talked with them alongside the regulation hedges. It
wasn't bad. It sounded a good deal like Jeffry Farnol
with the bitters left out. There seems to be no reasons why
Trudgeon shouldn't write this kind of stuff. There's no
law against it, not yet.

"But when it comes to Lionel's going around telling this country what he thinks of it, or what he believes he ought to think, then we're not so tolerant.

"If he says we're awful, that's okay by us. If he says we'll pass, that's okay. A lot of people, even in this great profession of influencing public opinion, or taking a shot at it, have made the mistake of supposing it matters a hoot whether he likes us or not. The point is, who the so-and-so ever supposed that the writing of a few volumes of pink pop qualified this fellow as an authority on this country, one way or the other?

"He comes here, for the first time, and tells us we've got a large wide country. That's news!

"He says we're pretty democratic, some ways. That's news!

"And people fall for it. We noted a piece right in the New York *Trumpet*, and that sheet, which we have hitherto, in our hoary-headed ignorance, regarded as the greatest newspaper in the world, uses up a lot of good white paper giving room to such novel information as that there's quite a few people in America who want to learn things.

"Next, we expect Trudgeon to walk into the White House and tell a certain gentleman there, 'Hoover, you are President of the United States.'

" 'The dickens you say!' says Herbert, struck all of a heap.

" 'Yes, and you have a lot of power.'

" 'Honest? Now that's real lovely of you, Brother Trudgeon. Now I understand why I have been staying around the White House. Nobody would tell me before. But now about this here power. Please go on, Maestro, and tell me what I'm going to do with it, now I've got it. And have you got any ideas about Shouse?'

"Yes, Lionel would be a help anywhere.

"Besides informing us that we have a lot of gold, gall, git, and gunmen, Lionel has assisted us a lot by putting Morton Norton in his place. He has defended the cowering 120,000,000 of us against that bold baddie mans. He

says we can cheer up. We're probably, he allows, a little
better than Norton says.

"We didn't know, till Lionel came, that we needed the
neighbors' help in spanking our own bad boy, Mort.

"Having a sneaking liking for an old-time dog fight,
we kind of preferred it when the great Trudgeon first
landed and said right out what he really thought—that
we were the back yard of the universe, the across-the-
railroad dump of the world, and that he expected to get
his patent leathers all muddy and didn't care a cuss who
knew it. But now he has gone soft.

"He has taken to praising us. We kind of crassly wonder whether it's just possible he saw a lot of lecture dates,
with a lot of lovely dollars, going glimmering if he did
not soft soap us. Anyway, that's where we got sore. We
don't mind his bawling us out, but when he tries to reach
up and pat us on the head, we don't like the spectacle—
we don't believe he can reach that high, and we hate to
see the little man wiggling."

Lionel looked displeased.

"Oh, you mustn't mind him. That's Colonel Snow. He's
an old grouch," said Tracy Goldblatt, in vulgar reference
to the venerable owner and editor of the *Advocate-Times*.
"Conservative, hide-bound old hyena—we don't pay any
attention to him."

"No, don't pay any attention to him," said the others.

But as Lionel looked down from his sleeper they were
looking again at the editorial, and giggling.

He sighed.

He felt full of gin and disillusion.

He fumbled in his pocket and brought out the flimsies
of his lecture schedule.

"Now what the deuce is the name of this next horrible
town where I have to perform?" he groaned.

Poor Lionel!

X

Lionel was eleven weeks out of New York and his lecture tour was almost over when he was invited to stay at Graybarn, the North Shore estate of G. Washburn Cockle, during his five consecutive lectures in Chicago.

The invitation amused him. He hadn't seen much of the social pretentiousness of America. He had stayed mostly at hotels, clubs, or the rather modest houses of clubwomen and college professors. He had read of Cockle as an ultra-rich car wheel manufacturer, with a villa in Florida and an apartment in New York, aside from Graybarn; he had seen pictures of Wash Cockle playing polo, and landing from his private plane.

It would be pretty funny.

Imagine Chicagoans trying to ape English country life! Cocktails before breakfast! Footmen dressed, as in the movies, like mediaeval pages! A Tudor hall with fake Spanish furniture! Bogus old masterpieces! Chicago heiresses trying to speak French! That would be a couple of chapters!

At the Birchmere station on the Northwestern, Lionel found a large limousine awaiting him. There was nothing particularly comic about the uniformed chauffeur, who bowed, tucked a rug about him, and drove off without once saying, "Hey, baby, I guess you're one of the birds for Graybarn, ain't you?" . . . Not but what the chauffeur did say it later, in the chapter on "The Humors of Democracy" in Mr. Lionel Trudgeon's *Babylon*.

Nor was there anything strikingly comic about Graybarn, a biggish Georgian house, very simple, in front of it a stone terrace below which were sunken gardens and lawns slipping down among oaks and birches to the shore of Lake Michigan. Had it been in England, Lionel would have exclaimed about it, and longed to be invited to enter it, and he would have put it in a novel as the residence of an earl. Even though it was in America, he couldn't feel entirely superior to it.

He was received by a butler whom Lionel would have believed to be pukka English, if it were not absurd to suppose that an English butler could ever be in Birchmere, Illinois. The butler showed him to a bedroom panelled in old pine; he rang, and as a meaching person in a red-striped waistcoat apologized himself into the room, observed, "Heebs will valet you, sir."

And Lionel was sore afraid.

He had never been valeted. He had never, so far as he knew, seen a valet. What the deuce did a valet do? Did you have to let him dress you? Agitatedly Lionel pictured himself hopping on one foot while this confounded fellow held out his trousers for him. His mind was a boil of anguish.

"Cocktails are being served in the library, sir," said the butler, and that was about all the comic American conversation Lionel had heard since leaving the train.

Nervously noting that Heebs, the demon valet, was already unpacking the one bag he had brought out from Chicago, Lionel washed his hands and fled downstairs. In the library which also had books, a dozen people were considering a silver cocktail-shaker the size of a trench mortar. Two people of perhaps forty came to greet him; a pretty woman with gardening gauntlets in one hand, and a tall man in riding clothes.

"Mr. Trudgeon? I'm Mrs. Cockle. It's frightfully nice of you to come. I'm supposed to do book-reviews once in a while for the Chicago *Item*, and I used the most unscrupulous pull with the literary set to down the other would-be hostesses and capture you. This is my husband."

Wash Cockle shook hands casually. He seemed neither excited nor acutely annoyed by the sight of an author. Neither did the other guests. The only remarkable incident was when one of the young men, presenting himself as a former Rhodes scholar, asked Lionel whether he had attended Oxford or Cambridge. Lionel adroitly said that he hadn't gone to Oxford, and the young man said that, after all, he admired Cambridge, too, and that was that.

When they went up to dress, Heebs the valet pounced on Lionel.

"Is one of your bags missing, sir?" he said, and Lionel meekly realized that Heebs as well as the butler seemed to be English. "I can find only two suits of underthings, and I have laid out one for tonight."

Now the reason why Heebs, blast him, could find only two suits of underclothes was because Lionel had brought only two suits of underclothes. He had thought that two nice clean suits were more than enough for just four days among the heathen.

"My man must have failed to send on one bag," he sighed. "We'll just have to make these do, my man."

"Verygoodsir, thenkyousir."

This seemed to be working out all right. In books, including those of Mr. Lionel Trudgeon, you kept saying "My man" to a servant and he kept answering "sir," and it really seemed to be the same in real life.

Heebs charitably left him alone, after drawing a bath and laying out dinner clothes and transferring the studs to a clean shirt from one which, Lionel unhappily remembered, he had intended to use two more times. He did not insist on scrubbing Lionel's back or otherwise terrifying him, and Lionel gave up his recent idea of having a telegram sent to recall him to Chicago.

Lionel had had a good sound bath that morning. He hadn't had the slightest notion of taking another before dinner, but he slid meekly into the bath Heebs had drawn.

He lay still and happy in the warm water, for into the mind of the master was coming an inspiration. A story! Topping!

He saw a house curiously like Graybarn, only it was in Kent. There was young Lord Delaligne, who strangely resembled Wash Cockle. To this unmistakably British Manor came an American visitor, Hiram Q. Pike of Pip Center, Oklahoma, and what do you think, this American bounder was so provincial that he had never had a valet, and when Lord Delaligne gave him one—a very quaint character named Sheebs—Hiram didn't know what the deuce to do with him! And Hiram hadn't even enough fresh underclothes along!

So Lionel happily rubbed his toes and resolved, through Hiram Q. Pike, to get back at America.

Lionel was happy at dinner. Among the twenty guests, there was, sitting opposite him, the perfect boisterous American business man whom he had been seeking. The fellow was clean-shaven, bald, and he wore horn-rimmed spectacles. He was, it comically appeared, a chewing-gum magnate. He called each of the women "sister," he peppered his conversation with "attaboy," "and how!" "yeah?" and "for crying out loud," and he drank four highballs during dinner instead of what seemed, Lionel condescended, to be a quite decent Johannisberger Cabinet.

Lionel remarked to the pretty, anonymous girl beside him, "It's so refreshing to meet an American like our friend opposite. He isn't ashamed of his natural heartiness. I rather hate to see so many American laddies repressing their good spirits. After all, if one really is an American, is there any sense in trying to hide it?"

"No, I suppose not," she said, "though that particular—laddie, is it?—doesn't happen to be an American. He's English. Been here fifteen years. Isn't it wonderful, just something out of Kipling, how quick all your Englishmen are at learning native dialects!"

For minutes Lionel was hurt and silent.

Then he became nervous.

His valet, Heebs, was apparently also a footman, or whatever they called it—outside of writing-hours, Lionel wasn't quite sure about these things. Anyway, he was one of the uniformed men assisting the butler in serving. Lionel noted that Heebs kept peeping at him throughout dinner, and it wasn't nice to have a valet-footman look owlishly at you over the leg of lamb. He might have been a detective. Lionel wondered what law he had broken; he understood that in America you were likely to be sent up for life any time, just because the judge didn't like your necktie.

After his first two days, he had become fairly certain that he wasn't likely to be shot down by gunmen, providing he didn't walk anywhere after nine P.M. But he was still anxious about being arrested. He was still wondering whether the editorial writer in the Atlanta *Picayune*, who had said "Whether deportation or enforced habitation in this wilderness would be the better for Mr. Trudgeon is a question for the Supreme Court" had meant it or, in his crude American way, been trying to be funny.

And suppose Heebs was a detective—the way he stared?

He was uncomfortable all evening, as he studied the vice and violence of the domestic life of the American rich.

He had rather expected to have his book enriched by beholding hired mulattos dancing, gin-crazed flappers in pajamas, and angry gentlemen assaulting one another with golf clubs. He was melancholy when he saw nothing more purple than guests playing bridge or talking politics and, after one highball, going to bed at eleven.

It did beat the devil how hard he had to look to find facts which would fit what he had already planned to write, so that his book would be accurate.

He went sullenly up to bed and, as he was undressing, Heebs tapped and tiptoed in, as genteel as a sidesman at St. Thomas's.

"Is there anything I can get you, sir?"

"No, my man, nothing, I think."

"At what time would you like to be called, sir?"

"Oh, about eight. I have to go into Chicago and lecture."

"Lecture, sir? Fancy!"

"Quite, my man."

"If you'll pardon my saying so, sir, we have been given to understand in servants' hall that you are a famous author."

"Oh, well, you know, I write."

"Detective or Westerns, sir, if I may ask?"

"Neither, my man, neither!"

Heebs was standing by the closed door, his hands clasped like a nervous bridesmaid; Lionel sat in an arm chair, his shirt and one shoe off. He felt that he ought to be annoyed by this conversation. But somehow he wasn't annoyed . . . famous author . . . servants' hall. And hadn't he read, hadn't he indeed written, that the real thing in English aristocrats chatted quite chummily with their old family retainers?

"If you will pardon my saying so, sir, it is very pleasant to have an English gentleman to valet. The American gentlemen are very kind to one, but one longs for one's own land, as one might say, doesn't one, sir!"

"Oh yes, doesn't one!"

And hastily afterward—he had darned near forgotten it!—"my man."

"May I ask, sir, if you live in London?"

"Oh yes, quite, my man!"

"Haven't I read, sir, that you were born in Essex?"

"No. Amazing how these journalistic Johnnies get things wrong. I was born in Cumberland."

"In what part, sir, if I may ask?"

"Oh, a little town. You wouldn't have heard of it, my man—a hamlet called Throslebury."

Then Lionel, who had been lolling happily, his lazy fingers tapping the breast of his undershirt, sat up in horror. For the immaculate Heebs went mad. Heebs rushed across the room, threw himself on the bed, kicked up his heels, sat up, leered at Lionel and, filling and lighting his pipe as he spoke, whooped:

"Old Snoopy! Snoopy Trudgeon! I thought it was you, but I wasn't sure—twenty-five years since I've seen you. And you've taken to bathing and having your hair cut—though not sufficiently, even yet, Snoopy! 'My man'! 'Sir'! A bit of all right, we two, what? Don't you remember me now? I was boots at His Lordship's when you used to deliver groceries. I remember when the butler, blast him, kicked you downstairs for stealing a wing of a pheasant. And you remember when I beat you for trying to steal my knife? Bit of a sniveller you was, always! But clever, me lad, clever, I will say that!

"Now don't you worry, Snoopy. I shan't tell the Master a word about you. We stand together, what? Neat, what, the way we cottagers can come to America and pose as gentry, sir—I mean Snoopy. I always do it on me vacations. Two weeks last summer I was the Right Honorable St. John Beauchamps at Atlantic City—invited to dine at the best hotels. I do it better than you, me lad—you still sniff at the wine as though you weren't used to it. But then, if I haven't the manners, I haven't your gab, and that's what brings in the tin, and that's all we're here for, isn't it, Snoopy! Serves the Yanks jolly well right for being so simple. Fancy you're like me, Snoopy. Get all you can out of the bleddy Yanks and go back to civilization. I have me eye on a pub in Lancashire. Haven't a bit of the ready to go into partnership with me, have you, Snoopy?"

Lionel had heard him out in one of the largest silences in history. He said mildly, "It's always very pleasant to meet old friends, Cricket. Strange I didn't recognize you. I, uh, I——"

"I say, Snoops, I'll go down and hook a bottle of Scotch, and we'll have a bit of chin tonight, what say?"

In approximately the tone of a man just lifted from the rack, Lionel murmured, "I have a terrible headache. I'm afraid I must go to bed."

Lionel dressed and slipped downstairs the next morning before Heebs could awaken him. He found Wash Cockle breakfasting alone in the vastness of the dining-room.

"What ho!" said Wash. "I say, you needn't have come down. Wouldn't you rather have a tray sent up to your room for breakfast?"

Remembering that something of the sort really had happened to him on one or two of the dozen week-end parties he had known in his life, Lionel condescended, "Usually I like it, but—such a splendid morning, you know!"

"I say. Your lecture is at eleven? Can you be out here for a spot of polo this afternoon, at the club?"

Now Lionel really had ridden. As a boy he had ridden the grocer's delivery horse. But until he was sixteen he had not known that the word "polo" referred to anything except an explorer.

"Thanks, but I don't play very well."

"But there'll be a friend of yours there—Bill Twyffort. You know him, of course—son of the Duke of Burnham. I heard you speaking of Burnham last evening."

At that second the horrible Heebs entered with fresh coffee. He winked at Lionel, and it was with the courage of being shot against the wall that Lionel said, and loudly, "Yes, good old buck, Burnham. Bill is a very decent chap, too. He married some Chicago gal, if I remember. Decent people."

He was satisfied to see the glassy awe with which Heebs stared at him. But his courage went no further.

He found a telephone under the stairs and desperately telephoned to the Chicago representative of Beaseley Lectures to send him instantly a telegram summoning him to Chicago for the rest of his visit.

The other three nights he spent in a Chicago hotel. During that time he was markedly polite to clerks, porters, bellboys, taxi-drivers, and even literary ladies. In fact he remained full of meekness and Americanomania until he had left New York. To the reporters, when he sailed, he explained that they had misunderstood what he had said on arrival. He had been joking. It was his peculiar Cumberland sense of humor.

When Lionel had vanished, Washburn Cockle fretted to his wife, "Wonder what made Trudgeon give us the gate and go back to town?"

"Why, he was called in for a conference. I saw the wire."

"My dear girl, that's the oldest dodge in the world. When Noah went off on that celebrated bat after the Ark landed, he had some buddy send him a fake wire. Do you suppose we offended him?"

"Of course we did! You and your friends, with your eternal talk of polo and aviation and business! Of course you bored him! I adore you, Wash, but when we do manage to get hold of a really distinguished Englishman, a thinker, not one of your eternal sportsmen, I do wish you'd make some little effort to profit by it and listen to him. Oh well, Sir Thompson Thompson, the explorer, is coming next week, and I think I have him hooked. Do try, this time, not to be so horribly American, will you?"

Three weeks after Lionel had safely and joyously arrived in England, there appeared in the New York Sunday *Dispatch-Chronicle-Star-Item-Register* his article summing up, for wistfully waiting America, his final verdict on that interesting land. The last paragraph of that article—which in all contained two facts, three ideas, and 12,000 words—proclaimed:

"Precisely that characteristic of America which caused traveling Americans and such idolators of Europeanism, or what, from much but not necessarily comprehending reading, they believe to be Europeanism, as Mr. Morton Norton, most to mock or even to scorn America as its greatest virtue. That it almost completely lacks culture, the practice of the arts, tradition, and a gentry, is, to the philosopher, its greatest merit. If the students of its universities chew gum instead of dactyls, they may yet make dactyls out of gum. If its plutocracy lacks the merits of a gentry, it may yet elevate our shabby gentry into plutocracy. If there is nowhere an insistence on the cold morning bath, the Americans may yet make the English gentleman perceive that a morning cold bath alone does not make the gentleman. If the American mob in general believes in too many absurd and childish things, it may yet show us of an older and wearier civilization that belief, that the practice of faith, is more important than that in which one believes. A little child shall lead them and to the mature mind of the European, who had come to believe that there was nothing but maturity, it is miraculous to discover that childishness can still beautifully exist."

It may have meant something, at that.

At exactly the time when New York was being edified by Lionel's article, in London, six hours later by the clock, Lionel was giving a mid-afternoon address to a large audience of twenty-seven persons at the St. John's Wood Arts Club:

"I trust that what I shall say here will not be reported. It is such a relief to be able to speak freely, without being hounded by the fiends of the American press who, for some reason not at all clear to me, seemed to find my slightest opinion of such great value.

"As so many of you are literary folk, doubtless you are thinking that when our brothers and sisters, as in politeness we call them, across the sea insist on your going over to lecture, you will be tempted. Don't! Resist! You may think you know all the faults of America—that there is no privacy, that their streets are the noisiest in the world. But beyond these faults, the Yankees are the touchiest people in the world. They want, as they call it, to be 'soft-soaped.' They simply do not want Englishmen like ourselves to tell them, for their own good, the simple unadorned truth. And everywhere you are in an atmosphere of dollar chasing. You may think that you will find the journey profitable, but you have no notion how people prey on you, over there. The fees sound large, but the lecture agent demands, and if necessary legally steals from you, the most appalling percentage. And you have to pay your own expenses. And since, being English, you cannot complain as would one of their own raucous countrymen, you are robbed in every hotel, every shop, every restaurant.

"It is true that I am myself going again next year. But I assure you that this will be my last venture into the land of the dollar chasers! What is the use of lavishing British culture on such people? It is idealism wasted. And what if I did make seven thousand pounds clear in thirteen weeks of lecturing? I am a simple man. So long as I have my town house, my country cottage—I have this past week taken one in Surrey, at which I should be happy to see any of you—and my modest little five-seater car, my wireless, my secretary, my garden, my library, my wine-cellar, my clubs, and just one month a year on the Riviera —so long as I can have these inexpensive pleasures, what, I ask you, could the land of dollar chasers, for all its barbaric splendor, give to me—and those of you who review books may be interested to know that in three weeks, now, you will be able to obtain advance proofs of my book, *Babylon.* I thank you."

Aldous Huxley

THE PALIO AT SIENA

Our rooms were in a tower. From the windows one looked across the brown tiled roofs to where, on its hills, stood the cathedral. A hundred feet below was the street, a narrow canyon between high walls, perennially sunless; the voices of the passers-by came up, reverberating, as out of a chasm. Down there they walked always in shadow; but in our tower we were the last to lose the sunlight. On the hot days it was cooler, no doubt, down in the street; but we at least had the winds. The waves of the air broke against our tower and flowed past it on either side. And at evening, when only the belfries and the domes and the highest roofs were still flushed by the declining sun, our windows were level with the flight of the swifts and swallows. Sunset after sunset all through the long summer, they wheeled and darted round our tower. There was always a swarm of them intricately manœuvring just outside the window. They swerved this way and that, they dipped and rose, they checked their headlong flight with a flutter of their long pointed wings and turned about within their own length. Compact, smooth and tapering, they seemed the incarnation of airy speed. And their thin, sharp, arrowy cry was speed made audible. I have sat at my window watching them tracing their intricate arabesques until I grew dizzy; till their shrill crying sounded as though from within my ears and their flying seemed a motion, incessant, swift and bewilderingly multitudinous, behind my eyes. And all the while the sun declined, the shadows climbed higher up the houses and towers, and the light with which they were tipped became more rosy. And at last the shadow had climbed to the very top and the city lay in a grey and violet twilight beneath the pale sky.

One evening, towards the end of June, as I was sitting

at the window looking at the wheeling birds, I heard
through the crying of the swifts the sound of a drum. I
looked down into the shadowy street, but could see nothing. Rub-a-dub, dub, dub, dub—the sound grew louder
and louder, and suddenly there appeared round the corner
where our street bent out of sight, three personages out
of a Pinturicchio fresco. They were dressed in liveries of
green and yellow—yellow doublets slashed and tagged
with green, parti-coloured hose and shoes, with feathered
caps of the same colours. Their leader played the drum.
The two who followed carried green and yellow banners.
Immediately below our tower the street opens out a little
into a tiny piazza. In this clear space the three Pinturicchio figures came to a halt and the crowd of little boys
and loafers who followed at their heels grouped themselves
round to watch. The drummer quickened his beat and the
two banner-bearers stepped forward into the middle of the
little square. They stood there for a moment quite still,
the right foot a little in advance of the other, the left
fist on the hip and the lowered banners drooping from
the right. Then, together, they lifted the banners and
began to wave them round their heads. In the wind of
their motion the flags opened out. They were the same
size and both of them green and yellow, but the colours
were arranged in a different pattern on each. And what
patterns! Nothing more "modern" was ever seen. They
might have been designed by Picasso for the Russian
Ballet. Had they been by Picasso, the graver critics
would have called them futuristic, the sprightlier (I must
apologize for both these expressions) jazz. But the flags
were not Picasso's; they were designed some four hundred years ago by the nameless genius who dressed the
Sienese for their yearly pageant. This being the case, the
critics can only take off their hats. The flags are classical,
they are High Art; there is nothing more to be said.

The drum beat on. The bannermen waved their flags,
so artfully that the whole expanse of patterned stuff was
always unfurled and tremulously stretched along the air.
They passed the flags from one hand to the other, behind

their backs, under a lifted leg. Then, at last, drawing
themselves together to make a supreme effort, they tossed
their banners into the air. High they rose, turning slowly,
over and over, hung for an instant at the height of their
trajectory, then dropped back, the weighted stave foremost, towards their throwers, who caught them as they
fell. A final wave, then the drum returned to its march
rhythm, the bannermen shouldered their flags, and followed by the anachronistic children and idlers from the
twentieth century, Pinturicchio's three young bravos
swaggered off up the dark street out of sight and at
length, the drum taps coming faintlier and ever faintlier,
out of hearing.

Every evening after that, while the swallows were in full
cry and flight about the tower, we heard the beating of
the drum. Every evening, in the little piazza below us, a
fragment of Pinturicchio came to life. Sometimes it was
our friends in green and yellow who returned to wave
their flags beneath our windows. Sometimes it was men
from the other *contrade* or districts of the town, in blue
and white, red and white, black, white and orange, white,
green and red, yellow and scarlet. Their bright pied
doublets and parti-coloured hose shone out from among
the drabs and funereal blacks of the twentieth-century
crowd that surrounded them. Their spread flags waved in
the street below, like the painted wings of enormous butterflies. The drummer quickened his beat, and to the
accompaniment of a long-drawn rattle, the banners leapt
up, furled and fluttering, into the air.

To the stranger who has never seen a Palio these little
dress rehearsals are richly promising and exciting.
Charmed by these present hints, he looks forward eagerly
to what the day itself holds in store. Even the Sienese are
excited. The pageant, however familiar, does not pall on
them. And all the gambler in them, all the local patriot
looks forward to the result of the race. Those last days
of June before the first Palio, that middle week of August
before the second, are days of growing excitement and

tension in Siena. One enjoys the Palio the more for having lived through them.

Even the mayor and corporation are infected by the pervading excitement. They are so far carried away that, in the last days of June, they send a small army of men down in the great square before the Palazzo Comunale to eradicate every blade of grass or tuft of moss that can be found growing in the crannies between the flagstones. It amounts almost to a national characteristic, this hatred of growing things among the works of men. I have often, in old Italian towns, seen workmen laboriously weeding the less frequented streets and squares. The Colosseum, mantled till thirty or forty years ago with a romantic, Piranesian growth of shrubs, grasses and flowers, was officially weeded with such extraordinary energy that its ruinousness was sensibly increased. More stones were brought down in those few months of weeding than had fallen of their own accord in the previous thousand years. But the Italians were pleased; which is, after all, the chief thing that matters. Their hatred of weeds is fostered by their national pride; a great country, and one which specially piques itself on being modern, cannot allow weeds to grow even among its ruins. I entirely understand and sympathise with the Italian point of view. If Mr. Ruskin and his disciples had talked about my house and me as they talked about Italy and the Italians, I too should pique myself on being up-to-date; I should put in bathrooms, central heating and a lift, I should have all the moss scratched off the walls, I should lay cork lino on the marble floors. Indeed, I think that I should probably, in my irritation, pull down the whole house and build a new one. Considering the provocation they have received, it seems to me that the Italians have been remarkably moderate in the matter of weeding, destroying and rebuilding. Their moderation is due in part, no doubt, to their comparative poverty. Their ancestors built with such prodigious solidity that it would cost as much to pull down one of their old houses as to build a new one. Imagine,

for example, demolishing the Palazzo Strozzi in Florence.
It would be about as easy to demolish the Matterhorn.
In Rome, which is predominantly a baroque, seventeenth-
century city, the houses are made of flimsier stuff. Consequently, modernisation progresses there much more
rapidly than in most other Italian towns. In wealthier
England very little antiquity has been permitted to stand.
Thus, most of the great country houses of England were
rebuilt during the eighteenth century. If Italy had preserved her independence and her prosperity during the
seventeenth, eighteenth and nineteenth centuries, there
would probably be very much less mediæval or Renaissance work now surviving than is actually the case. Money
is lacking to modernize completely. Weeding has the merit
of being cheap and, at the same time, richly symbolic.
When you say of a town that the grass grows in its
streets, you mean that it is utterly dead. Conversely, if
there is no grass in its streets, it must be alive. No doubt
the mayor and corporation of Siena did not put the argument quite so explicitly. But that the argument was put
somehow, obscurely and below the surface of the mind, I
do not doubt. The weeding was symbolic of modernity.

With the weeders came other workmen who built up
round the curving flanks of the great piazza a series of
wooden stands, six tiers high, for the spectators. The
piazza which is shaped, whether by accident or design I
do not know, like an ancient theatre, became for the time
being indeed a theatre. Between the seats and the central
area of the place, a track was railed off and the slippery
flags covered parsimoniously with sand. Expectation rose
higher than ever.

And at last the day came. The swallows and swifts
wove their arabesques as usual in the bright golden light
above the town. But their shrill crying was utterly inaudible, through the deep, continuous, formless murmur
of the crowd that thronged the streets and the great
piazza. Under its canopy of stone the great bell of the
Mangia tower swung incessantly backwards and forwards; it too seemed dumb. The talking, the laughter, the

shouting of forty thousand people rose up from the piazza in a column of solid sound, impenetrable to any ordinary noise.

It was after six. We took our places in one of the stands opposite the Palazzo Comunale. Our side of the piazza was already in the shade; but the sun still shone on the palace and its tall slender tower, making their rosy brickwork glow as though by inward fire. An immense concourse of people filled the square and all the tiers of seats round it. There were people in every window, even on the roofs. At the Derby, on boat-race days, at Wembley I have seen larger crowds; but never, I think, so many people confined within so small a space.

The sound of a gunshot broke through the noise of voices; and at the signal a company of mounted carabiniers rode into the piazza, driving the loungers who still thronged the track before them. They were in full dress uniform, black and red, with silver trimmings; cocked hats on their heads and swords in their hands. On their handsome little horses, they looked like a squadron of smart Napoleonic cavalry. The idlers retreated before them, squeezing their way through every convenient opening in the rails into the central area, which was soon densely packed. The track was cleared at a walk and, cleared, was rounded again at the trot, dashingly, in the best Carle Vernet style. The carabiniers got their applause and retired. The crowd waited expectantly. For a moment there was almost a silence. The bell on the tower ceased to be dumb. Some one in the crowd let loose a couple of balloons. They mounted perpendicularly into the still air, a red sphere and a purple. They passed out of the shadow into the sunlight; and the red became a ruby, the purple a glowing amethyst. When they had risen above the level of the roofs, a little breeze caught them and carried them away, still mounting all the time, over our heads, out of sight.

There was another gunshot and Vernet was exchanged for Pinturicchio. The noise of the crowd grew louder as they appeared, the bell swung, but gave no sound, and

across the square the trumpets of the procession were all
but inaudible. Slowly they marched round, the representatives of all the seventeen *contrade* of the city. Besides its
drummer and its two bannermen, each *contrada* had a
man-at-arms on horseback, three or four halbardiers and
young pages and, if it happened to be one of the ten
competing in the race, a jockey, all of them wearing the
Pinturicchian livery in its own particular colours. Their
progress was slow; for at every fifty paces they stopped,
to allow the bannermen to give an exhibition of their skill
with the flags. They must have taken the best part of an
hour to get round. But the time seemed only too short.
The Palio is a spectacle of which one does not grow tired.
I have seen it three times now and was as much delighted
on the last occasion as on the first.

English tourists are often sceptical about the Palio.
They remember those terrible "pageants" which were all
the rage some fifteen years ago in their own country, and
they imagine that the Palio will turn out to be something
of the same sort. But let me reassure them; it is not. There
is no poetry by Louis Napoleon Parker at Siena. There
are no choruses of young ladies voicing high moral senti-
ments in low voices. There are no flabby actor-managers
imperfectly disguised as Hengist and Horsa, no crowd
of gesticulating supernumeraries dressed in the worst of
taste and the cheapest of bunting. Nor finally does one
often meet at Siena with that almost invariable accompaniment of the English pageant—rain. No, the Palio is
just a show; having no "meaning" in particular, but by
the mere fact of being traditional and still alive, signify-
ing infinitely more than the dead-born English affairs for
all their Parkerian blank verse and their dramatic re-
evocations. For these pages and men-at-arms and bannermen come straight out of the Pinturicchian past. Their
clothes are those designed for their ancestors, copied faithfully, once in a generation, in the same colours and the
same rich materials. They walk, not in cotton or flannel-
ette, but in silks and furs and velvets. And the colours

were matched, the clothes originally cut by men whose taste was the faultless taste of the early Renaissance. To be sure there are costumiers with as good a taste in these days. But it was not Paquin, not Lanvin or Poiret who dressed the actors of the English pageants; it was professional wig-makers and lady amateurs. I have already spoken of the beauty of the flags—the bold, fantastic, "modern" design of them. Everything else at the Palio is in keeping with the flags, daring, brilliant and yet always right, always irreproachably refined. The one false note is always the *Palio* itself—the painted banner which is given to the *contrada* whose horse wins the race. This banner is specially painted every year for the occasion. Look at it, where it comes along, proudly exposed on the great mediæval war chariot which closes the procession—look at it, or preferably don't look at it. It is a typical property from the wardrobe of an English pageant committee. It is a lady amateur's masterpiece. Shuddering, one averts the eyes.

Preceded by a line of *quattrocento* pages carrying festoons of laurel leaves and escorted by a company of mounted knights, the war chariot rolled slowly and ponderously past, bearing aloft the unworthy trophy. And by now the trumpets at the head of the procession sounded, almost inaudibly for us, from the farther side of the piazza. And at last the whole procession had made its round and was lined up in close order in front of the Palazzo Comunale. Over the heads of the spectators standing in the central area, we could see all the thirty-four banners waving and waving in a last concerted display and at last, together, all leaping high into the air, hesitating at the top of their leap, falling back, out of sight. There was a burst of applause. The pageant was over. Another gunshot. And in the midst of more applause, the racehorses were ridden to the starting place.

The course is three times round the piazza, whose shape, as I have said, is something like that of an ancient theatre. Consequently, there are two sharp turns, where the ends of the semicircle meet the straight diameter. One of these, owing to the irregularity of the plan, is sharper than the other. The outside wall of the track is padded with mattresses at this point, to prevent impetuous jockeys who take the corner too fast from dashing themselves to pieces. The jockeys ride bareback; the horses run on a thin layer of sand spread over the flagstones of the piazza. The Palio is probably the most dangerous flat-race in the world. And it is made the more dangerous by the excessive patriotism of the rival *contrade*. For the winner of the race as he reins in his horse after passing the post, is set upon by the supporters of the other *contrade* (who all think that *their* horse should have won), with so real and earnest a fury that the carabiniers must always intervene to protect man and beast from lynching. Our places were at a point some two or three hundred yards beyond the post, so that we had an excellent view of the battle waged round the winning horse, as he slackened speed. Scarcely was the post passed when the crowd broke its ranks and rushed out into the course. Still cantering, the horse came up the track. A gang of young men ran in pursuit, waving sticks and shouting. And with them, their Napoleonic coat tails streaming in the wind of their own speed, their cocked hats bobbing, and brandishing their swords in their white-gloved hands, ran the rescuing carabiniers. There was a brief struggle round the now stationary horse, the young men were repulsed, and surrounded by cocked hats, followed by a crowd of supporters from its native *contrada*, the beast was led off in triumph. We climbed down from our places. The piazza was now entirely shaded. It was only on the upper part of the tower and the battlements of the great Palazzo that the sun still shone. Rosily against the pale blue sky, they glowed. The swifts still turned and turned overhead in the light. It is said that at evening and at dawn these light-loving birds mount on their strong wings into the sky to bid a last farewell or earliest good-morrow to the sinking or the rising sun. While we lie sleeping or have resigned ourselves to darkness the swifts are looking down from their watch-tower in the height of heaven over the edge of the turning planet towards the light. Was it a fable, I wondered, looking up at the wheeling birds? Or was it true? Meanwhile, some one was swearing at me for not looking where I was going. I postponed the speculation.

Edna Ferber

FRÄULEIN

Mrs. CARLTON SCHURTZ had everything. In the order of
their (to her) importance she had money, position, looks,
children, health, and love—of a sort. Two of these treas-
ures she had had before marriage, four she had acquired
with marriage, all of them she had possessed and valued
for six years. Yet Mrs. Carlton Schurtz did a good deal
of tossing and turning on her pillow these days—nights,
rather—the while Carlton Schurtz II, in his bed an arm's
length away, slept the quiescent sleep of the man of fifty-
seven who has had eighteen holes of golf, a massage, a
matutinal highball, and two handsome, healthy infants
now growing handsomer and healthier by the minute as
they slumbered in their airy quarters on the floor above.

Usually she managed to drop off by three o'clock. She
awoke at ten, or thereabouts, when Fräulein brought the
children in before taking them to the park. Faintly there
reached her ears the not-unpleasant sounds of a well-
ordered household in a well-built house in New York's
East Sixties. Bath water running. The far-away drone of
a vacuum cleaner used discreetly on another floor. The
zing of a telephone bell, nipped at the beginning of its
third peal. The voices of small children, muted to the
tones of a ménage whose mistress must not be disturbed.

Carlton was up at half-past seven, but he was most
considerate about it. He dressed in the dressing room.
Carlton made a virtue of getting up at half-past seven.
Yessir, no matter how late I go to bed, I'm up at seven-
thirty. At my office desk by nine. He did not realize that
this virtue, if virtue it was, existed only as a habit due to
the solid training given him by Mama Schurtz in his boyhood Brooklyn days when he was little William Carl
Schurtz.

His name had shrunk as his fortune had grown. William Carl Schurtz, Junior, at high school in Brooklyn. Then, as a very young man, W. Carl Schurtz, Jr. The Carlton had burgeoned with his first million. It was as Carlton Schurtz II, the eligible bachelor of fifty-one, that he had married Nancy Ravenet, of the Charleston, South Carolina, Ravenets.

He had, by this time, learned the American-rich pattern. At certain seasons of the year you went here, you went there. You went to Florida for the Sun. You went to Carolina for the Golf. You went to Virginia for the Riding. You went to Canada for the Fishing. You went to England for the Racing. It was like an army, moving under relentless orders. The ironclad programme admitted of no fairways in the Dominion of Canada; ignored the existence of piscatorial life in Western waters.

Carlton Schurtz had been amazed—had been delighted —to discover how simple it all was, once you had a great deal of money, even though born above the butcher shop in Brooklyn. You made money. Then you listened to what they said. You played certain games at certain times. You talked little, but in dry deliberate tones, with a quizzical look in the eye. You retained enough of your native flavor to win the reputation of being an Original: a judicious mixture of Dawes, Al Smith, Will Rogers, and Artemus Ward.

You sat tight while some terrifically important figure held forth in a roomful of people. Then, drawlingly, in a temporary silence, you boldly disagreed with him. The effect was electric. Finally, you acquired one thing—a horse, a car, a picture, a house, a boat, a mistress—that was, of its kind, more precious, more nearly flawless, than any other of its kind in the world.

"Carlton Schurtz—you know, he owns the Oompah." Or Streak-o'-Lightning. Or Sea King. Or grows black orchids.

At fifty-one, then, Carlton Schurtz had become so secure that he was unsafe in such open hunting grounds as Asheville, White Sulphur, or Palm Beach, infested as these spots were with carnivorous mothers of marriageable daughters.

"Come in any time, dear Carlton," the mothers said, a glitter in the eye. "Don't bother to phone. You're like one of the family. There's always a bed and a plate."

"You are too kind," Carton replied. And he meant it.

Daughters said, "I'm so sick of kids with hip flasks. It's wonderful to talk to somebody like you, who understands. You're like an older brother or a ——" Panic. Blushes.

"Father?"

"Oh, no! I wasn't going to say father at all. I almost said——"

He never finished the sentence for them. He knew that for less than that men have found themselves selecting cuff links for groomsmen at Cartier's.

It was when he was golfing discreetly in the protection of the magic ring made by the magnificent live oaks encircling Yeaman's Hall, just outside Charleston, that he met Nancy Ravenet, slim, ashen-blonde, anæmic, twenty-six. Nancy was so Charleston, so French Huguenot, that she did not even bother to talk with a Southern accent. She left that to eighteenth-century upstarts from Virginia, Tennessee, and North Carolina.

The Ravenets had a great deal of fine old family, handsome old mahogany, beautiful old silver (very thin) and linen sheets and damask tablecloths the size of a carnival tent, exquisitely darned in patches as big as your palm. These, together with Miss Nancy, were contained in the lovely crumbling Ravenet mansion on the Battery.

Miss Nancy herself was good and sick of all this ghostly splendor. She was tired of homemade underwear and impecunious Charleston beaux, all of whom gave the effect, somehow, of wearing black satin stocks and looking like Lafayette in modern (but not very modern) clothes. Layer by layer, like the choicest sweets in a box of candy, these had offered themselves for Miss Nancy's taking. Layer by layer she had rejected them, and they had been gobbled up elsewhere. She hoped for richer fare, but the years slipped by and now she was twenty-six, and the box held only those moldy uninviting items vulgarly known as spit-backs—green bonbons with a tooth-mark on them; candied violets; hard pellets covered with tarnished silver coating.

The adjectives "beautiful" and "Southern" have learned automatically to leap into position behind belle. But Nancy Ravenet was beautiful, and she was Southern, and she was a belle. She was not one of your black-haired, smoldering jujubes. She was all creamy, like a magnolia. Her pale gold hair was like thick smooth yellow cream, and hers was the cream-white Southern skin about which so many poets have so romantically sung— and which is due to the habits of eating hot breads, sitting in dim, jalousied rooms, and taking no exercise. Her languorous manner was largely anæmia.

When she met Carlton Schurtz II she did not raise her Southern voice in accents of vivacity; she did not lift a finger; she scarcely fluttered an eyelash. He dined at the Ravenets' and was served beaten biscuit, which he found completely indigestible, and tough old chicken and homemade wine, and said he hadn't eaten anything like it in years—which certainly was true.

He got, by some magic wangling, an invitation to the St. Cecilia Ball and saw her there queening it in an evening dress so shabby that, even in that collection of dated finery, it stood out with a kind of splendid distinction. Carlton, the rankest of outsiders at this almost sacred function, had difficulty in getting a dance with her. She drifted dreamily off, in dance after dance, with this or that lafayette. Carlton Schurtz, in his London clothes, stood in the ballroom doorway, his eyes suddenly misting (sentimental Negro music and bad punch) as they followed the shabby figure of distinction moving languorously about the dance floor.

"An emerald," he resolved, his gaze resting a moment on her ringless left hand against a black coat sleeve. "Square-cut, the size of a Bronx-express headlight. Black velvet by Worth. Gray crêpe, with handmade collar and

cuff things, by Molyneux. Dull green tea gowns. Schia-
parelli sports things to watch me drive off from the first
tee. One whole closet for shoes and another for hats.
Stockings you can stuff into a thimble."

For he, with his millions, had been around by the time
he was fifty-one.

Twenty-five years older than she, but not too unattrac-
tive. Bald, eyeglassed, but a fair waistline saved by golf,
massage, and the New York Athletic Club. The sun—
when sun was available—and the sun-ray lamp when it
was not, gave him a look of tanned health the year round.

His nails were too well manicured. He was terribly
neat. He wore a dark burgundy dinner suit at home. A
house in East Sixty-seventh Street. A house at South-
ampton.

If Camilla, now aged three, had been a boy, there would
have been no Camilla. Carlton Schurtz, in his mid-fifties,
must have male issue to prove his virility and satisfy the
egotism of an old bachelor who has married a young wife.
Like a last amazing floral setpiece of fireworks terminat-
ing an evening of conventional skyrockets and Roman
candles, Carlton Schurtz III was produced to the accompaniment of rapturous oh's and ah's. Then darkness. The
entertainment was ended. Camilla, three. Carlton III,
eighteen months.

As Mrs. Carlton Schurtz opened her eyes on this particular March morning it was to the dim consciousness of
something not quite pleasant lying in store for her to-
day. She lay a moment, still half asleep. The room was
pleasant, orderly, accustomed. The angular rods, tubes,
slabs, and metals of the modernistic had no part in this
room of soft curves, of blurred chintz, of cushions and
curtains and gleaming taffetas. The French windows
opened on the garden at the back of the house.

The day, she saw, was one of those fantastically blue-
and-gold April days with which New York, the show-off,
occasionally struts its stuff in March. When Mrs. Schurtz
pressed the enameled knob at the side of her bed, her

breakfast tray would appear. All this she saw and knew. Still, the heavy-hearted half-consciousness.

Today—something—something not quite pleasant. Today—oh, yes. It came over her, depressingly. Today was Fräulein's day out.

During the week Mrs. Schurtz was hardly conscious of Fräulein Berta's presence in the household, except as an admirable machine that functioned perfectly. It was on Fräulein Berta's day out that her presence made itself felt. On Fräulein's day out, Mrs. Carlton Schurtz, inexpertly assisted by Millie, the parlor maid, was in charge of her offspring from two in the afternoon, when Berta left, until midnight, or thereabouts, when she returned. It required all the following day to restore Mrs. Schurtz to a normal state of nerves, health, and self-respect.

"I don't know how she does it," Nancy confessed to her husband, at the end of these nurseless days. "I follow her routine exactly. I do every single thing that she does— food, nap, park, bath—everything. And they behave like fiends. Perhaps it's because I love them too much. Children sense these things in electric waves."

"Maybe she drugs 'em," Carlton suggested.

Whatever the cause, certainly the Schurtz cherubs became demons the moment they opened their eyes after their afternoon nap to find their lovely parent bending over them. They were like spirited horses who sense the inexpert seat in the saddle. Fräulein was able, day after day, to stuff incredible masses of food into them—lamb chops, mashed vegetables, stewed fruits, eggs, cereal, milk, junket, bacon. Under their mother's loving eye Camilla messed her food round and round on her plate, and even dropped plops of it on the nursery floor, while Carlton III flatly refused to perform the act of swallowing but allowed his cereal or his egg to drool out of the corners of his mouth and down his chin, a revolting sight. That rosebud orifice, opening like an obedient flower at Berta's behest, now became a maddening, twisting trap.

True to the daily ritual, Mrs. Schurtz, with Millie, took the children to the park in the afternoon, choosing

a spot near—but not too near—the nursemaids with
whom Fräulein consorted on her workdays. Long before
the allotted time you saw them returning to Sixty-seventh
Street, tired, disheveled. The children had a wild gleam
in their eyes. Sometimes (when they had been particularly devilish) Nancy Schurtz thought it was a glare of
actual triumph.

Bath time was as bad. Camilla threw her new white
shoes into the tub. Carlton III slapped his mother's magnolia cheek with a wet, soapy, and astonishingly forceful
fist. They howled.

The Schurtzes never went out on the evening of Fräulein's day off. Nancy wore one of her softly gleaming
house gowns and dined alone with Carlton, looking pale
and drooping and flower-like, as always—a magnolia
gone a little brown around the edges.

Mrs. Schurtz did not mind staying home on the evening of Fräulein's day out. She would have liked it better, perhaps, if she could have spent the evening alone.
She had very few evenings alone. She and Carlton went
to the theater. They had friends to dinner. They dined
out. They played bridge.

Carlton had made hundreds—sometimes she thought
thousands—of friends in those fifty-one years of his
bachelorhood. He was loyal to all of them. He took for
granted that Nancy would like them all. Sometimes she
thought longingly of the crumbling old house on the Battery, and the shabby lafayettes, and the wild-turkey dinners of her Charleston days. The house had been sold to
Northerners.

She was, though she never confessed it to herself,
bored. She was bored with the everlasting dinners, and
the Schurtz friends, and the emerald as big as a Bronx-
express headlight, and the velvet house gowns, and having her hair waved and her nails done a deep rose. She
was bored, in a word, with Carlton Schurtz II, though
fond of him. She was luckier, she knew, than most women.
She urged him to go down to Asheville or to White Sulphur for the golf. Alone.

"It will do you good. You look sort of washed-out."

"I need a shave."

"Nonsense. You've been looking fagged for a month."

"When do you want to go?"

"Oh, I don't want to go. You. Besides, I wouldn't leave the children. All this flu around."

"Fräulein'll handle them. She's a wonder, that girl." Carlton stood a moment, collar and tie in hand, as though struck by a sudden thought. "What a life for a young girl! She can't be more than twenty-three. Taking care of somebody else's kids, stuffing food into 'em and wiping their noses. A good-looking girl, too. Fresh-looking." Unconsciously his gaze rested a moment on Nancy, seated before her dressing table.

Nancy selected a bracelet from her box, slipped it on her wrist, surveyed the effect, her hand and arm outstretched in the immemorial gesture that Helen used, and Cleopatra, and all women who have been decked with jewels by men.

"She isn't bad-looking, really, in a wholesome, peasant kind of way. Of course her cheekbones—and those thick ankles. I think, given a choice, that I'd almost rather have an ugly face than thick ankles."

"Are they thick? She just wears those sensible shoes, doesn't she? Working?"

Nancy glanced down at her own slim, delicate feet. Her ankles could be encircled with a thumb and second finger.

"They're sensible, goodness knows. So is she. And a little thick, too, like her ankles. I suppose if she weren't she couldn't stand it, poor thing. I wonder if she ever has any fun. I don't think she even has a beau. What do you suppose she does, from two until midnight, on her day out? Goes and sits with some friend, I suppose, who's taking care of somebody else's children."

Carlton laughed appreciatively. "Busman's holiday."

Some of these thoughts were drifting through Nancy's mind now as she finished her breakfast. There was a scuffling sound at the door, voices, then a firm little rap.

"Come in!"

Fräulein, with the children. Suddenly the quiet dim bedroom burst into a thousand sparks of light, color, sound. Camilla, in broadcloth and fur and leggings, looking perversely like Carlton II; Carlton III, in broadcloth and fur and leggings, looking like an exquisite edition of Nancy. Their faces glowed, bloomed, seemed to give out actual light. The whites of their eyes were a healthy blue.

Fräulein brought them to the slim pale figure in the bed. There was about Fräulein a quiet vitality. She did not bustle. This vital quality went from her body in warm, sustaining waves. The children felt it, thrived on it. You rested on it, drew life from it as from the earth when you throw yourself upon it, gratefully, in the first days of spring. Both blonde, Nancy's blondeness, beside Fräulein's, was that of an exotic orchid beside a sturdy plume of stock.

"Oh. Hello, darlings. . . . Don't *do* that, Camilla dearest. Mother has a tiny headache this morning. . . . Did you put the drops up his nose, Fräulein? . . . You don't think he ought to stay in the house today with Millie, do you, while I take Camilla out? . . . Well, I just thought . . . Oh, is it? Just the same, it isn't spring yet —not really, I mean. This is the dangerous time of year, when it's too warm for winter things and too cold for summer—and I'd hate to have Camilla catch Carlton's cold. . . . Well, whatever it is. . . . I—uh—suppose you wouldn't want to stay in today just until four, instead of leaving at two? I just thought if you hadn't planned to do anything special."

"I have planned," said Fräulein. She spoke with the least trace of an accent. Her *v* was likely to be more *f* than *v*. Her voice vibrated now with a strange intensity.

"Oh. Well." Privately she thought—planned, fiddlesticks! Planned what!

Carlton on her arm, Camilla by the hand, Fräulein moved toward the door. The room seemed close. She longed to be out in the crisp air. She was dressed for the street, as were the children. She descended with them in the little electric lift. Carlton puffed out his cheeks and made big eyes and pounded the brilliantly painted metal walls with his soft fist. He was feeling the spring. Camilla leaned against Fräulein's thigh for balance. She did not like riding in the lift.

"So!" said Fräulein, stepping out at the street floor. "The park, the park! In the sun, the sun!"

"Park the park in the sun the sun!" echoed Camilla, skipping. Carlton III, catching the spirit of the thing, squealed.

Frederick was dusting the hall. For the past twenty minutes he had been dusting the hall, which contained three articles of furniture. Fräulein was fifteen minutes past her usual schedule. The drops in Carlton's nose.

He stood in their way. His eyes glowed. He put a hand on Camilla's head, patting it. The hand would have trembled had it not patted. "Are you off today?"

"What do you care?"

"I'm off, too, after dinner tonight. They're only having two, for bridge, after dinner. Millie will serve them. We'll go to a movie. Will you? A dollar one, downtown."

Fräulein shook her head from side to side.

"Why not? Why not? You haven't got a date." This was bravado.

Fräulein shook her head, up and down, this time.

"With who?" He transferred the hand from Camilla's head to Fräulein's arm. The fingers tightened. "With who? Not with that wop! That greasy mechanic—that Louie!"

"Co-*mon!*" whined Camilla, tired of the dark hallway. She jerked Fräulein's skirts. "Co-*mon*, Fräu'n."

"Yes, my darling." She plumped Carlton into his English pram, tucked the rich robes about him.

"Berta! Answer me."

"I have an engagement."

"Yes. All right. But is it with him? Is it——"

She opened the front door. There at the curb stood Louie, the chauffeur. He was doing something to the car, with his eyes on the front door. When he saw Fräulein he pinned down the engine hood and sprang to help her as she bumped the heavy pram down the two steps to the sidewalk. A tall, thin Italian with a scar on the left cheek. His uniform—tightly fitted and buttoned coat and smart cap—gave him a false air of distinction.

"I'll drive you over to the park," he said. "The madam don't want me till eleven."

"The baby's buggy."

"I'll put it in the front."

"I'd rather walk. It's only three blocks. It's healthier. Such a beautiful morning."

She turned toward the park. Louie followed her. Frederick, in his work apron, stood helpless in the doorway gazing after them. Camilla trotted by Fräulein's side. Fräulein's hands rested lightly on the pram handle.

Louie glanced sharply round at the discreetly curtained house windows. Then he put one lean brown hand over one of hers. "Listen, golden-haired darling. They are at home tonight. I am off. We'll go to dinner— Italian, with red wine, at Salvatore's. And a movie."

She shook her head.

"A show, then. A real show, with dancing. Or we could go somewhere and dance. Roseland."

"I can't. I have a date."

The dark face grew darker. The scar leaped out, queerly purple. "With that Austrian? With that Frederick?"

"It is no business of yours who with. You must go back. If the madam sees you like this from the window!"

They had reached the corner. She grasped Camilla's hand, looked right and left, smiled at the corner policeman, received his nod and wave to come on, made a dash for it. Louie stood a moment on the curb; turned, defeated, his smart black boots glittering in the sunlight.

The East Sixties and the East Seventies were dotted with nursemaids stepping briskly along toward the park with their charges. They wore good cloth coats with real fur collars, thick and soft; and smart felt hats and good gloves and silk stockings and excellent shoes, sometimes

with trim galoshes over them as protection against the
nipping cold. They were the most expensively dressed
nursemaids in the world. Everything they wore was good
and modish. They and their charges had been up since
seven. They were all full of prunes and cereal and bacon
and toast and milk and orange juice.

An April day, gone completely mad, had leaped ahead
of its fellows and plumped itself wantonly into the lap
of March. New York was sharp-cut in outline. The high
white buildings pierced the blue of the sky. The Pierre,
at Sixty-third, dazzled the eye. The trees in the park had
not yet budded, yet to the knowing gaze there was dis-
cernible just the faintest hint of swelling along the
branches etched against the blue.

Fräulein's sentimental Teutonic soul could stand it no
longer, what with the signs of spring, the importunings
of butler and chauffeur, and the prospect of the day
ahead of her. She must find relief in poetry.

" '. . . das Saatkorn dort, und wartet still,
    Ob's wieder Frühling werden will.' "

She looked up at the trees. She looked down at Camilla. She gave a little skip and a rush with the pram.
"Frühling! Frühling, mein Kind," she trilled.

Camilla skipped, too, catching the spirit of the thing.
"Fweeling! Fweeling!"

Life was very agreeable, Fräulein thought.

She had her special little place in the park, where her
exclusive coterie of nursemaid friends forgathered. They
were very snobbish and select. Their charges were all children of the rich. These played primly on the cement
paths, or slept in their perambulators. They wore tiny
fur coats, miniature editions of the pelts in which their
mothers were swathed; and white or pale blue broadcloth
leggings and chic bonnets to match. As you strolled past
the little group in the lemon-yellow spring sunshine there
came up to sensitive nostrils the scent which—next to
new-mown hay—is in the whole world the most pure and

exquisite: the scent given out by the flesh of very small clean babies.

They were all there, for she was a little late—Fräulein Lotta and Fräulein Hedwig and Fräulein Carola and Fräulein Greta, and Mademoiselle Marcelle, and Miss Peake in her English uniform of blue, with cape and veil, *fesch* but silly, that uniform, Berta always thought. Quite an international little group. They looked very blooming, these girls, for they were out of doors every day from ten to twelve, and from three to five, sitting or walking in the brilliant New York sunshine. In the winter their knees, as they ranged along the park benches, were snugly tucked in warm woolen robes.

They conversed in English, in German, in French— but mostly in English. They talked of their employers, they talked of their households, of international politics, of economics, of books, of the *Valuta*, of this mad America, of their memories of Europe, of their parents in the old country. All this interspersed with calls or commands to their little charges trotting about the confines of the park path.

"I have got off today."

"I wish I had. Such a day. What will you make?"

"Oh, plenty."

"He's got off, too?"

"Sure. Every two weeks, only."

". . . fighting in Düsseldorf on the streets. It was never like that in the old days of the Kaiser."

"Kaiser! That old *Narr!* He made all the trouble."

"They are like children here in America. They play golf and backgammon and ride around in automobiles going nowhere and drink out of bottles gin and whisky like coachmen, when the whole world is falling in pieces. Well, they will fall, too."

"Was machts du denn! 'Wirst schmutzig! Komm 'mal hier, du!"

"Ca-mee-la! Give it to him back! But yes, I say! It belongs to him; give it to him back. Play with your own dolly."

"She gets a new fur coat for summer, my madam. Did you ever hear of such foolishness!"

"Mine works on committees now and says it is sinful to buy new clothes. I thought she would give me that dress with the white satin tie, but no, she wears it."

They sewed. They read a little. They scrutinized the world going by, and commented on it—plump matrons bound for the two-mile walk around the reservoir; a boy and a girl deep in their own affairs, the boy talking, talking, his voice low and urgent, the girl listening with bent head; rheumy old men, shuffling by in the sun. Sometimes their men friends, temporarily free, or unemployed, strolled round to chat with them. But this they discouraged. They did not approve. It was common.

Twelve o'clock. Like so many noonday Cinderellas, they rose and vanished.

Fräulein kept a sharp eye out for Frederick and Louie. She did not want to encounter them again. The silly fools.

Dinner in the nursery—meat and vegetables and junket. The children ate well, and obediently, not playing with their food as they sometimes did. *Gott sei Dank*, she would be out by two, or even one-thirty, if they fell asleep quickly. Would she wait until four! Ha! That was good, that was. She, too, ate her good, hot, nourishing dinner from a leaden tray in the nursery.

Now they were in bed, each tucked in a little downy cell, Camilla in a pink silk cell, Carlton III in a blue. She tried not to communicate to them the waves of her own inner excitement. That would keep them from sleeping.

There. They slept. Full of food, they slept, their arms above their heads. Berta, too, was fed, not only by good food but by the warmth of their sturdy growing bodies, by the velvet touch of their clinging fingers, by their trust in her, their nearness to her, their very demands on her. She gave to them, but they, too, gave to her, and sustained her. The sound of their soft rhythmic breathing was like music in her ears.

Fräulein dressed quickly. Her best coat, with the real fox fur collar, that She had given her, and the smart

tight hat that exposed one whole side of her rich golden
hair, and her Christmas gloves and her strap slippers
with the high heels that made her ankles look quite slim.
She had seen people on the streets—on Park Avenue and
Fifth, with straw hats already, in March and even Febru-
ary. Let them, the simpletons. She had better use than
that for her money.

There. She was dressed. It was not yet two. The door
opened and She came in. "Oh, Fräulein. Are you going
al——"

"Sh-sh! Please. They are asleep."

"But——"

Fräulein's blue eyes blazed. She tiptoed swiftly toward
the door, ushering Her through it by the very force of her
resentment, closed it firmly, soundlessly, behind her.
"Everything is done. They are sleeping. Their milk is in
the ice box ready for them at three. Take it out fifteen
minutes before, so it is not too cold. The drops in Carlchen's nose before he goes to bed . . . Scraped apple
. . . no egg . . ."

She was gone. As nurse, she was entitled to leave
through the front door, but Louie knew this and Frederick. She would go through the service door and fly up the
street toward Madison, giving them the slip. They would
be watching the front door. She stole toward the kitchen.
She was early. Perhaps they still were there. Voices, high,
in argument or anger. She stopped, listened.

"Yeah, wouldn't you like to know!" sneeringly. Frederick's voice.

"Go on, Dutchy! She's meeting me at seven, and what
do you know about that!"

"Lying wop!"

The clatter of a knife or fork thrown down violently
among the china; the sound of a chair pushed back,
scraping, against the floor. Slap! A little yelping scream.
Cook's voice. They were fighting! Frederick and Louie
were fighting over her! She turned, fled, up to the front
hall, out to the street, up toward Madison Avenue. Her
eyes sparkled. Her lips were parted in a smile. Two men

fighting over her. Poor sticks they were, and that Louie had a wife, and both were beneath her notice, but men, nevertheless, young and personable. It gave one a feeling of power.

She took the Madison Avenue street car. She was not used to walking in these high heels, and then, too, she must save time. She got off at her bank corner, and went in and sent the usual monthly money order to her mother in Germany. Ten good American dollars. Here in America ten dollars was considered nothing. There it would buy the old people meat, and heat and clothes, even. It meant the difference between comfort and starvation. She knew.

Over to Fifty-ninth Street. In the big block-square department store she did a little wise, scanty shopping. A pair of silk stockings, fifty-nine cents, very good. A suit of men's pajamas, blue, and a man's necktie at the sale counter. Men should wear blue. It made their skin look clear and fresh. She paid for these, took the bundles with her. Over to the Five and Ten. A comb, a spool of white thread, a little packet of tacks, and a yard of oilcloth shelving in a bluebird pattern. The aisles were packed with women pawing over bead necklaces, ribbons, candy, bracelets. She eyed them contemptuously. Throwing away good money.

She took the subway to Ninety-sixth Street, walked back a block to Ninety-fifth and entered a huge brick modern tenement that was a hive for human beings. Her strong young legs made nothing of the five flights up which she must walk. Down to the very end of the long, prisonlike corridor with its double row of shut doors.

She took the key from her purse, unlocked the door at the end of the passage, closed it, locked it again. She stood a moment, looking about her. Her back to the door, she shut her eyes a moment, as if in ecstasy, breathed deeply, opened them quickly as though in fear that the sight before her might vanish.

A small, square, low-ceilinged room, clean, bright, but untidy. Two good windows facing south. The March mid-afternoon sun came in beneath the partly drawn shades. The shades were a little awry, one up, one down. Her bundles still in her arms, she marched toward the windows, threw them open, straightened the shades.

A double bed, unmade. A table, with books and papers and a green-shaded lamp. A shelf with books. A commode with drawers. A comfortable armchair covered neatly with cretonne. Fräulein had covered it. Two straight-backed chairs. The floor was bare except for three small rugs made of carpet-squares that had been scoured in soap and water, very bright.

Fräulein took another long, deep, soul-filling breath, tossed her packages on the table and plunged in. She took off her dress, her corset, her high-heeled shoes, her stockings. From the closet she took an enveloping work apron and a pair of loose old slippers. Then, barelegged and unstayed, she snatched the covering from the bed, rolled the sheets into a ball and tossed them to one side, turned the heavy mattress with a single gesture of her strong young arms. She placed the stripped feather pillows on the sills of the open windows, to catch the sun.

Leaving the bed to air, she sprinkled some clothes which had been left rolled up in a dry wrinkled ball, for ironing. She washed out two sets of pajamas and some handkerchiefs and underwear extracted from the laundry bag on the closet door, turned the laundry bag inside out, hung it at the window. She went into the tiny bathroom, cleaned and dried the safety razor that lay there, gathered up various small scraps of soap and threw them into a scrub pail.

Next she washed some dishes found, unwashed, in the corner of the room, back of the screen. She attached a small electric iron, ironed the clothes, pressed two pairs of trousers, made up the bed with fresh linen, wiped up with luke-warm water and soap every inch of floor—main room, bathroom, closet. She wasted no step, no gesture. She was like a terribly efficient machine.

In a corner, on a stout little table behind the screen, was a five-gallon crock. This she inspected minutely, sniffing its brownish aromatic contents. It was still fermenting a little. By day after tomorrow the beer would be ready for bottling. She must tell him. Otherwise it would lose its good strength.

That reminded her. She went to the tiny tin ice box. A little cube of ice, and on it two bottles of beer, a little butter, a packet of thin ham slices. He remembered everything.

Half-past four. Otto would be there at quarter after five. She peeled off the work apron, bent over the basin in her underthings and washed her hair. She dried it feverishly, tossing it, rubbing her scalp with a dry towel. She twisted it, still damp, into a knot (Otto would not let her bob it), and bending over the absurdly small bathtub that was little more than an enameled box, she scoured it with powdered cleanser—tub, faucets, waste plate, pipes, everything.

Otto was neater than most men, and very clean, but all men were alike. Still, she thought of old Schurtz, and her nose wrinkled. He was neat, too, old Schurtz. He perfumed his handkerchiefs and was quite the dandy for Her. He wore beautiful silk pajamas that were made for him, measured, like a woman's dress, and fresh bed linen on his bed every night.

"I would rather have Otto in a *Nachthemd* made of flour sacking," she thought, "than that old one with his silk and his sweet-smelling stuff. I wouldn't be in Her shoes, not for any money."

She bathed. She lay in the warm water, relaxing. Out she jumped, rubbed herself briskly with a rough towel, put on a bright wrapper she had taken from its hook in the closet, slipped her feet into coquettisth mules, let down her hair to dry, took a last comprehensive look around. Bright. Shining. Orderly.

She was deliciously relaxed and a little weary, but the weariness was delicious, too. She lay down a minute on the bed; flung herself across it, the mules dangling. The dollar clock ticked on the corner shelf. The bath water dripped a little from that loose faucet. She must tell him

to tighten it. The roar of the street came up, subdued,
even soothing. The heartening smell of something cooking in one of the flats—pot roast, it smelled like.

A key in the lock; the door opened, shut. Wordlessly,
in the dim light, he strode to the bed, gathered her in
his arms, buried his face in the masses of her damp, fragrant hair.

At half-past six they had a bottle of beer each and a
little of the spicy cold ham and one slice of rye bread.
Just enough for an appetizer; not enough to spoil their
good dinner later on.

The lamp lighted, and the top lights, too, she could see
his beloved face. It was the face of a little boy, grown up.
The features had never quite crystallized into maturity.
A high, rather bulging brow, like a child's. A full mouth,
with curling corners, very appealing. Not much chin.
Dark curling hair and brown eyes with a hurt look in
them because he was a little nearsighted and must not
wear glasses. A waiter cannot wear glasses. A weak face,
but sweet for a strong woman to look at. She was strong,
Fräulein. She had strength and courage and resource-
fulness for two.

He was in rebellion, Otto was, against what he called
the Capitalistic Class. He was always saying Capitalism
must go. The people in the hotel in which he worked
were Capitalists, and they must Go. He didn't say where.
He took their tips and handed the money over to the
thrifty Berta, and said that the Capitalistic Class must
Go. Pigs. Slave drivers.

"Of course," Berta agreed. "In two years more, or
three, at the most. Carlchen will be four and Camilla six,
and they will not need me any more, and we shall have
enough money saved, and we can go back home and buy
the little farm. Oh, Otto! Otto! My darling, my darling,
my darling!"

Well, she must dress.

"How brown you are! Golden, like a little high-yellow
girl from Harlem."

"Yes, isn't it beautiful! Every day, when Carlchen and

Camilla have the sun-lamp I have it, too, longer than they, because their skin is too delicate. It makes me strong and healthy, the sun-lamp. And golden all over. She never takes it. She likes her skin white. Ugh!"

Arm in arm, very close together, they walked at a swinging gait down to Eighty-sixth Street in the York-ville section. The neighbourhood was dotted with restaurants bearing roguish German names—Maxl's; Drei Mäderl; Brau Stüberl.

Into the warm bright odorous depths of one of these they popped. Gay checked tablecloths; waiters in Bavarian peasant garb; round shining faces; music in which everybody joined. Emil, the *Ober*, was a *Landsmann* of Otto. Otto, the waiter, was received by this head waiter as he himself, in his waiter's uniform, received a guest of the hated Capitalistic Class. Otto enjoyed this very much.

He and Berta ordered their dinner. Herring salad, chicken noodle soup, *Sauerbraten* with potato balls, apple strudel, coffee. Awaiting this, they buried their faces in enormous foaming steins of beer. They looked at each other across the table. Each reached out for the hand of the other, clasped it a moment, hard; sat back, drank again.

They ate with excellent appetite. Otto had another stein of beer.

Berta shook her head. "Not for me. I don't want to get fat."

"You are just right. I don't like thin."

"Yes. Not thin, like Her, with legs like sticks. But not fat, either. It is not stylish to be fat. Besides, Her good clothes won't fit me if I am not careful."

"Her clothes! You don't need her clothes!" cried Otto, full of class hatred and beer.

"Don't be foolish, Otto darling. Certainly I do. I could not afford to buy anything one tenth as good."

They must go to the Meeting now. Berta was not especially interested in the movement, but Otto was. And the speeches were sometimes interesting, and even exciting. Berta listened and learned and remembered, and held forth, sometimes, to her friends in the park. Otto was a member of a German Nationalistic party with a desire to rule the ruling classes. They set certain dates on which to do it, but it never quite came off. Otto said it would, though, some day, and soon.

The hall was in Eighty-sixth Street, near the East River. It was crowded and hot and hung with emblems, red muslin, posters of a silly-looking man with a Chaplin mustache, no chin, and one mad and one sane eye. Berta, studying it during the speeches, arrived at this conclusion. She did not speak of it to Otto. The speaker said everything three times.

. . . and so, Comrades, we must give the Worker hands, we must give the Worker feet, we must give the Worker strength . . . until we have the knowledge, until we have the power, until we have the Capital . . . we must prepare for the struggle, we must plan for the struggle, we must be ready for the struggle . . .

But I thought Capital was what they didn't want, Berta thought. It all sounded pretty silly to her, but interesting, too, some of it. It stirred you up. Otto was rapt. His knobby forehead shone. Tiny beads stood on his upper lip. She longed to wipe them away with her handkerchief.

It was ten o'clock. Beer was being served. "Let's go. It is so hot in here. We can go to a movie, for the second show, on Lexington."

They emerged into the clear cold March night. A passing boat hooted hoarsely on the river. The secondary picture was finished, the main picture was not yet started, the weekly news pictures were being shown. They were in luck. Blissfully they sat through the picture, in the warm dark intimacy of the luxurious seats. Gorgeously dressed and unbelievably slim creatures glided across the screen.

There was music with this picture, sensual and sentimental music. Otto's hand rested on Berta's knee; her head touched his shoulder. She felt lulled, blissful, a little sleepy, what with food, love, work, talk, beer, and the close air.

Five minutes to twelve.

"Otto! Quick! I must take a taxi."

"Oh, what do you care! What can they do? Come home with me. Please. Darling. *Liebchen.*"

"Don't be foolish, my dearest."

They kissed, there in the bright lights of Lexington and Eighty-sixth. They clung. This the taxi driver regarded with an urban eye.

"Quick. I am late."

"Where to, lady?"

She reached Sixty-seventh Street not more than three minutes after twelve. She let herself in quietly, quietly, but she need not have bothered. The air was rent, shattered, by the screams from the nursery on the top floor.

"*Gott!*" She mounted nimbly, spurning the lift.

Lights blazed in the larger room where Fräulein was wont to sleep with Carlton III, the son, the heir, the Link. Lights blazed in the smaller adjoining room, where lay Camilla in the solitary independence of her adult three years. Fräulein blinked a little, dazedly, what with the lights, and weariness, and the rush up the stairs.

Nancy Schurtz turned, a distraught figure, looking yellow and drawn in her pale blue robe. She turned on a torrent of words above the shrieks of the two infants.

"I thought you'd never come. I can't do anything with them. It's after midnight. We had just got to sleep. The Frasers left at eleven. I was dead. I dreamed that I was riding a horse I used to own, long ago, in Charleston, and I felt myself slipping, and I was under the horse's hoofs and he was trampling me, and neighing in a perfect scream and I woke up and it was Carlton, here, screaming. I had left his nursery door open, of course, because you were out.

"There isn't a thing the matter with him. Not a thing. I've had every stitch off him, and put him on his chair, and he wouldn't. I took his temperature. He hasn't stopped screaming for fifteen minutes. It's sheer devilment, and Camilla, too. I'm worn out. Such a day. They've been fiends. Everything's been horrible. Fred-

erick and Louis had some quarrel, and Frederick gave
notice. I'm sure I don't know—and—— Listen to that!
I'll spank him, that's what I'll——"

"Go to bed," said Fräulein, calmly. She hung up her
coat, went over to the red-faced, howling infant in the
blue silk cell. "They will be quiet now." She felt the boy's
sleeping garment, wet with sweat. She unbuttoned it,
peeled him deftly, wiped him, powdered him, dressed him
in a dry garment. She turned out the top lights. His
howls abated, and with his, Camilla's. "Go to bed,
madam."

The child's arm reached up, the hand rested on her
cheek; she turned her head and kissed the soft warm
palm. Deep, quivering sighs shook him. Suddenly, miraculously, in that instant, he was asleep. Fräulein made
motions with her lips, with her free hand, with her head.
They spelled go—go.

Mrs. Carlton Schurtz went back to bed. Carlton
Schurtz II opened one fishy gray eye. Whazza?

"Nothing. She's here. They're quieter. Little devils.
Poor thing. I wouldn't take her job—not if I were starving. What a life!"

Edna St. Vincent Millay

SONNETS

XXXVI

HEARING your words, and not a word among them
Tuned to my liking, on a salty day
When inland woods were pushed by winds that flung them
Hissing to leeward like a ton of spray,
I thought how off Matinicus the tide
Came pounding in, came running through the Gut,
While from the Rock the warning whistle cried,
And children whimpered, and the doors blew shut;
There in the autumn when the men go forth,
With slapping skirts the island women stand
In gardens stripped and scattered, peering north,
With dahlia tubers dripping from the hand:
The wind of their endurance, driving south,
Flattened your words against your speaking mouth.

XLV

I know my mind and I have made my choice;
Not from your temper does my doom depend;
Love me or love me not, you have no voice
In this, my portion to the end.
Your presence and your favours, the full part
That you could give, you now can take away:
What lies between your beauty and my heart
Not even you can trouble or betray.
Mistake me not—unto my inmost core
I do desire your kiss upon my mouth;
They have not craved a cup of water more
That bleach upon the deserts of the south;
Here might you bless me; what you cannot do
Is bow me down, that have been loved by you.

XLVII

Well, I have lost you; and I lost you fairly;
In my own way, and with my full consent.
Say what you will, kings in a tumbrel rarely
Went to their deaths more proud than this one went.
Some nights of apprehension and hot weeping
I will confess; but that's permitted me;
Day dried my eyes; I was not one for keeping
Rubbed in a cage a wing that would be free.
If I had loved you less or played you slyly
I might have held you for a summer more,
But at the cost of words I value highly,
And no such summer as the one before.
Should I outlive this anguish—and men do—
I shall have only good to say of you.

H. G. Wells

THE FLOWERING OF THE STRANGE ORCHID

THE buying of orchids always has in it a certain speculative flavour. You have before you the brown shrivelled lump of tissue, and for the rest you must trust your judgment, or the auctioneer, or your good-luck, as your taste may incline. The plant may be moribund or dead, or it may be just a respectable purchase, fair value for your money, or perhaps—for the thing has happened again and again—there slowly unfolds before the delighted eyes of the happy purchaser, day after day, some new variety, some novel richness, a strange twist of the labellum, or some subtler coloration or unexpected mimicry. Pride, beauty, and profit blossom together on one delicate green spike, and, as it may be, even immortality. For the new miracle of Nature may stand in need of a new specific name, and what so convenient as that of its discoverer? "Johnsmithia"! There have been worse names.

It was perhaps the hope of some such happy discovery that made Winter-Wedderburn such a frequent attendant at these sales—that hope, and also, maybe, the fact that he had nothing else of the slightest interest to do in the world. He was a shy, lonely, rather ineffectual man, provided with just enough income to keep off the spur of necessity, and not enough nervous energy to make him seek any exacting employment. He might have collected stamps or coins, or translated Horace, or bound books, or invented new species of diatoms. But, as it happened, he grew orchids, and had one ambitious little hothouse.

"I have a fancy," he said over his coffee, "that something is going to happen to me to-day." He spoke—as he moved and thought—slowly.

"Oh, don't say *that!*" said his housekeeper—who was

also his remote cousin. For "something happening" was a euphemism that meant only one thing to her.

"You misunderstand me. I mean nothing unpleasant . . . though what I do mean I scarcely know.

"To-day," he continued, after a pause, "Peters' are going to sell a batch of plants from the Andamans and the Indies. I shall go up and see what they have. It may be I shall buy something good, unawares. That may be it."

He passed his cup for his second cupful of coffee.

"Are those the things collected by that poor young fellow you told me of the other day?" asked his cousin as she filled his cup.

"Yes," he said, and became meditative over a piece of toast.

"Nothing ever does happen to me," he remarked presently, beginning to think aloud. "I wonder why? Things enough happen to other people. There is Harvey. Only the other week—on Monday he picked up sixpence, on Wednesday his chicks all had the staggers, on Friday his cousin came home from Australia, and on Saturday he broke his ankle. What a whirl of excitement!—compared to me."

"I think I would rather be without so much excitement," said his housekeeper. "It can't be good for you."

"I suppose it's troublesome. Still . . . you see, nothing ever happens to me. When I was a little boy I never had accidents. I never fell in love as I grew up. Never married. . . . I wonder how it feels to have something happen to you, something really remarkable.

"That orchid-collector was only thirty-six—twenty years younger than myself—when he died. And he had been married twice and divorced once; he had had malarial fever four times, and once he broke his thigh. He killed a Malay once, and once he was wounded by a poisoned dart. And in the end he was killed by jungle-leeches. It must have all been very troublesome, but then it must have been very interesting, you know—except, perhaps, the leeches."

"I am sure it was not good for him," said the lady, with conviction.

"Perhaps not." And then Wedderburn looked at his watch. "Twenty-three minutes past eight. I am going up by the quarter to twelve train, so that there is plenty of time. I think I shall wear my alpaca jacket—it is quite warm enough—and my grey felt hat and brown shoes. I suppose——"

He glanced out of the window at the serene sky and sunlit garden, and then nervously at his cousin's face.

"I think you had better take an umbrella if you are going to London," she said in a voice that admitted of no denial. "There's all between here and the station coming back."

When he returned he was in a state of mild excitement. He had made a purchase. It was rare that he could make up his mind quickly enough to buy, but this time he had done so.

"There are Vandas," he said, "and a Dendrobe and some Palæonophis." He surveyed his purchases lovingly as he consumed his soup. They were laid out on the spotless tablecloth before him, and he was telling his cousin all about them as he slowly meandered through his dinner. It was his custom to live all his visits to London over again in the evening for her and his own entertainment.

"I knew something would happen to-day. And I have bought all these. Some of them—some of them—I feel sure, do you know, that some of them will be remarkable. I don't know how it is, but I feel just as sure as if some-one had told me that some of these will turn out remarkable.

"That one"—he pointed to a shrivelled rhizome—"was not identified. It may be a Palæonophis—or it may not. It may be a new species, or even a new genus. And it was the last that poor Batten ever collected."

"I don't like the look of it," said his housekeeper. "It's such an ugly shape."

"To me it scarcely seems to have a shape."

"I don't like those things that stick out," said his house-keeper.

"It shall be put away in a pot to-morrow."

"It looks," said the housekeeper, "like a spider sham-ming dead."

Wedderburn smiled and surveyed the root with his head on one side. "It is certainly not a pretty lump of stuff. But you can never judge of these things from their dry appearance. It may turn out to be a very beautiful orchid indeed. How busy I shall be to-morrow! I must see to-night just exactly what to do with these things, and to-morrow I shall set to work.

"They found poor Batten lying dead, or dying, in a mangrove swamp—I forget which," he began again pres-ently, "with one of these very orchids crushed up under his body. He had been unwell for some days with some kind of native fever, and I suppose he fainted. These man-grove swamps are very unwholesome. Every drop of blood, they say, was taken out of him by the jungle-leeches. It may be that very plant that cost him his life to obtain."

"I think none the better of it for that."

"Men must work though women may weep," said Wed-derburn with profound gravity.

"Fancy dying away from every comfort in a nasty swamp! Fancy being ill of fever with nothing to take but chlorodyne and quinine—if men were left to themselves they would live on chlorodyne and quinine—and no one round you but horrible natives! They say the Andaman islanders are most disgusting wretches—and, anyhow, they can scarcely make good nurses, not having the neces-sary training. And just for people in England to have orchids!"

"I don't suppose it was comfortable, but some men seem to enjoy that kind of thing," said Wedderburn. "Any-how, the natives of his party were sufficiently civilised to take care of all his collection until his colleague, who was an ornithologist, came back again from the interior; though they could not tell the species of the orchid and had let it wither. And it makes these things more interesting."

"It makes them disgusting. I should be afraid of some of the malaria clinging to them. And just think, there has been a dead body lying across that ugly thing! I never thought of that before. There! I declare I cannot eat another mouthful of dinner."

"I will take them off the table if you like, and put them in the window-seat. I can see them just as well there."

The next few days he was indeed singularly busy in his steamy little hothouse, fussing about with charcoal, lumps of teak, moss, and all the other mysteries of the orchid cultivator. He considered he was having a wonderfully eventful time. In the evening he would talk about these new orchids to his friends, and over and over again he reverted to his expectation of something strange.

Several of the Vandas and the Dendrobium died under his care, but presently the strange orchid began to show signs of life. He was delighted and took his housekeeper right away from jam-making to see it at once, directly he made the discovery.

"That is a bud," he said, "and presently there will be a lot of leaves there, and those little things coming out here are aërial rootlets."

"They look to me like little white fingers poking out of the brown," said his housekeeper. "I don't like them."

"Why not?"

"I don't know. They look like fingers trying to get at you. I can't help my likes and dislikes."

"I don't know for certain, but I don't *think* there are any orchids I know that have aërial rootlets quite like that. It may be my fancy, of course. You see they are a little flattened at the ends."

"I don't like 'em," said his housekeeper, suddenly shivering and turning away. "I know it's very silly of me—and I'm very sorry, particularly as you like the thing so much. But I can't help thinking of that corpse."

"But it may not be that particular plant. That was merely a guess of mine."

His housekeeper shrugged her shoulders. "Anyhow I don't like it," she said.

Wedderburn felt a little hurt at her dislike to the plant. But that did not prevent his talking to her about orchids generally, and this orchid in particular, whenever he felt inclined.

"There are such queer things about orchids," he said one day; "such possibilities of surprises. You know, Darwin studied their fertilisation, and showed that the whole structure of an ordinary orchid-flower was contrived in order that moths might carry the pollen from plant to plant. Well, it seems that there are lots of orchids known the flower of which cannot possibly be used for fertilisation in that way. Some of the Cypripediums, for instance; there are no insects known that can possibly fertilise them, and some of them have never been found with seed."

"But how do they form new plants?"

"By runners and tubers, and that kind of outgrowth. That is easily explained. The puzzle is, what are the flowers for?"

"Very likely," he added, "*my* orchid may be something extraordinary in that way. If so I shall study it. I have often thought of making researches as Darwin did. But hitherto I have not found the time, or something else has happened to prevent it. The leaves are beginning to unfold now. I do wish you would come and see them!"

But she said that the orchid-house was so hot it gave her the headache. She had seen the plant once again, and the aërial rootlets, which were now some of them more than a foot long, had unfortunately reminded her of tentacles reaching out after something; and they got into her dreams, growing after her with incredible rapidity. So that she had settled to her entire satisfaction that she would not see that plant again, and Wedderburn had to admire its leaves alone. They were of the ordinary broad form, and a deep glossy green, with splashes and dots of deep red towards the base. He knew of no other leaves quite like them. The plant was placed on a low bench near the thermometer, and close by was a simple arrangement by which a tap dripped on the hot-water pipes and kept the air steamy. And he spent his afternoons now with some regularity meditating on the approaching flowering of this strange plant.

And at last the great thing happened. Directly he entered the little glass house he knew that the spike had burst out, although his great *Palæonophis Lowii* hid the corner where his new darling stood. There was a new odour in the air, a rich, intensely sweet scent, that overpowered every other in that crowded, steaming little greenhouse.

Directly he noticed this he hurried down to the strange orchid. And, behold! the trailing green spikes bore now three great splashes of blossom, from which this overpowering sweetness proceeded. He stopped before them in an ecstasy of admiration.

The flowers were white, with streaks of golden orange upon the petals; the heavy labellum was coiled into an intricate projection, and a wonderful bluish purple mingled there with the gold. He could see at once that the genus was altogether a new one. And the insufferable scent! How hot the place was! The blossoms swam before his eyes.

He would see if the temperature was right. He made a step towards the thermometer. Suddenly everything appeared unsteady. The bricks on the floor were dancing up and down. Then the white blossoms, the green leaves behind them, the whole greenhouse, seemed to sweep sideways, and then in a curve upward.

· · · · · · · · ·

At half-past four his cousin made the tea, according to their invariable custom. But Wedderburn did not come in for his tea.

"He is worshipping that horrid orchid," she told herself, and waited ten minutes. "His watch must have stopped. I will go and call him."

She went straight to the hothouse, and, opening the door, called his name. There was no reply. She noticed that the air was very close, and loaded with an intense

perfume. Then she saw something lying on the bricks between the hot-water pipes.

For a minute, perhaps, she stood motionless.

He was lying, face upward, at the foot of the strange
orchid. The tentacle-like aërial rootlets no longer swayed
freely in the air, but were crowded together, a tangle of
grey ropes, and stretched tight with their ends closely
applied to his chin and neck and hands.

She did not understand. Then she saw from under one
of the exultant tentacles upon his cheek there trickled a
little thread of blood.

With an inarticulate cry she ran towards him, and tried
to pull him away from the leech-like suckers. She snapped
two of these tentacles, and their sap dripped red.

Then the overpowering scent of the blossom began to
make her head reel. How they clung to him! She tore at
the tough ropes, and he and the white inflorescence swam
about her. She felt she was fainting, knew she must not.
She left him and hastily opened the nearest door, and,
after she had panted for a moment in the fresh air, she
had a brilliant inspiration. She caught up a flower-pot
and smashed in the windows at the end of the greenhouse.
Then she reëntered. She tugged now and with renewed
strength at Wedderburn's motionless body, and brought
the strange orchid crashing to the floor. It still clung
with the grimmest tenacity to its victim. In a frenzy, she
lugged it and him into the open air.

Then she thought of tearing through the sucker rootlets one by one, and in another minute she had released
him and was dragging him away from the horror.

He was white and bleeding from a dozen circular
patches.

The odd-job man was coming up the garden, amazed
at the smashing of glass, and saw her emerge, hauling the
inanimate body with red-stained hands. For a moment he
thought impossible things.

"Bring some water!" she cried, and her voice dispelled
his fancies. When, with unnatural alacrity, he returned
with the water, he found her weeping with excitement,

and with Wedderburn's head upon her knee, wiping the blood from his face.

"What's the matter?" said Wedderburn, opening his eyes feebly, and closing them again at once.

"Go and tell Annie to come out here to me, and then go for Doctor Haddon at once," she said to the odd-job man so soon as he brought the water; and added, seeing he hesitated, "I will tell you all about it when you come back."

Presently Wedderburn opened his eyes again, and, seeing that he was troubled by the puzzle of his position, she explained to him, "You fainted in the hothouse."

"And the orchid?"

"I will see to that," she said.

Wedderburn had lost a good deal of blood, but beyond that he had suffered no very great injury. They gave him brandy mixed with some pink extract of meat, and carried him upstairs to bed. His housekeeper told her incredible story in fragments to Dr. Haddon. "Come to the orchid-house and see," she said.

The cold outer air was blowing in through the open door, and the sickly perfume was almost dispelled. Most of the torn aëial rootlets lay already withered amidst a number of dark stains upon the bricks. The stem of the inflorescence was broken by the fall of the plant, and the flowers were growing limp and brown at the edges of the petals. The doctor stooped towards it, then saw that one of the aërial rootlets still stirred feebly, and hesitated.

The next morning the strange orchid still lay there, black now and putrescent. The door banged intermittently in the morning breeze, and all the array of Wedderburn's orchids was shrivelled and prostrate. But Wedderburn himself was bright and garrulous upstairs in the glory of his strange adventure.

Joseph Conrad

TYPHOON

Captain macwhirr, of the steamer *Nan-Shan,* had a physiognomy that, in the order of material appearances, was the exact counterpart of his mind: it presented no marked characteristics of firmness or stupidity; it had no pronounced characteristics whatever; it was simply ordinary, irresponsive, and unruffled.

The only thing his aspect might have been said to suggest, at times, was bashfulness; because he would sit, in business offices ashore, sunburnt and smiling faintly, with downcast eyes. When he raised them, they were perceived to be direct in their glance and of blue colour. His hair was fair and extremely fine, clasping from temple to temple the bald dome of his skull in a clamp as of fluffy silk. The hair of his face, on the contrary, carroty and flaming, resembled a growth of copper wire clipped short to the line of the lip; while, no matter how close he shaved, fiery metallic gleams passed, when he moved his head, over the surface of his cheeks. He was rather below the medium height, a bit round-shouldered, and so sturdy of limb that his clothes always looked a shade too tight for his arms and legs. As if unable to grasp what is due to the difference of latitudes, he wore a brown bowler hat, a complete suit of a brownish hue, and clumsy black boots. These harbour togs gave to his thick figure an air of stiff and uncouth smartness. A thin silver watch-chain looped his waistcoat, and he never left his ship for the shore without clutching in his powerful, hairy fist an elegant umbrella of the very best quality, but generally unrolled. Young Jukes, the chief mate, attending his commander to the gangway, would sometimes venture to say, with the greatest gentleness, "Allow me, sir"—and possessing himself of the umbrella deferentially, would elevate the ferule, shake the folds, twirl a neat furl in a jiffy, and hand it

back; going through the performance with a face of such
portentous gravity, that Mr. Solomon Rout, the chief
engineer, smoking his morning cigar over the skylight,
would turn away his head in order to hide a smile. "Oh!
aye! The blessed gamp. . . . Thank 'ee, Jukes, thank
'ee," would mutter Captain MacWhirr, heartily, without
looking up.

Having just enough imagination to carry him through
each successive day, and no more, he was tranquilly sure
of himself; and from the very same cause he was not in
the least conceited. It is your imaginative superior who is
touchy, overbearing, and difficult to please; but every
ship Captain MacWhirr commanded was the floating
abode of harmony and peace. It was, in truth, as impossible for him to take a flight of fancy as it would be for a
watchmaker to put together a chronometer with nothing
except a two-pound hammer and a whip-saw in the way
of tools. Yet the uninteresting lives of men so entirely
given to the actuality of the bare existence have their
mysterious side. It was impossible in Captain Mac-
Whirr's case, for instance, to understand what under
heaven could have induced that perfectly satisfactory son
of a petty grocer in Belfast to run away to sea. And yet
he had done that very thing at the age of fifteen. It was
enough, when you thought it over, to give you the idea of
an immense, potent, and invisible hand thrust into the
ant-heap of the earth, laying hold of shoulders, knocking
heads together, and setting the unconscious faces of the
multitude towards inconceivable goals and in undreamt-of
directions.

His father never really forgave him for this undutiful
stupidity. "We could have got on without him," he used
to say later on, "but there's the business. And he an only
son, too!" His mother wept very much after his disappearance. As it had never occurred to him to leave word
behind, he was mourned over for dead till, after eight
months, his first letter arrived from Talcahuano. It was
short, and contained the statement: "We had very fine
weather on our passage out." But evidently, in the writ-

er's mind, the only important intelligence was to the effect that his captain had, on the very day of writing, entered him regularly on the ship's articles as Ordinary Seaman. "Because I can do the work," he explained. The mother again wept copiously, while the remark, "Tom's an ass," expressed the emotions of the father. He was a corpulent man, with a gift for sly chaffing, which to the end of his life he exercised in his intercourse with his son, a little pityingly, as if upon a half-witted person.

MacWhirr's visits to his home were necessarily rare, and in the course of years he despatched other letters to his parents, informing them of his successive promotions and of his movements upon the vast earth. In these missives could be found sentences like this: "The heat here is very great." Or: "On Christmas day at 4 P. M. we fell in with some icebergs." The old people ultimately became acquainted with a good many names of ships, and with the names of the skippers who commanded them—with the names of Scots and English shipowners—with the names of seas, oceans, straits, promontories—with outlandish names of lumber-ports, of rice-ports, of cotton-ports— with the names of islands—with the name of their son's young woman. She was called Lucy. It did not suggest itself to him to mention whether he thought the name pretty. And then they died.

The great day of MacWhirr's marriage came in due course, following shortly upon the great day when he got his first command.

All these events had taken place many years before the morning when, in the chart-room of the steamer *Nan-Shan*, he stood confronted by the fall of a barometer he had no reason to distrust. The fall—taking into account the excellence of the instrument, the time of the year, and the ship's position on the terrestrial globe—was of a nature ominously prophetic; but the red face of the man betrayed no sort of inward disturbance. Omens were as nothing to him, and he was unable to discover the message of a prophecy till the fulfilment had brought it home to his very door. "That's a fall, and no mistake," he thought.

"There must be some uncommonly dirty weather knocking about."

The *Nan-Shan* was on her way from the southward to the treaty port of Fu-chau, with some cargo in her lower holds, and two hundred Chinese coolies returning to their village homes in the province of Fo-kien, after a few years of work in various tropical colonies. The morning was fine, the oily sea heaved without a sparkle, and there was a queer white misty patch in the sky like a halo of the sun. The fore-deck, packed with Chinamen, was full of sombre clothing, yellow faces, and pigtails, sprinkled over with a good many naked shoulders, for there was no wind, and the heat was close. The coolies lounged, talked, smoked, or stared over the rail; some, drawing water over the side, sluiced each other; a few slept on hatches, while several small parties of six sat on their heels surrounding iron trays with plates of rice and tiny teacups; and every single Celestial of them was carrying with him all he had in the world—a wooden chest with a ringing lock and brass on the corners, containing the savings of his labours: some clothes of ceremony, sticks of incense, a little opium maybe, bits of nameless rubbish of conventional value, and a small hoard of silver dollars, toiled for in coal lighters, won in gambling-houses or in petty trading, grubbed out of earth, sweated out in mines, on railway lines, in deadly jungle, under heavy burdens—amassed patiently, guarded with care, cherished fiercely.

A cross swell had set in from the direction of Formosa Channel about ten o'clock, without disturbing these passengers much, because the *Nan-Shan*, with her flat bottom, rolling chocks on bilges, and great breadth of beam, had the reputation of an exceptionally steady ship in a seaway. Mr. Jukes, in moments of expansion on shore, would proclaim loudly that the "old girl was as good as she was pretty." It would never have occurred to Captain Mac-Whirr to express his favourable opinion so loud or in terms so fanciful.

She was a good ship, undoubtedly, and not old either. She had been built in Dumbarton less than three years

before, to the order of a firm of merchants in Siam—
Messrs. Sigg and Son. When she lay afloat, finished in
every detail and ready to take up the work of her life, the
builders contemplated her with pride.

"Sigg has asked us for a reliable skipper to take her
out," remarked one of the partners; and the other, after
reflecting for a while, said: "I think MacWhirr is ashore
just at present." "Is he? Then wire him at once. He's the
very man," declared the senior, without a moment's hesitation.

Next morning MacWhirr stood before them unper-
turbed, having travelled from London by the midnight
express after a sudden but undemonstrative parting with
his wife. She was the daughter of a superior couple who
had seen better days.

"We had better be going together over the ship, Captain," said the senior partner; and the three men started
to view the perfections of the *Nan-Shan* from stem to
stern, and from her keelson to the trucks of her two
stumpy pole-masts.

Captain MacWhirr had begun by taking off his coat,
which he hung on the end of a steam windlass embodying
all the latest improvements.

"My uncle wrote of you favourably by yesterday's mail
to our good friends—Messrs. Sigg, you know—and doubtless they'll continue you out there in command," said the
junior partner. "You'll be able to boast of being in charge
of the handiest boat of her size on the coast of China, Captain," he added.

"Have you? Thank 'ee," mumbled vaguely MacWhirr,
to whom the view of a distant eventuality could appeal no
more than the beauty of a wide landscape to a purblind
tourist; and his eyes happening at the moment to be at
rest upon the lock of the cabin door, he walked up to it,
full of purpose, and began to rattle the handle vigorously,
while he observed, in his low, earnest voice, "You can't
trust the workmen nowadays. A brand-new lock, and it
won't act at all. Stuck fast. See? See?"

As soon as they found themselves alone in their office

across the yard: "You praised that fellow up to Sigg. What is it you see in him?" asked the nephew, with faint contempt.

"I admit he has nothing of your fancy skipper about him, if that's what you mean," said the elder man, curtly. "Is the foreman of the joiners on the *Nan-Shan* outside? . . . Come in, Bates. How is it that you let Tait's people put us off with a defective lock on the cabin door? The Captain could see directly he set eye on it. Have it replaced at once. The little straws, Bates . . . the little straws. . . ."

The lock was replaced accordingly, and a few days afterwards the *Nan-Shan* steamed out to the East, without MacWhirr having offered any further remark as to her fittings, or having been heard to utter a single word hinting at pride in his ship, gratitude for his appointment, or satisfaction at his prospects.

With a temperament neither loquacious nor taciturn he found very little occasion to talk. There were matters of duty, of course—directions, orders, and so on; but the past being to his mind done with, and the future not there yet, the more general actualities of the day required no comment—because facts can speak for themselves with overwhelming precision.

Old Mr. Sigg liked a man of few words, and one that "you could be sure would not try to improve upon his instructions." MacWhirr satisfying these requirements, was continued in command of the *Nan-Shan*, and applied himself to the careful navigation of his ship in the China seas. She had come out on a British register, but after some time Messrs. Sigg judged it expedient to transfer her to the Siamese flag.

At the news of the contemplated transfer Jukes grew restless, as if under a sense of personal affront. He went about grumbling to himself, and uttering short scornful laughs. "Fancy having a ridiculous Noah's Ark elephant in the ensign of one's ship," he said once at the engine-room door. "Dash me if I can stand it: I'll throw up the billet. Don't it make *you* sick, Mr. Rout?" The chief engineer only cleared his throat with the air of a man who knows the value of a good billet.

The first morning the new flag floated over the stern of the *Nan-Shan* Jukes stood looking at it bitterly from the bridge. He struggled with his feelings for a while, and then remarked, "Queer flag for a man to sail under, sir."

"What's the matter with the flag?" inquired Captain MacWhirr. "Seems all right to me." And he walked across to the end of the bridge to have a good look.

"Well, it looks queer to me," burst out Jukes, greatly exasperated, and flung off the bridge.

Captain MacWhirr was amazed at these manners. After a while he stepped quietly into the chart-room, and opened his International Signal Code-book at the plate where the flags of all the nations are correctly figured in gaudy rows. He ran his finger over them, and when he came to Siam he contemplated with great attention the red field and the white elephant. Nothing could be more simple; but to make sure he brought the book out on the bridge for the purpose of comparing the coloured drawing with the real thing at the flag-staff astern. When next Jukes, who was carrying on the duty that day with a sort of suppressed fierceness, happened on the bridge, his commander observed:

"There's nothing amiss with that flag."

"Isn't there?" mumbled Jukes, falling on his knees before a deck-locker and jerking therefrom viciously a spare lead-line.

"No. I looked up the book. Length twice the breadth and the elephant exactly in the middle. I thought the people ashore would know how to make the local flag. Stands to reason. You were wrong, Jukes. . . ."

"Well, sir," began Jukes, getting up excitedly, "all I can say——" He fumbled for the end of the coil of line with trembling hands.

"That's all right." Captain MacWhirr soothed him, sitting heavily on a little canvas folding-stool he greatly affected. "All you have to do is to take care they don't

hoist the elephant upside-down before they get quite used
to it."

Jukes flung the new lead-line over on the fore-deck with
a loud "Here you are, bo'ss'en—don't forget to wet it
thoroughly," and turned with immense resolution towards
his commander; but Captain MacWhirr spread his elbows on the bridge-rail comfortably.

"Because it would be, I suppose, understood as a signal of distress," he went on. "What do you think? That
elephant there, I take it, stands for something in the nature of the Union Jack in the flag. . . ."

"Does it!" yelled Jukes, so that every head on the *Nan-
Shan's* decks looked towards the bridge. Then he sighed,
and with sudden resignation: "It would certainly be a
dam' distressful sight," he said, meekly.

Later in the day he accosted the chief engineer with a
confidential, "Here, let me tell you the old man's latest."

Mr. Solomon Rout (frequently alluded to as Long Sol,
Old Sol, or Father Rout), from finding himself almost
invariably the tallest man on board every ship he joined,
had acquired the habit of a stooping, leisurely condescen-
sion. His hair was scant and sandy, his flat cheeks were
pale, his bony wrists and long scholarly hands were pale,
too, as though he had lived all his life in the shade.

He smiled from on high at Jukes, and went on smoking
and glancing about quietly, in the manner of a kind uncle
lending an ear to the tale of an excited schoolboy. Then,
greatly amused but impassive, he asked:

"And did you throw up the billet?"

"No," cried Jukes, raising a weary, discouraged voice
above the harsh buzz of the *Nan-Shan's* friction winches.
All of them were hard at work, snatching slings of cargo,
high up, to the end of long derricks, only, as it seemed, to
let them rip down recklessly by the run. The cargo chains
groaned in the gins, clinked on coamings, rattled over the
side; and the whole ship quivered, with her long gray
flanks smoking in wreaths of steam. "No," cried Jukes,
"I didn't. What's the good? I might just as well fling my
resignation at this bulkhead. I don't believe you can make

a man like that understand anything. He simply knocks me over."

At that moment Captain MacWhirr, back from the shore, crossed the deck, umbrella in hand, escorted by a mournful, self-possessed Chinaman, walking behind in paper-soled silk shoes, and who also carried an umbrella. The master of the *Nan-Shan*, speaking just audibly and gazing at his boots as his manner was, remarked that it would be necessary to call at Fu-chau this trip, and desired Mr. Rout to have steam up to-morrow afternoon at one o'clock sharp. He pushed back his hat to wipe his forehead, observing at the same time that he hated going ashore anyhow; while overtopping him Mr. Rout, without deigning a word, smoked austerely, nursing his right elbow in the palm of his left hand. Then Jukes was directed in the same subdued voice to keep the forward 'tween-deck clear of cargo. Two hundred coolies were going to be put down there. The Bun Hin Company were sending that lot home. Twenty-five bags of rice would be coming off in a sampan directly, for stores. All seven-years'-men they were, said Captain MacWhirr, with a camphor-wood chest to every man. The carpenter should be set to work nailing three-inch battens along the deck below, fore and aft, to keep these boxes from shifting in a sea-way. Jukes had better look to it at once. "D'ye hear, Jukes?" This Chinaman here was coming with the ship as far as Fu-chau—a sort of interpreter he would be. Bun Hin's clerk he was, and wanted to have a look at the space. Jukes had better take him forward. "D'ye hear, Jukes?"

Jukes took care to punctuate these instructions in proper places with the obligatory "Yes, sir," ejaculated without enthusiasm. His brusque "Come along, John; make look see" set the Chinaman in motion at his heels.

"Wanchee look see, all same look see can do," said Jukes, who having no talent for foreign languages mangled the very pidgin-English cruelly. He pointed at the open hatch. "Catchee number one piecie place to sleep in. Eh?"

He was gruff, as became his racial superiority, but not

unfriendly. The Chinaman, gazing sad and speechless
into the darkness of the hatchway, seemed to stand at the
head of a yawning grave.

"No catchee rain down there—savee?" pointed out
Jukes. "Suppose all'ee same fine weather, one piecie coolie-
man come topside," he pursued, warming up imagina-
tively. "Make so—Phooooo!" He expanded his chest and
blew out his cheeks. "Savee, John? Breathe—fresh air.
Good. Eh? Washee him piecie pants, chow-chow top-side
—see, John?"

With his mouth and hands he made exuberant motions
of eating rice and washing clothes; and the Chinaman,
who concealed his distrust of this pantomime under a collected demeanour tinged by a gentle and refined melancholy, glanced out of his almond eyes from Jukes to the
hatch and back again. "Velly good," he murmured, in a
disconsolate undertone, and hastened smoothly along the
decks, dodging obstacles in his course. He disappeared,
ducking low under a sling of ten dirty gunny-bags full of
some costly merchandise and exhaling a repulsive smell.

Captain MacWhirr meantime had gone on the bridge,
and into the chart-room, where a letter, commenced two
days before, awaited termination. These long letters began with the words, "My darling wife," and the steward,
between the scrubbing of the floors and the dusting of
chronometer-boxes, snatched at every opportunity to read
them. They interested him much more than they possibly
could the woman for whose eye they were intended; and
this for the reason that they related in minute detail each
successive trip of the *Nan-Shan.*

Her master, faithful to facts, which alone his consciousness reflected, would set them down with painstak-
ing care upon many pages. The house in a northern sub-
urb to which these pages were addressed had a bit of
garden before the bow-windows, a deep porch of good
appearance, coloured glass with imitation lead frame in
the front door. He paid five-and-forty pounds a year for
it, and did not think the rent too high, because Mrs. Mac-
Whirr (a pretentious person with a scraggy neck and a

disdainful manner) was admittedly ladylike, and in the neighbourhood considered as "quite superior." The only secret of her life was her abject terror of the time when her husband would come home to stay for good. Under the same roof there dwelt also a daughter called Lydia and a son, Tom. These two were but slightly acquainted with their father. Mainly, they knew him as a rare but privileged visitor, who of an evening smoked his pipe in the dining-room and slept in the house. The lanky girl, upon the whole, was rather ashamed of him; the boy was frankly and utterly indifferent in a straightforward, delightful, unaffected way manly boys have.

And Captain MacWhirr wrote home from the coast of China twelve times every year, desiring quaintly to be "remembered to the children," and subscribing himself "your loving husband," as calmly as if the words so long used by so many men were, apart from their shape, worn-out things, and of a faded meaning.

The China seas north and south are narrow seas. They are seas full of every-day, eloquent facts, such as islands, sand-banks, reefs, swift and changeable currents—tangled facts that nevertheless speak to a seaman in clear and definite language. Their speech appealed to Captain MacWhirr's sense of realities so forcibly that he had given up his state-room below and practically lived all his days on the bridge of his ship, often having his meals sent up, and sleeping at night in the chart-room. And he indited there his home letters. Each of them, without exception, contained the phrase, "The weather has been very fine this trip," or some other form of a statement to that effect. And this statement, too, in its wonderful persistence, was of the same perfect accuracy as all the others they contained.

Mr. Rout likewise wrote letters; only no one on board knew how chatty he could be pen in hand, because the chief engineer had enough imagination to keep his desk locked. His wife relished his style greatly. They were a childless couple, and Mrs. Rout, a big high-bosomed, jolly woman of forty, shared with Mr. Rout's toothless and venerable mother a little cottage near Teddington. She would run over her correspondence, at breakfast, with lively eyes, and scream out interesting passages in a joyous voice at the deaf old lady, prefacing each extract by the warning shout, "Solomon says!" She had the trick of firing off Solomon's utterances also upon strangers, astonishing them easily by the unfamiliar text and the unexpectedly jocular vein of these quotations. On the day the new curate called for the first time at the cottage, she found occasion to remark, "As Solomon says: 'the engineers that go down to the sea in ships behold the wonders of sailor nature';" when a change in the visitor's countenance made her stop and stare.

"Solomon. . . . Oh! . . . Mrs. Rout," stuttered the young man, very red in the face, "I must say . . . I don't. . . ."

"He's my husband," she announced in a great shout, throwing herself back in the chair. Perceiving the joke, she laughed immoderately with a handkerchief to her eyes, while he sat wearing a forced smile, and, from his inexperience of jolly women, fully persuaded that she must be deplorably insane. They were excellent friends afterwards; for, absolving her from irreverent intention, he came to think she was a very worthy person indeed; and he learned in time to receive without flinching other scraps of Solomon's wisdom.

"For my part," Solomon was reported by his wife to have said once, "give me the dullest ass for a skipper before a rogue. There is a way to take a fool; but a rogue is smart and slippery." This was an airy generalization drawn from the particular case of Captain MacWhirr's honesty, which, in itself, had the heavy obviousness of a lump of clay. On the other hand, Mr. Jukes, unable to generalize, unmarried, and unengaged, was in the habit of opening his heart after another fashion to an old chum and former shipmate, actually serving as second officer on board an Atlantic liner.

First of all he would insist upon the advantages of the Eastern trade, hinting at its superiority to the Western

ocean service. He extolled the sky, the seas, the ships, and
the easy life of the Far East. The *Nan-Shan*, he affirmed,
was second to none as a sea-boat.

"We have no brass-bound uniforms, but then we are
like brothers here," he wrote. "We all mess together and
live like fighting-cocks. . . . All the chaps of the black-
squad are as decent as they make that kind, and old Sol,
the Chief, is a dry stick. We are good friends. As to our
old man, you could not find a quieter skipper. Sometimes
you would think he hadn't sense enough to see anything
wrong. And yet it isn't that. Can't be. He has been in
command for a good few years now. He doesn't do anything actually foolish, and gets his ship along all right
without worrying anybody. I believe he hasn't brains
enough to enjoy kicking up a row. I don't take advantage of him. I would scorn it. Outside the routine of duty
he doesn't seem to understand more than half of what you
tell him. We get a laugh out of this at times; but it is dull,
too, to be with a man like this—in the long-run. Old Sol
says he hasn't much conversation. Conversation! O Lord!
He never talks. The other day I had been yarning under
the bridge with one of the engineers, and he must have
heard us. When I came up to take my watch, he steps out
of the chart-room and has a good look all round, peeps
over at the sidelights, glances at the compass, squints upwards at the stars. That's his regular performance. By-
and-by he says: 'Was that you talking just now in the
port alleyway?' 'Yes, sir.' 'With the third engineer?'
'Yes, sir.' He walks off to starboard, and sits under the
dodger on a little campstool of his, and for half an hour
perhaps he makes no sound, except that I heard him sneeze
once. Then after a while I hear him getting up over there,
and he strolls across to port, where I was. 'I can't understand what you can find to talk about,' says he. 'Two solid
hours. I am not blaming you. I see people ashore at it all
day long, and then in the evening they sit down and keep
at it over the drinks. Must be saying the same things over
and over again. I can't understand.'

"Did you ever hear anything like that? And he was so

patient about it. It made me quite sorry for him. But he is exasperating, too, sometimes. Of course one would not do anything to vex him even if it were worth while. But it isn't. He's so jolly innocent that if you were to put your thumb to your nose and wave your finges at him he would only wonder gravely to himself what got into you. He told me once quite simply that he found it very difficult to make out what made people always act so queerly. He's too dense to trouble about, and that's the truth."

Thus wrote Mr. Jukes to his chum in the Western ocean trade, out of the fulness of his heart and the liveliness of his fancy.

He had expressed his honest opinion. It was not worth while trying to impress a man of that sort. If the world had been full of such men, life would have probably appeared to Jukes an unentertaining and unprofitable business. He was not alone in his opinion. The sea itself, as if sharing Mr. Jukes' good-natured forbearance, had never put itself out to startle the silent man, who seldom looked up, and wandered innocently over the waters with the only visible purpose of getting food, raiment, and houseroom for three people ashore. Dirty weather he had known, of course. He had been made wet, uncomfortable, tired in the usual way, felt at the time and presently forgotten. So that upon the whole he had been justified in reporting fine weather at home. But he had never been given a glimpse of immeasurable strength and of immoderate wrath, the wrath that passes exhausted but never appeased—the wrath and fury of the passionate sea. He knew it existed, as we know that crime and abomination exist; he had heard of it as a peaceable citizen in a town hears of battles, famines, and floods, and yet knows nothing of what these things mean—though, indeed, he may have been mixed up in a street row, have gone without his dinner once, or been soaked to the skin in a shower. Captain MacWhirr had sailed over the surface of the oceans as some men go skimming over the years of existence to sink gently into a placid grave, ignorant of life to the last, without ever having been made to see all it may contain

of perfidy, of violence, and of terror. There are on sea and
land such men thus fortunate—or thus disdained by destiny or by the sea.

II

Observing the steady fall of the barometer, Captain
MacWhirr thought, "There's some dirty weather knocking about." This is precisely what he thought. He had
had an experience of moderately dirty weather—the term
dirty as applied to the weather implying only moderate
discomfort to the seaman. Had he been informed by an
indisputable authority that the end of the world was to
be finally accomplished by a catastrophic disturbance of
the atmosphere, he would have assimilated the information under the simple idea of dirty weather, and no other,
because he had no experience of cataclysms, and belief
does not necessarily imply comprehension. The wisdom of
his county had pronounced by means of an Act of Parliament that before he could be considered as fit to take
charge of a ship he should be able to answer certain simple questions on the subject of circular storms such as
hurricanes, cyclones, typhoons; and apparently he had
answered them, since he was now in command of the *Nan-
Shan* in the China seas during the season of typhoons.
But if he had answered he remembered nothing of it. He
was, however, conscious of being made uncomfortable by
the clammy heat. He came out on the bridge, and found
no relief to this oppression. The air seemed thick. He
gasped like a fish, and began to believe himself greatly
out of sorts.

The *Nan-Shan* was ploughing a vanishing furrow upon
the circle of the sea that had the surface and the shimmer of an undulating piece of gray silk. The sun, pale
and without rays, poured down leaden heat in a strangely
indecisive light, and the Chinamen were lying prostrate
about the decks. Their bloodless, pinched, yellow faces
were like the faces of bilious invalids. Captain MacWhirr
noticed two of them especially, stretched out on their

backs below the bridge. As soon as they had closed their
eyes they seemed dead. Three others, however, were quarrelling barbarously away forward; and one big fellow,
half naked, with herculean shoulders, was hanging limply
over a winch; another, sitting on the deck, his knees up
and his head drooping sideways in a girlish attitude, was
plaiting his pigtail with infinite languor depicted in his
whole person and in the very movement of his fingers.
The smoke struggled with difficulty out of the funnel,
and instead of streaming away spread itself out like an
infernal sort of cloud, smelling of sulphur and raining
soot all over the decks.

"What the devil are you doing there, Mr. Jukes?"
asked Captain MacWhirr.

This unusual form of address, though mumbled rather
than spoken, caused the body of Mr. Jukes to start as
though it had been prodded under the fifth rib. He had
had a low bench brought on the bridge, and sitting on it,
with a length of rope curled about his feet and a piece of
canvas stretched over his knees, was pushing a sail-needle
vigorously. He looked up, and his surprise gave to his
eyes an expression of innocence and candour.

"I am only roping some of that new set of bags we
made last trip for whipping up coals," he remonstrated,
gently. "We shall want them for the next coaling, sir."

"What became of the others?"

"Why, worn out of course, sir."

Captain MacWhirr, after glaring down irresolutely at
his chief mate, disclosed the gloomy and cynical conviction that more than half of them had been lost overboard, "if only the truth was known," and retired to the
other end of the bridge. Jukes, exasperated by this un-
provoked attack, broke the needle at the second stitch,
and dropping his work got up and cursed the heat in a
violent undertone.

The propeller thumped, the three Chinamen forward
had given up squabbling very suddenly, and the one who
had been plaiting his tail clasped his legs and stared de-
jectedly over his knees. The lurid sunshine cast faint and

sickly shadows. The swell ran higher and swifter every moment, and the ship lurched heavily in the smooth, deep hollows of the sea.

"I wonder where that beastly swell comes from," said Jukes aloud, recovering himself after a stagger.

"North-east," grunted the literal MacWhirr, from his side of the bridge. "There's some dirty weather knocking about. Go and look at the glass."

When Jukes came out of the chart-room, the cast of his countenance had changed to thoughtfulness and concern. He caught hold of the bridge-rail and stared ahead.

The temperature in the engine-room had gone up to a hundred and seventeen degrees. Irritated voices were ascending through the skylight and through the fiddle of the stokehold in a harsh and resonant uproar, mingled with angry clangs and scrapes of metal, as if men with limbs of iron and throats of bronze had been quarrelling down there. The second engineer was falling foul of the stokers for letting the steam go down. He was a man with arms like a blacksmith, and generally feared; but that afternoon the stokers were answering him back recklessly, and slammed the furnace doors with the fury of despair. Then the noise ceased suddenly, and the second engineer appeared, emerging out of the stokehold streaked with grime and soaking wet like a chimney-sweep coming out of a well. As soon as his head was clear of the fiddle he began to scold Jukes for not trimming properly the stokehold ventilators; and in answer Jukes made with his hands deprecatory soothing signs meaning: "No wind—can't be helped—you can see for yourself." But the other wouldn't hear reason. His teeth flashed angrily in his dirty face. He didn't mind, he said, the trouble of punching their blanked heads down there, blank his soul, but did the condemned sailors think you could keep steam up in the God-forsaken boilers simply by knocking the blanked stokers about? No, by George! You had to get some draught, too—may he be everlastingly blanked for a swab-headed deck-hand if you didn't! And the chief, too, rampaging before the steam-gauge and carrying on

like a lunatic up and down the engine-room ever since
noon. What did Jukes think he was stuck up there for,
if he couldn't get one of his decayed, good-for-nothing
deck-cripples to turn the ventilators to the wind?

The relations of the "engine-room" and the "deck" of
the *Nan-Shan* were, as is known, of a brotherly nature;
therefore Jukes leaned over and begged the other in a
restrained tone not to make a disgusting ass of himself;
the skipper was on the other side of the bridge. But the
second declared mutinously that he didn't care a rap who
was on the other side of the bridge, and Jukes, passing in
a flash from lofty disapproval into a state of exaltation,
invited him in unflattering terms to come up and twist
the beastly things to please himself, and catch such wind
as a donkey of his sort could find. The second rushed up
to the fray. He flung himself at the port ventilator as
though he meant to tear it out bodily and toss it overboard. All he did was to move the cowl round a few inches,
with an enormous expenditure of force, and seemed spent
in the effort. He leaned against the back of the wheelhouse, and Jukes walked up to him.

"Oh, Heavens!" ejaculated the engineer in a feeble
voice. He lifted his eyes to the sky, and then let his glassy
stare descend to meet the horizon that, tilting up to an
angle of forty degrees, seemed to hang on a slant for a
while and settled down slowly. "Heavens! Phew! What's
up, anyhow?"

Jukes, straddling his long legs like a pair of com-
passes, put on an air of superiority. "We're going to
catch it this time," he said. "The barometer is tumbling
down like anything, Harry. And you trying to kick up
that silly row. . . ."

The word "barometer" seemed to revive the second
engineer's mad animosity. Collecting afresh all his
energies, he directed Jukes in a low and brutal tone to
shove the unmentionable instrument down his gory
throat. Who cared for his crimson barometer? It was the
steam—the steam—that was going down; and what between the firemen going faint and the chief going silly,

it was worse than a dog's life for him; he didn't care a tinker's curse how soon the whole show was blown out of the water. He seemed on the point of having a cry, but after regaining his breath he muttered darkly, "I'll faint them," and dashed off. He stopped upon the fiddle long enough to shake his fist at the unnatural daylight, and dropped into the dark hole with a whoop.

When Jukes turned, his eyes fell upon the rounded back and the big red ears of Captain MacWhirr, who had come across. He did not look at his chief officer, but said at once, "That's a very violent man, that second engineer."

"Jolly good second, anyhow," grunted Jukes. "They can't keep up steam," he added, rapidly, and made a grab at the rail against the coming lurch.

Captain MacWhirr, unprepared, took a run and brought himself up with a jerk by an awning stanchion.

"A profane man," he said, obstinately. "If this goes on, I'll have to get rid of him the first chance."

"It's the heat," said Jukes. "The weather's awful. It would make a saint swear. Even up here I feel exactly as if I had my head tied up in a woollen blanket."

Captain MacWhirr looked up. "D'ye mean to say, Mr. Jukes, you ever had your head tied up in a blanket? What was that for?"

"It's a manner of speaking, sir," said Jukes, stolidly.

"Some of you fellows do go on! What's that about saints swearing? I wish you wouldn't talk so wild. What sort of saint would that be that would swear? No more saint than yourself, I expect. And what's a blanket got to do with it—or the weather either. . . . The heat does not make me swear—does it? It's filthy bad temper. That's what it is. And what's the good of your talking like this?"

Thus Captain MacWhirr expostulated against the use of images in speech, and at the end electrified Jukes by a contemptuous snort, followed by words of passion and resentment: "Damme! I'll fire him out of the ship if he don't look out."

And Jukes, incorrigible, thought: "Goodness me! Somebody's put a new inside to my old man. Here's temper, if you like. Of course it's the weather; what else? It would make an angel quarrelsome—let alone a saint."

All the Chinamen on deck appeared at their last gasp.

At its setting the sun had a diminished diameter and an expiring brown, rayless glow, as if millions of centuries elapsing since the morning had brought it near its end. A dense bank of cloud became visible to the northward; it had a sinister dark olive tint, and lay low and motionless upon the sea, resembling a solid obstacle in the path of the ship. She went floundering towards it like an exhausted creature driven to its death. The coppery twilight retired slowly, and the darkness brought out overhead a swarm of unsteady, big stars, that, as if blown upon, flickered exceedingly and seemed to hang very near the earth. At eight o'clock Jukes went into the chartroom to write up the ship's log.

He copied neatly out of the rough-book the number of miles, the course of the ship, and in the column for "wind" scrawled the word "calm" from top to bottom of the eight hours since noon. He was exasperated by the continuous, monotonous rolling of the ship. The heavy inkstand would slide away in a manner that suggested perverse intelligence in dodging the pen. Having written in the large space under the head of "Remarks" "Heat very oppressive," he stuck the end of the penholder in his teeth, pipe fashion, and mopped his face carefully.

"Ship rolling heavily in a high cross swell," he began again, and commented to himself, "Heavily is no word for it." Then he wrote: "Sunset threatening, with a low bank of clouds to N. and E. Sky clear overhead."

Sprawling over the table with arrested pen, he glanced out of the door, and in that frame of his vision he saw all the stars flying upwards between the teakwood jambs on a black sky. The whole lot took flight together and disappeared, leaving only a blackness flecked with white flashes, for the sea was as black as the sky and speckled with foam afar. The stars that had flown to the roll came back on the return swing of the ship, rushing downwards in their glittering multitude, not of fiery points, but enlarged to tiny discs brilliant with a clear wet sheen.

Jukes watched the flying big stars for a moment, and then wrote: "8 P.M. Swell increasing. Ship labouring and taking water on her decks. Battened down the coolies for the night. Barometer still falling." He paused, and thought to himself, "Perhaps nothing whatever'll come of it." And then he closed resolutely his entries: "Every appearance of a typhoon coming on."

On going out he had to stand aside, and Captain MacWhirr strode over the doorstep without saying a word or making a sign.

"Shut the door, Mr. Jukes, will you?" he cried from within.

Jukes turned back to do so, muttering ironically: "Afraid to catch cold, I suppose." It was his watch below, but he yearned for communion with his kind; and he remarked cheerily to the second mate: "Doesn't look so bad, after all—does it?"

The second mate was marching to and fro on the bridge, tripping down with small steps one moment, and the next climbing with difficulty the shifting slope of the deck. At the sound of Jukes' voice he stood still, facing forward, but made no reply.

"Hallo! That's a heavy one," said Jukes, swaying to meet the long roll till his lowered hand touched the planks. This time the second mate made in his throat a noise of an unfriendly nature.

He was an oldish, shabby little fellow, with bad teeth and no hair on his face. He had been shipped in a hurry in Shanghai, that trip when the second officer brought from home had delayed the ship three hours in port by contriving (in some manner Captain MacWhirr could never understand) to fall overboard into an empty coal-lighter lying alongside, and had to be sent ashore to the hospital with concussion of the brain and a broken limb or two.

Jukes was not discouraged by the unsympathetic sound. "The Chinamen must be having a lovely time of it down there," he said. "It's lucky for them the old girl has the easiest roll of any ship I've ever been in. There now! This one wasn't so bad."

"You wait," snarled the second mate.

With his sharp nose, red at the tip, and his thin pinched lips, he always looked as though he were raging inwardly; and he was concise in his speech to the point of rudeness. All his time off duty he spent in his cabin with the door shut, keeping so still in there that he was supposed to fall asleep as soon as he had disappeared; but the man who came in to wake him for his watch on deck would invariably find him with his eyes wide open, flat on his back in the bunk, and glaring irritably from a soiled pillow. He never wrote any letters, did not seem to hope for news from anywhere; and though he had been heard once to mention West Hartlepool, it was with extreme bitterness, and only in connection with the extortionate charges of a boarding-house. He was one of those men who are picked up at need in the ports of the world. They are competent enough, appear hopelessly hard up, show no evidence of any sort of vice, and carry about them all the signs of manifest failure. They come aboard on an emergency, care for no ship afloat, live in their own atmosphere of casual connection amongst their shipmates who know nothing of them, and make up their minds to leave at inconvenient times. They clear out with no words of leave-taking in some God-forsaken port other men would fear to be stranded in, and go ashore in company of a shabby sea-chest, corded like a treasure-box, and with an air of shaking the ship's dust off their feet.

"You wait," he repeated, balanced in great swings with his back to Jukes, motionless and implacable.

"Do you mean to say we are going to catch it hot?" asked Jukes with boyish interest.

"Say? . . . I say nothing. You don't catch me," snapped the little second mate, with a mixture of pride, scorn, and cunning, as if Jukes' question had been a trap cleverly detected. "Oh, no! None of you here shall make a fool of me if I know it," he mumbled to himself.

Jukes reflected rapidly that this second mate was a mean little beast, and in his heart he wished poor Jack Allen had never smashed himself up in the coal-lighter. The far-off blackness ahead of the ship was like another night seen through the starry night of the earth—the starless night of the immensities beyond the created universe, revealed in its appalling stillness through a low fissure in the glittering sphere of which the earth is the kernel.

"Whatever there might be about," said Jukes, "we are steaming straight into it."

"*You've* said it," caught up the second mate, always with his back to Jukes. "You've said it, mind—not I."

"Oh, go to Jericho!" said Jukes, frankly; and the other emitted a triumphant little chuckle.

"You've said it," he repeated.

"And what of that?"

"I've known some real good men get into trouble with their skippers for saying a dam' sight less," answered the second mate feverishly. "Oh, no! You don't catch me."

"You seem deucedly anxious not to give yourself away," said Jukes, completely soured by such absurdity. "I wouldn't be afraid to say what I think."

"Aye, to me! That's no great trick. I am nobody, and well I know it."

The ship, after a pause of comparative steadiness, started upon a series of rolls, one worse than the other, and for a time Jukes, preserving his equilibrium, was too busy to open his mouth. As soon as the violent swinging had quieted down somewhat, he said: "This is a bit too much of a good thing. Whether anything is coming or not I think she ought to be put head on to that swell. The old man is just gone in to lie down. Hang me if I don't speak to him."

But when he opened the door of the chart-room he saw his captain reading a book. Captain MacWhirr was not lying down: he was standing up with one hand grasping the edge of the bookshelf and the other holding open before his face a thick volume. The lamp wriggled in the gimbals, the loosened books toppled from side to side on the shelf, the long barometer swung in jerky circles, the table altered its slant every moment. In the midst of all this stir and movement Captain MacWhirr, holding on, showed his eyes above the upper edge, and asked, "What's the matter?"

"Swell getting worse, sir."

"Noticed that in here," muttered Captain MacWhirr. "Anything wrong?"

Jukes, inwardly disconcerted by the seriousness of the eyes looking at him over the top of the book, produced an embarrassed grin.

"Rolling like old boots," he said, sheepishly.

"Aye! Very heavy—very heavy. What do you want?"

At this Jukes lost his footing and began to flounder.

"I was thinking of our passengers," he said, in the manner of a man clutching at a straw.

"Passengers?" wondered the Captain, gravely. "What passengers?"

"Why, the Chinamen, sir," explained Jukes, very sick of this conversation.

"The Chinamen! Why don't you speak plainly? Couldn't tell what you meant. Never heard a lot of coolies spoken of as passengers before. Passengers, indeed! What's come to you?"

Captain MacWhirr, closing the book on his forefinger, lowered his arm and looked completely mystified. "Why are you thinking of the Chinamen, Mr. Jukes?" he inquired.

Jukes took a plunge, like a man driven to it. "She's rolling her decks full of water, sir. Thought you might put her head on perhaps—for a while. Till this goes down a bit—very soon, I dare say. Head to the eastward. I never knew a ship roll like this."

He held on in the doorway, and Captain MacWhirr, feeling his grip on the shelf inadequate, made up his mind to let go in a hurry, and fell heavily on the couch.

"Head to the eastward?" he said, struggling to sit up. "That's more than four points off her course."

"Yes, sir. Fifty degrees. . . . Would just bring her head far enough round to meet this. . . ."

Captain MacWhirr was now sitting up. He had not dropped the book, and he had not lost his place.

"To the eastward?" he repeated, with dawning astonishment. "To the . . . Where do you think we are bound to? You want me to haul a full-powered steamship four points off her course to make the Chinamen comfortable! Now, I've heard more than enough of mad things done in the world—but this. . . . If I didn't know you, Jukes, I would think you were in liquor. Steer four points off. . . . And what afterwards? Steer four points over the other way, I suppose, to make the course good. What put it into your head that I would start to tack a steamer as if she were a sailing-ship?"

"Jolly good thing she isn't," threw in Jukes, with bitter readiness. "She would have rolled every blessed stick out of her this afternoon."

"Aye! And you just would have had to stand and see them go," said Captain MacWhirr, showing a certain animation. "It's a dead calm, isn't it?"

"It is, sir. But there's something out of the common coming, for sure."

"Maybe. I suppose you have a notion I should be getting out of the way of that dirt," said Captain MacWhirr, speaking with the utmost simplicity of manner and tone, and fixing the oilcloth on the floor with a heavy stare. Thus he noticed neither Jukes' discomfiture nor the mixture of vexation and astonished respect on his face.

"Now, here's this book," he continued with deliberation, slapping his thigh with the closed volume. "I've been reading the chapter on the storms there."

This was true. He had been reading the chapter on the storms. When he had entered the chart-room, it was with no intention of taking the book down. Some influence in the air—the same influence, probably, that caused the steward to bring without orders the Captain's sea-boots and oilskin coat up to the chart-room—had as it were guided his hand to the shelf; and without taking the time to sit down he had waded with a conscious effort into the terminology of the subject. He lost himself amongst advancing semi-circles, left- and right-hand quadrants, the curves of the tracks, the probable bearing of the centre, the shifts of wind and the readings of barometer. He tried to bring all these things into a definite relation to himself, and ended by becoming contemptuously angry with such a lot of words and with so much advice, all head-work and supposition, without a glimmer of certitude.

"It's the damnedest thing, Jukes," he said. "If a fellow was to believe all that's in there, he would be running most of his time all over the sea trying to get behind the weather."

Again he slapped his leg with the book; and Jukes opened his mouth, but said nothing.

"Running to get behind the weather! Do you understand that, Mr. Jukes? It's the maddest thing!" ejaculated Captain MacWhirr, with pauses, gazing at the floor profoundly. "You would think an old woman had been writing this. It passes me. If that thing means anything useful, then it means that I should at once alter the course away, away to the devil somewhere, and come booming down on Fu-chau from the northward at the tail of this dirty weather that's supposed to be knocking about in our way. From the north! Do you understand, Mr. Jukes? Three hundred extra miles to the distance, and a pretty coal bill to show. I couldn't bring myself to do that if every word in there was gospel truth, Mr. Jukes. Don't you expect me. . . ."

And Jukes, silent, marvelled at this desplay of feeling and loquacity.

"But the truth is that you don't know if the fellow is right, anyhow. How can you tell what a gale is made of till you get it? He isn't aboard here, is he? Very well. Here he says that the centre of them things bears eight points off the wind; but we haven't got any wind, for all the barometer falling. Where's his centre now?"

"We will get the wind presently," mumbled Jukes.

"Let it come, then," said Captain MacWhirr, with dignified indignation. "It's only to let you see, Mr. Jukes, that you don't find everything in books. All these rules for dodging breezes and circumventing the winds of heaven, Mr. Jukes, seem to me the maddest thing, when you come to look at it sensibly."

He raised his eyes, saw Jukes gazing at him dubiously, and tried to illustrate his meaning.

"About as queer as your extraordinary notion of dodging the ship head to sea, for I don't know how long, to make the Chinamen comfortable; whereas all we've got to do is to take them to Fu-chau, being timed to get there before noon on Friday. If the weather delays me—very well. There's your log-book to talk straight about the weather. But suppose I went swinging off my course and came in two days late, and they asked me: 'Where have you been all that time, Captain?' What could I say to that? 'Went around to dodge the bad weather,' I would say. 'It must've been dam' bad,' they would say. 'Don't know,' I would have to say; 'I've dodged clear of it.' See that, Jukes? I have been thinking it all out this afternoon."

He looked up again in his unseeing, unimaginative way. No one had ever heard him say so much at one time. Jukes, with his arms open in the doorway, was like a man invited to behold a miracle. Unbounded wonder was the intellectual meaning of his eye, while incredulity was seated in his whole countenance.

"A gale is a gale, Mr. Jukes," resumed the Captain, "and a full-powered steam-ship has got to face it. There's just so much dirty weather knocking about the world, and the proper thing is to go through it with none of what old Captain Wilson of the *Melita* calls 'storm strategy.' The other day ashore I heard him hold forth about it to a lot of shipmasters who came in and sat at a table next to mine. It seemed to me the greatest nonsense. He was telling them how he out-manœuvred, I think he said, a terrific gale, so that it never came nearer than fifty miles to him. A neat piece of head-work he called it. How he knew there was a terrific gale fifty miles off beats me altogether. It was like listening to a crazy man. I would have thought Captain Wilson was old enough to know better."

Captain MacWhirr ceased for a moment, then said, "It's your watch below, Mr. Jukes?"

Jukes came to himself with a start. "Yes, sir."

"Leave orders to call me at the slightest change," said the Captain. He reached up to put the book away, and tucked his legs upon the couch. "Shut the door so that it don't fly open, will you? I can't stand a door banging. They've put a lot of rubbishy locks into this ship, I must say."

Captain MacWhirr closed his eyes.

He did so to rest himself. He was tired, and he experienced that state of mental vacuity which comes at the end of an exhaustive discussion that has liberated some belief matured in the course of meditative years. He had indeed been making his confession of faith, had he only known it; and its effect was to make Jukes, on the other side of the door, stand scratching his head for a good while.

Captain MacWhirr opened his eyes.

He thought he must have been asleep. What was that loud noise? Wind? Why had he not been called? The lamp wriggled in its gimbals, the barometer swung in circles, the table altered its slant every moment; a pair of limp sea-boots with collapsed tops went sliding past the couch. He put out his hand instantly, and captured one.

Jukes' face appeared in a crack of the door: only his face, very red, with staring eyes. The flame of the lamp leaped, a piece of paper flew up, a rush of air enveloped Captain MacWhirr. Beginning to draw on the boot, he directed an expectant gaze at Jukes' swollen, excited features.

"Came on like this," shouted Jukes, "five minutes ago . . . all of a sudden."

The head disappeared with a bang, and a heavy splash and patter of drops swept past the closed door as if a

pailful of melted lead had been flung against the house.
A whistling could be heard now upon the deep vibrating
noise outside. The stuffy chart-room seemed as full of
draughts as a shed. Captain MacWhirr collared the other
sea-boot on its violent passage along the floor. He was
not flustered, but he could not find at once the opening
for inserting his foot. The shoes he had flung off were
scurrying from end to end of the cabin, gambolling play-
fully over each other like puppies. As soon as he stood
up he kicked at them viciously, but without effect.

He threw himself into the attitude of a lunging fencer,
to reach after his oilskin coat; and afterwards he staggered all over the confined space while he jerked himself
into it. Very grave, straddling his legs far apart, and
stretching his neck, he started to tie deliberately the
strings of his sou-wester under his chin, with thick fingers that trembled slightly. He went through all the
movements of a woman putting on her bonnet before a
glass, with a strained, listening attention, as though he
had expected every moment to hear the shout of his name
in the confused clamour that had suddenly beset his ship.
Its increase filled his ears while he was getting ready to
go out and confront whatever it might mean. It was
tumultuous and very loud—made up of the rush of the
wind, the crashes of the sea, with that prolonged deep
vibration of the air, like the roll of an immense and remote drum beating the charge of the gale.

He stood for a moment in the light of the lamp, thick,
clumsy, shapeless in his panoply of combat, vigilant and
red-faced.

"There's a lot of weight in this," he muttered.

As soon as he attempted to open the door the wind
caught it. Clinging to the handle, he was dragged out
over the doorstep, and at once found himself engaged
with the wind in a sort of personal scuffle whose object
was the shutting of that door. At the last moment a
tongue of air scurried in and licked out the flame of the
lamp.

Ahead of the ship he perceived a great darkness lying

upon a multitude of white flashes; on the starboard beam a few amazing stars drooped, dim and fitful, above an immense waste of broken seas, as if seen through a mad drift of smoke.

On the bridge a knot of men, indistinct and toiling, were making great efforts in the light of the wheelhouse windows that shone mistily on their heads and backs. Suddenly darkness closed upon one pane, then on another. The voices of the lost group reached him after the manner of men's voices in a gale, in shreds and fragments of forlorn shouting snatched past the ear. All at once Jukes appeared at his side, yelling, with his head down.

"Watch—put in—wheelhouse shutters—glass—afraid —blow in."

Jukes heard his commander upbraiding.

"This—come—anything—warning—call me."

He tried to explain, with the uproar pressing on his lips.

"Light air—remained—bridge—sudden—north-east— could turn—thought—you—sure—hear."

They had gained the shelter of the weather-cloth, and could converse with raised voices, as people quarrel.

"I got the hands along to cover up all the ventilators. Good job I had remained on deck. I didn't think you would be asleep, and so . . . What did you say, sir? What?"

"Nothing," cried Captain MacWhirr. "I said—all right."

"By all the powers! We've got it this time," observed Jukes in a howl.

"You haven't altered her course?" inquired Captain MacWhirr, straining his voice.

"No, sir. Certainly not. Wind came out right head. And here comes the head sea."

A plunge of the ship ended in a shock as if she had landed her forefoot upon something solid. After a moment of stillness a lofty flight of sprays drove hard with the wind upon their faces.

"Keep her at it as long as we can," shouted Captain MacWhirr.

Before Jukes had squeezed the salt water out of his eyes all the stars had disappeared.

III

Jukes was as ready a man as any half-dozen young mates that may be caught by casting a net upon the waters; and though he had been somewhat taken aback by the startling viciousness of the first squall, he had pulled himself together on the instant, had called out the hands and had rushed them along to secure such openings about the deck as had not been already battened down earlier in the evening. Shouting in his fresh, stentorian voice, "Jump, boys, and bear a hand!" he led in the work, telling himself the while that he had "just expected this."

But at the same time he was growing aware that this was rather more than he had expected. From the first stir of the air felt on his cheek the gale seemed to take upon itself the accumulated impetus of an avalanche. Heavy sprays enveloped the *Nan-Shan* from stem to stern, and instantly in the midst of her regular rolling she began to jerk and plunge as though she had gone mad with fright.

Jukes thought, "This is no joke." While he was exchanging explanatory yells with his captain, a sudden lowering of the darkness came upon the night, falling before their vision like something palpable. It was as if the masked lights of the world had been turned down. Jukes was uncritically glad to have his captain at hand. It relieved him as though that man had, by simply coming on deck, taken most of the gale's weight upon his shoulders. Such is the prestige, the privilege, and the burden of command.

Captain MacWhirr could expect no relief of that sort from any one on earth. Such is the loneliness of command. He was trying to see, with that watchful manner

of a seaman who stares into the wind's eye as if into the
eye of an adversary, to penetrate the hidden intention and
guess the aim and force of the thrust. The strong wind
swept at him out of a vast obscurity; he felt under his
feet the uneasiness of his ship, and he could not even discern the shadow of her shape. He wished it were not so;
and very still he waited, feeling stricken by a blind man's
helplessness.

To be silent was natural to him, dark or shine. Jukes,
at his elbow, made himself heard yelling cheerily in the
gusts, "We must have got the worst of it at once, sir."
A faint burst of lightning quivered all round, as if flashed
into a cavern—into a black and secret chamber of the
sea, with a floor of foaming crests.

It unveiled for a sinister, fluttering moment a ragged
mass of clouds hanging low, the lurch of the long outlines
of the ship, the black figures of men caught on the bridge,
heads forward, as if petrified in the act of butting. The
darkness palpitated down upon all this, and then the real
thing came at last.

It was something formidable and swift, like the sudden smashing of a vial of wrath. It seemed to explode all
round the ship with an overpowering concussion and a
rush of great waters, as if an immense dam had been blown
up to windward. In an instant the men lost touch of each
other. This is the disintegrating power of a great wind:
it isolates one from one's kind. An earthquake, a landslip,
an avalanche, overtake a man incidentally, as it were—
without passion. A furious gale attacks him like a personal enemy, tries to grasp his limbs, fastens upon his
mind, seeks to rout his very spirit out of him.

Jukes was driven away from his commander. He
fancied himself whirled a great distance through the air.
Everything disappeared—even, for a moment, his power
of thinking; but his hand had found one of the rail-
stanchions. His distress was by no means alleviated by
an inclination to disbelieve the reality of this experience.
Though young, he had seen some bad weather, and had
never doubted his ability to imagine the worst; but this

was so much beyond his powers of fancy that it appeared
incompatible with the existence of any ship whatever. He
would have been incredulous about himself in the same
way, perhaps, had he not been so harassed by the necessity of exerting a wrestling effort against a force trying
to tear him away from his hold. Moreover, the conviction
of not being utterly destroyed returned to him through
the sensations of being half-drowned, bestially shaken,
and partly choked.

It seemed to him he remained there precariously alone
with the stanchion for a long, long time. The rain poured
on him, flowed, drove in sheets. He breathed in gasps;
and sometimes the water he swallowed was fresh and
sometimes it was salt. For the most part he kept his eyes
shut tight, as if suspecting his sight might be destroyed
in the immense flurry of the elements. When he ventured
to blink hastily, he derived some moral support from the
green gleam of the starboard light shining feebly upon
the flight of rain and sprays. He was actually looking at
it when its ray fell upon the uprearing sea which put it
out. He saw the head of the wave topple over, adding the
mite of its crash to the tremendous uproar raging around
him, and almost at the same instant the stanchion was
wrenched away from his embracing arms. After a crush-
ing thump on his back he found himself suddenly afloat
and borne upwards. His first irresistible notion was that
the whole China Sea had climbed on the bridge. Then,
more sanely, he concluded himself gone overboard. All the
time he was being tossed, flung, and rolled in great volumes of water, he kept on repeating mentally, with the
utmost precipitation, the words: "My God! My God! My
God! My God!"

All at once, in a revolt of misery and despair, he
formed the crazy resolution to get out of that. And he
began to thresh about with his arms and legs. But as soon
as he commenced his wretched struggles he discovered
that he had become somehow mixed up with a face, an oilskin coat, somebody's boots. He clawed ferociously all
these things in turn, lost them, found them again, lost

them once more, and finally was himself caught in the firm clasp of a pair of stout arms. He returned the embrace closely round a thick solid body. He had found his captain.

They tumbled over and over, tightening their hug. Suddenly the water let them down with a brutal bang; and, stranded against the side of the wheelhouse, out of breath and bruised, they were left to stagger up in the wind and hold on where they could.

Jukes came out of it rather horrified, as though he had escaped some unparalleled outrage directed at his feelings. It weakened his faith in himself. He started shouting aimlessly to the man he could feel near him in that fiendish blackness, "Is it you, sir? Is it you, sir?" till his temples seemed ready to burst. And he heard in answer a voice, as if crying far away, as if screaming to him fretfully from a very great distance, the one word "Yes!" Other seas swept again over the bridge. He received them defencelessly right over his bare head, with both his hands engaged in holding.

The motion of the ship was extravagant. Her lurches had an appalling helplessness: she pitched as if taking a header into a void, and seemed to find a wall to hit every time. When she rolled she fell on her side headlong, and she would be righted back by such a demolishing blow that Jukes felt her reeling as a clubbed man reels before he collapses. The gale howled and scuffled about gigantically in the darkness, as though the entire world were one black gully. At certain moments the air streamed against the ship as if sucked through a tunnel with a concentrated solid force of impact that seemed to lift her clean out of the water and keep her up for an instant with only a quiver running through her from end to end. And then she would begin her tumbling again as if dropped back into a boiling cauldron. Jukes tried hard to compose his mind and judge things coolly.

The sea, flattened down in the heavier gusts, would uprise and overwhelm both ends of the *Nan-Shan* in snowy rushes of foam, expanding wide, beyond both rails, into the night. And on this dazzling sheet, spread under the blackness of the clouds and emitting a bluish glow, Captain MacWhirr could catch a desolate glimpse of a few tiny specks black as ebony, the tops of the hatches, the battened companions, the heads of the covered winches, the foot of a mast. This was all he could see of his ship. Her middle structure, covered by the bridge which bore him, his mate, the closed wheelhouse where a man was steering shut up with the fear of being swept overboard together with the whole thing in one great crash—her middle structure was like a half-tide rock awash upon a coast. It was like an outlying rock with the water boiling up, streaming over, pouring off, beating round—like a rock in the surf to which shipwrecked people cling before they let go—only it rose, it sank, it rolled continuously, without respite and rest, like a rock that should have miraculously struck adrift from a coast and gone wallowing upon the sea.

The *Nan-Shan* was being looted by the storm with a senseless, destructive fury: trysails torn out of the extra gaskets, double-lashed awnings blown away, bridge swept clean, weather-cloths burst, rails twisted, light-screens smashed—and two of the boats had gone already. They had gone unheard and unseen, melting, as it were, in the shock and smother of the wave. It was only later, when upon the white flash of another high sea hurling itself amidships, Jukes had a vision of two pairs of davits leaping black and empty out of the solid blackness, with one overhauled fall flying and an iron-bound block capering in the air, that he became aware of what had happened within about three yards of his back.

He poked his head forward, groping for the ear of his commander. His lips touched it—big, fleshy, very wet. He cried in an agitated tone, "Our boats are going now, sir."

And again he heard that voice, forced and ringing feebly, but with a penetrating effect of quietness in the enormous discord of noises, as if sent out from some remote spot of peace beyond the black wastes of the gale; again he heard a man's voice—the frail and indomitable sound that can be made to carry an infinity of thought, resolution and purpose, that shall be pronouncing confident words on the last day, when heavens fall, and justice is done—again he heard it, and it was crying to him, as if from very, very far—"All right."

He thought he had not managed to make himself understood. "Our boats—I say boats—the boats, sir! Two gone!"

The same voice, within a foot of him and yet so remote, yelled sensibly, "Can't be helped."

Captain MacWhirr had never turned his face, but Jukes caught some more words on the wind.

"What can—expect—when hammering through— such—— Bound to leave—something behind—stands to reason."

Watchfully Jukes listened for more. No more came. This was all Captain MacWhirr had to say; and Jukes could picture to himself rather than see the broad squat back before him. An impenetrable obscurity pressed down upon the ghostly glimmers of the sea. A dull conviction seized upon Jukes that there was nothing to be done.

If the steering-gear did not give way, if the immense volumes of water did not burst the deck in or smash one of the hatches, if the engines did not give up, if way could be kept on the ship against this terrific wind, and she did not bury herself in one of these awful seas, of whose white crests alone, topping high above her bows, he could now and then get a sickening glimpse—then there was a chance of her coming out of it. Something within him seemed to turn over, bringing uppermost the feeling that the *Nan-Shan* was lost.

"She's done for," he said to himself, with a surprising mental agitation, as though he had discovered an unexpected meaning in this thought. One of these things was bound to happen. Nothing could be prevented now, and nothing could be remedied. The men on board did not count, and the ship could not last. This weather was too impossible.

Jukes felt an arm thrown heavily over his shoulders;

and to this overture he responded with great intelligence by catching hold of his captain round the waist.

They stood clasped thus in the blind night, bracing each other against the wind, cheek to cheek and lip to ear, in the manner of two hulks lashed stem to stern together.

And Jukes heard the voice of his commander hardly any louder than before, but nearer, as though, starting to march athwart the prodigious rush of the hurricane, it had approached him, bearing that strange effect of quietness like the serene glow of a halo.

"D'ye know where the hands got to?" it asked, vigorous and evanescent at the same time, overcoming the strength of the wind, and swept away from Jukes instantly.

Jukes didn't know. They were all on the bridge when the real force of the hurricane struck the ship. He had no idea where they had crawled to. Under the circumstances they were nowhere, for all the use that could be made of them. Somehow the Captain's wish to know distressed Jukes.

"Want the hands, sir?" he cried, apprehensively.

"Ought to know," asserted Captain MacWhirr. "Hold hard."

They held hard. An outburst of unchained fury, a vicious rush of the wind absolutely steadied the ship; she rocked only, quick and light like a child's cradle, for a terrific moment of suspense, while the whole atmosphere, as it seemed, streamed furiously past her, roaring away from the tenebrous earth.

It suffocated them, and with eyes shut they tightened their grasp. What from the magnitude of the shock might have been a column of water running upright in the dark, butted against the ship, broke short, and fell on her bridge, crushingly, from on high, with a dead burying weight.

A flying fragment of that collapse, a mere splash, enveloped them in one swirl from their feet over their heads, filling violently their ears, mouths and nostrils with salt water. It knocked out their legs, wrenched in haste at their arms, seethed away swiftly under their chins; and opening their eyes, they saw the piled-up masses of foam dashing to and fro amongst what looked like the fragments of a ship. She had given way as if driven straight in. Their panting hearts yielded, too, before the tremendous blow; and all at once she sprang up again to her desperate plunging, as if trying to scramble out from under the ruins.

The seas in the dark seemed to rush from all sides to keep her back where she might perish. There was hate in the way she was handled, and a ferocity in the blows that fell. She was like a living creature thrown to the rage of a mob: hustled terribly, struck at, borne up, flung down, leaped upon. Captain MacWhirr and Jukes kept hold of each other, deafened by the noise, gagged by the wind; and the great physical tumult beating about their bodies, brought, like an unbridled display of passion, a profound trouble to their souls. One of those wild and appalling shrieks that are heard at times passing mysteriously overhead in the steady roar of a hurricane, swooped, as if borne on wings, upon the ship, and Jukes tried to outscream it.

"Will she live through this?"

The cry was wrenched out of his breast. It was as unintentional as the birth of a thought in the head, and he heard nothing of it himself. It all became extinct at once —thought, intention, effort—and of his cry the inaudible vibration added to the tempest waves of the air.

He expected nothing from it. Nothing at all. For indeed what answer could be made? But after a while he heard with amazement the frail and resisting voice in his ear, the dwarf sound, unconquered in the giant tumult.

"She may!"

It was a dull yell, more difficult to seize than a whisper. And presently the voice returned again, half submerged in the vast crashes, like a ship battling against the waves of an ocean.

"Let's hope so!" it cried—small, lonely and unmoved,

a stranger to the visions of hope or fear; and it flickered into disconnected words: "Ship. . . . This. . . . Never —Anyhow . . . for the best." Jukes gave it up.

Then, as if it had come suddenly upon the one thing fit to withstand the power of a storm, it seemed to gain force and firmness for the last. broken shouts:

"Keep on hammering . . . builders . . . good men. . . . And chance it . . . engines. . . . Rout . . . good man."

Captain MacWhirr removed his arm from Jukes' shoulders, and thereby ceased to exist for his mate, so dark it was; Jukes, after a tense stiffening of every muscle, would let himself go limp all over. The gnawing of profound discomfort existed side by side with an incredible disposition to somnolence, as though he had been buffeted and worried into drowsiness. The wind would get hold of his head and try to shake it off his shoulders; his clothes, full of water, were as heavy as lead, cold and dripping like an armour of melting ice: he shivered—it lasted a long time; and with his hands closed hard on his hold, he was letting himself sink slowly into the depths of bodily misery. His mind became concentrated upon himself in an aimless, idle way, and when something pushed lightly at the back of his knees he nearly, as the saying is, jumped out of his skin.

In the start forward he bumped the back of Captain MacWhirr, who didn't move; and then a hand gripped his thigh. A lull had come, a menacing lull of the wind, the holding of a stormy breath—and he felt himself pawed all over. It was the boatswain. Jukes recognized these hands, so thick and enormous that they seemed to belong to some new species of man.

The boatswain had arrived on the bridge, crawling on all fours against the wind, and had found the chief mate's legs with the top of his head. Immediately he crouched and began to explore Jukes' person upwards with prudent, apologetic touches, as became an inferior.

He was an ill-favoured, undersized, gruff sailor of fifty, coarsely hairy, short-legged, long-armed, resembling an elderly ape. His strength was immense; and in his great lumpy paws, bulging like brown boxing-gloves on the end of furry forearms, the heaviest objects were handled like playthings. Apart from the grizzled pelt on his chest, the menacing demeanour and the hoarse voice, he had none of the classical attributes of his rating. His good nature almost amounted to imbecility: the men did what they liked with him, and he had not an ounce of initiative in his character, which was easy-going and talkative. For these reasons Jukes disliked him; but Captain MacWhirr, to Jukes' scornful disgust, seemed to regard him as a first-rate petty officer.

He pulled himself up by Jukes' coat, taking that liberty with the greatest moderation, and only so far as it was forced upon him by the hurricane.

"What is it, boss'n, what is it?" yelled Jukes, impatiently. What could that fraud of a boss'n want on the bridge? The typhoon had got on Jukes' nerves. The husky bellowings of the other, though unintelligible, seemed to suggest a state of lively satisfaction. There could be no mistake. The old fool was pleased with something.

The boatswain's other hand had found some other body, for in a changed tone he began to inquire: "Is it you, sir? Is it you, sir?" The wind strangled his howls.

"Yes!" cried Captain MacWhirr.

IV

All that the boatswain, out of a superabundance of yells, could make clear to Captain MacWhirr was the bizarre intelligence that "All them Chinamen in the fore 'tween deck have fetched away, sir."

Jukes to leeward could hear these two shouting within six inches of his face, as you may hear on a still night half a mile away two men conversing across a field. He heard Captain MacWhirr's exasperated "What? What?" and the strained pitch of the other's hoarseness. "In a

lump . . . seen them myself. . . . Awful sight, sir . . .
thought . . . tell you.''

Jukes remained indifferent, as if rendered irresponsible
by the force of the hurricane, which made the very
thought of action utterly vain. Besides, being very young,
he had found the occupation of keeping his heart completely steeled against the worst so engrossing that he had
come to feel an overpowering dislike towards any other
form of activity whatever. He was not scared; he knew
this because, firmly believing he would never see another
sunrise, he remained calm in that belief.

These are the moments of do-nothing heroics to which
even good men surrender at times. Many officers of ships
can no doubt recall a case in their experience when just
such a trance of confounded stoicism would come all at
once over a whole ship's company. Jukes, however, had no
wide experience of men or storms. He conceived himself
to be calm—inexorably calm; but as a matter of fact he
was daunted; not abjectly, but only so far as a decent
man may, without becoming loathsome to himself.

It was rather like a forced-on numbness of spirit. The
long, long stress of a gale does it; the suspense of the
interminably culminating catastrophe; and there is a
bodily fatigue in the mere holding on to existence within
the excessive tumult; a searching and insidious fatigue
that penetrates deep into a man's breast to cast down and
sadden his heart, which is incorrigible, and of all the gifts
of the earth—even before life itself—aspires to peace.

Jukes was benumbed much more than he supposed. He
held on—very wet, very cold, stiff in every limb; and in
a momentary hallucination of swift visions (it is said that
a drowning man thus reviews all his life) he beheld all
sorts of memories altogether unconnected with his present
situation. He remembered his father, for instance: a
worthy business man, who at an unfortunate crisis in his
affairs went quietly to bed and died forthwith in a state
of resignation. Jukes did not recall these circumstances,
of course, but remaining otherwise unconcerned he seemed
to see distinctly the poor man's face; a certain game of

nap played when quite a boy in Table Bay on board a ship, since lost with all hands; the thick eyebrows of his first skipper; and without any emotion, as he might years ago have walked listlessly into her room and found her sitting there with a book, he remembered his mother— dead, too, now—the resolute woman, left badly off, who had been very firm in his bringing up.

It could not have lasted more than a second, perhaps not so much. A heavy arm had fallen about his shoulders; Captain MacWhirr's voice was speaking his name into his ear.

"Jukes! Jukes!"

He detected the tone of deep concern. The wind had thrown its weight on the ship, trying to pin her down amongst the seas. They made a clean breach over her, as over a deep-swimming log; and the gathered weight of crashes menaced monstrously from afar. The breakers flung out of the night with a ghostly light on their crests —the light of sea-foam that in a ferocious, boiling-up pale flash showed upon the slender body of the ship the toppling rush, the downfall, and the seething mad scurry of each wave. Never for a moment could she shake herself clear of the water; Jukes, rigid, perceived in her motion the ominous sign of haphazard floundering. She was no longer struggling intelligently. It was the beginning of the end; and the note of busy concern in Captain Mac-Whirr's voice sickened him like an exhibition of blind and pernicious folly.

The spell of the storm had fallen upon Jukes. He was penetrated by it, absorbed by it; he was rooted in it with a rigour of dumb attention. Captain MacWhirr persisted in his cries, but the wind got between them like a solid wedge. He hung round Jukes' neck as heavy as a mill-stone, and suddenly the sides of their heads knocked together.

"Jukes! Mr. Jukes, I say!"

He had to answer that voice that would not be silenced. He answered in the customary manner: ". . . Yes, sir."

And directly, his heart, corrupted by the storm that

breeds a craving for peace, rebelled against the tyranny of training and command.

Captain MacWhirr had his mate's head fixed firm in the crook of his elbow, and pressed it to his yelling lips mysteriously. Sometimes Jukes would break in, admonishing hastily: "Look out, sir!" or Captain MacWhirr would bawl an earnest exhortation to "Hold hard, there!" and the whole black universe seemed to reel together with the ship. They paused. She floated yet. And Captain MacWhirr would resume his shouts. ". . . . Says . . . whole lot . . . fetched away. . . . Ought to see . . . what's the matter."

Directly the full force of the hurricane had struck the ship, every part of her deck became untenable; and the sailors, dazed and dismayed, took shelter in the port alleyway under the bridge. It had a door aft, which they shut; it was very black, cold, and dismal. At each heavy fling of the ship they would groan all together in the dark, and tons of water could be heard scuttling about as if trying to get at them from above. The boatswain had been keeping up a gruff talk, but a more unreasonable lot of men, he said afterwards, he had never been with. They were snug enough there, out of harm's way, and not wanted to do anything, either; and yet they did nothing but grumble and complain peevishly like so many sick lads. Finally, one of them said that if there had been at least some light to see each other's noses by, it wouldn't be so bad. It was making him crazy, he declared, to lie there in the dark waiting for the blamed hooker to sink.

"Why don't you step outside, then, and be done with it at once?" the boatswain turned on him.

This called up a shout of execration. The boatswain found himself overwhelmed with reproaches of all sorts. They seemed to take it ill that a lamp was not instantly created for them out of nothing. They would whine after a light to get drowned by—anyhow! And though the unreason of their revilings was patent—since no one could hope to reach the lamp-room, which was forward—he became greatly distressed. He did not think it was decent

of them to be nagging at him like this. He told them so,
and was met by general contumely. He sought refuge,
therefore, in an embittered silence. At the same time their
grumbling and sighing and muttering worried him
greatly, but by-and-by it occurred to him that there were
six globe lamps hung in the 'tween-deck, and that there
could be no harm in depriving the coolies of one of them.

The *Nan-Shan* had an athwartship coal-bunker, which,
being at times used as cargo space, communicated by an
iron door with the fore 'tween-deck. It was empty then,
and its manhole was the foremost one in the alleyway.
The boatswain could get in, therefore, without coming
out on deck at all; but to his great surprise he found he
could induce no one to help him in taking off the manhole cover. He groped for it all the same, but one of the
crew lying in his way refused to budge.

"Why, I only want to get you that blamed light you
are crying for," he expostulated, almost pitifully.

Somebody told him to go and put his head in a bag.
He regretted he could not recognize the voice, and that
it was too dark to see, otherwise, as he said, he would have
put a head on *that* son of a sea-cook, anyway, sink or
swim. Nevertheless, he had made up his mind to show
them he could get a light, if he were to die for it.

Through the violence of the ship's rolling, every movement was dangerous. To be lying down seemed labour
enough. He nearly broke his neck dropping into the
bunker. He fell on his back, and was sent shooting help-
lessly from side to side in the dangerous company of a
heavy iron bar—a coal-trimmer's slice probably—left
down there by somebody. This thing made him as nervous as though it had been a wild beast. He could not see
it, the inside of the bunker coated with coal-dust being
perfectly and impenetrably black; but he heard it sliding
and clattering, and striking here and there, always in
the neighbourhood of his head. It seemed to make an
extraordinary noise, too—to give heavy thumps as
though it had been as big as a bridge girder. This was
remarkable enough for him to notice while he was flung

from port to starboard and back again, and clawing desperately the smooth sides of the bunker in the endeavour
to stop himself. The door into the 'tween-deck not fitting
quite true, he saw a thread of dim light at the bottom.

Being a sailor, and a still active man, he did not want
much of a chance to regain his feet; and as luck would
have it, in scrambling up he put his hand on the iron slice,
picking it up as he rose. Otherwise he would have been
afraid of the thing breaking his legs, or at least knocking him down again. At first he stood still. He felt unsafe in this darkness that seemed to make the ship's motion unfamiliar, unforeseen, and difficult to counteract.
He felt so much shaken for a moment that he dared not
move for fear of "taking charge again." He had no mind
to get battered to pieces in that bunker.

He had struck his head twice; he was dazed a little.
He seemed to hear yet so plainly the clatter and bangs
of the iron slice flying about his ears that he tightened
his grip to prove to himself he had it there safely in his
hand. He was vaguely amazed at the plainness with which
down there he could hear the gale raging. Its howls and
shrieks seemed to take on, in the emptiness of the bunker,
something of the human character, of human rage and
pain—being not vast but infinitely poignant. And there
were, with every roll, thumps, too—profound, ponder-
ous thumps, as if a bulky object of five-ton weight or so
had got play in the hold. But there was no such thing
in the cargo. Something on deck? Impossible. Or alongside? Couldn't be.

He thought all this quickly, clearly, competently, like
a seaman, and in the end remained puzzled. This noise,
though, came deadened from outside, together with the
washing and pouring of water on deck above his head.
Was it the wind? Must be. It made down there a row like
the shouting of a big lot of crazed men. And he discovered in himself a desire for a light, too—if only to get
drowned by—and a nervous anxiety to get out of that
bunker as quickly as possible.

He pulled back the bolt: the heavy iron plate turned

on its hinges; and it was though he had opened the door to the sounds of the tempest. A gust of hoarse yelling met him: the air was still; and the rushing of water overhead was covered by a tumult of strangled, throaty shrieks that produced an effect of desperate confusion. He straddled his legs the whole width of the doorway and stretched his neck. And at first he perceived only what he had come to seek: six small yellow flames swinging violently on the great body of the dusk.

It was stayed like the gallery of a mine, with a row of stanchions in the middle, and cross-beams overhead, penetrating into the gloom ahead—indefinitely. And to port there loomed, like the caving in of one of the sides, a bulky mass with a slanting outline. The whole place, with the shadows and the shapes, moved all the time. The boatswain glared: the ship lurched to starboard, and a great howl came from that mass that had the slant of fallen earth.

Pieces of wood whizzed past. Planks, he thought, inexpressibly startled, and flinging back his head. At his feet a man went sliding over, open-eyed, on his back, straining with uplifted arms for nothing: and another came bounding like a detached stone with his head between his legs and his hands clenched. His pigtail whipped in the air; he made a grab at the boatswain's legs, and from his opened hand a bright white disc rolled against the boatswain's foot. He recognized a silver dollar, and yelled at it with astonishment. With a precipitated sound of trampling and shuffling of bare feet, and with guttural cries, the mound of writhing bodies piled up to port detached itself from the ship's side and sliding, inert and struggling, shifted to starboard, with a dull, brutal thump. The cries ceased. The boatswain heard a long moan through the roar and whistling of the wind; he saw an inextricable confusion of heads and shoulders, naked soles kicking upwards, fists raised, tumbling backs, legs, pigtails, faces.

"Good Lord!" he cried, horrified, and banged-to the iron door upon this vision.

This was what he had come on the bridge to tell. He could not keep it to himself; and on board ship there is only one man to whom it is worth while to unburden yourself. On his passage back the hands in the alleyway swore at him for a fool. Why didn't he bring that lamp? What the devil did the coolies matter to anybody? And when he came out, the extremity of the ship made what went on inside of her appear of little moment.

At first he thought he had left the alleyway in the very moment of her sinking. The bridge ladders had been washed away, but an enormous sea filling the after-deck floated him up. After that he had to lie on his stomach for some time, holding to a ring-bolt, getting his breath now and then, and swallowing salt water. He struggled farther on his hands and knees, too frightened and distracted to turn back. In this way he reached the after-part of the wheelhouse. In that comparatively sheltered spot he found the second mate. The boatswain was pleasantly surprised—his impression being that everybody on deck must have been washed away a long time ago. He asked eagerly where the Captain was.

The second mate was lying low, like a malignant little animal under a hedge.

"Captain? Gone overboard, after getting us into this mess." The mate, too, for all he knew or cared. Another fool. Didn't matter. Everybody was going by-and-by.

The boatswain crawled out again into the strength of the wind; not because he much expected to find anybody, he said, but just to get away from "that man." He crawled out as outcasts go to face an inclement world. Hence his great joy at finding Jukes and the Captain. But what was going on in the 'tween-deck was to him a minor matter by that time. Besides, it was difficult to make yourself heard. But he managed to convey the idea that the Chinamen had broken adrift together with their boxes, and that he had come up on purpose to report this. As to the hands, they were all right. Then, appeased, he subsided on the deck in a sitting posture, hugging with his arms and legs the stand of the engine-room telegraph

—an iron casting as thick as a post. When that went, why, he expected he would go, too. He gave no more thought to the coolies.

Captain MacWhirr had made Jukes understand that he wanted him to go down below—to see.

"What am I to do then, sir?" And the trembling of his whole wet body caused Jukes' voice to sound like bleating.

"See first . . . Boss'n . . . says . . . adrift."

"That boss'n is a confounded fool," howled Jukes, shakily.

The absurdity of the demand made upon him revolted Jukes. He was as unwilling to go as if the moment he had left the deck the ship were sure to sink.

"I must know . . . can't leave. . . ."

"Fight . . . boss'n says they fight. . . . Why? Can't have . . . fighting . . . board ship. . . . Much rather keep you here . . . case . . . I should . . . washed overboard myself. . . . Stop it . . . some way. You see and tell me . . . through engine-room tube. Don't want you . . . come up here . . . too often. Dangerous . . . moving about . . . deck."

Jukes, held with his head in chancery, had to listen to what seemed horrible suggestions.

"Don't want . . . you get lost . . . so long . . . ship isn't. . . . Rout . . . Good man . . . Ship . . . may . . . through this . . . all right yet."

All at once Jukes understood he would have to go.

"Do you think she may?" he screamed.

But the wind devoured the reply, out of which Jukes heard only the one word, pronounced with great energy ". . . Always. . . ."

Captain MacWhirr released Jukes, and bending over the boatswain, yelled, "Get back with the mate." Jukes only knew that the arm was gone off his shoulders. He was dismissed with his orders—to do what? He was exasperated into letting go his hold carelessly, and on the instant was blown away. It seemed to him that nothing could stop him from being blown right over the stern.

He flung himself down hastily, and the boatswain, who was following, fell on him.

"Don't you get up yet, sir," cried the boatswain. "No hurry!"

A sea swept over. Jukes understood the boatswain to splutter that the bridge ladders were gone. "I'll lower you down, sir, by your hands," he screamed. He shouted also something about the smoke-stack being as likely to go overboard as not. Jukes thought it very possible, and imagined the fires out, the ship helpless. . . . The boatswain by his side kept on yelling. "What? What is it?" Jukes cried distressfully; and the other repeated, "What would my old woman say if she saw me now?"

In the alleyway, where a lot of water had got in and splashed in the dark, the men were still as death, till Jukes stumbled against one of them and cursed him savagely for being in the way. Two or three voices then asked, eager and weak, "Any chance for us, sir?"

"What's the matter with you fools?" he said brutally. He felt as though he could throw himself down amongst them and never move any more. But they seemed cheered; and in the midst of obsequious warnings, "Look out! Mind that manhole lid, sir," they lowered him into the bunker. The boatswain tumbled down after him, and as soon as he had picked himself up he remarked, "She would say, 'Serve you right, you old fool, for going to sea.' "

The boatswain had some means, and made a point of alluding to them frequently. His wife—a fat woman— and two grown-up daughters kept a greengrocer's shop in the East-end of London.

In the dark, Jukes, unsteady on his legs, listened to a faint thunderous patter. A deadened screaming went on steadily at his elbow, as it were; and from above the louder tumult of the storm descended upon these near sounds. His head swam. To him, too, in that bunker, the motion of the ship seemed novel and menacing, sapping his resolution as though he had never been afloat before.

He had half a mind to scramble out again; but the re-membrance of Captain MacWhirr's voice made this impossible. His orders were to go and see. What was the good of it, he wanted to know. Enraged, he told himself he would see—of course. But the boatswain, staggering clumsily, warned him to be careful how he opened that door; there was a blamed fight going on. And Jukes, as if in great bodily pain, desired irritably to know what the devil they were fighting for.

"Dollars! Dollars, sir. All their rotten chests got burst open. Blamed money skipping all over the place, and they are tumbling after it head over heels—tearing and biting like anything. A regular little hell in there."

Jukes convulsively opened the door. The short boat-swain peered under his arm.

One of the lamps had gone out, broken perhaps. Rancorous, guttural cries burst out loudly on their ears, and a strange panting sound, the working of all these straining breasts. A hard blow hit the side of the ship: water fell above with a stunning shock, and in the forefront of the gloom, where the air was reddish and thick, Jukes saw a head bang the deck violently, two thick calves waving on high, muscular arms twined round a naked body, a yellow-face, open-mouthed and with a set wild stare, look up and slide away. An empty chest clattered turning over; a man fell head first with a jump, as if lifted by a kick; and farther off, indistinct, others streamed like a mass of rolling stones down a bank, thumping the deck with their feet and flourishing their arms wildly. The hatchway ladder was loaded with coolies swarming on it like bees on a branch. They hung on the steps in a crawling, stirring cluster, beating madly with their fists the underside of the battened hatch, and the headlong rush of the water above was heard in the intervals of their yelling. The ship heeled over more, and they began to drop off: first one, then two, then all the rest went away together, falling straight off with a great cry.

Jukes was confounded. The boatswain, with gruff anxiety, begged him, "Don't you go in there, sir."

The whole place seemed to twist upon itself, jumping incessantly the while; and when the ship rose to a sea

Jukes fancied that all these men would be shot upon him in a body. He backed out, swung the door to, and with trembling hands pushed at the bolt. . . .

As soon as his mate had gone Captain MacWhirr, left alone on the bridge, sidled and staggered as far as the wheelhouse. Its door being hinged forward, he had to fight the gale for admittance, and when at last he managed to enter, it was with an instantaneous clatter and a bang, as though he had been fired through the wood. He stood within, holding on to the handle.

The steering-gear leaked steam, and in the confined space the glass of the binnacle made a shiny oval of light in a thin white fog. The wind howled, hummed, whistled, with sudden booming gusts that rattled the doors and shutters in the vicious patter of sprays. Two coils of lead-line and a small canvas bag hung on a long lanyard, swung wide off, and came back clinging to the bulkheads. The gratings underfoot were nearly afloat; with every sweeping blow of a sea, water squirted violently through the cracks all round the door, and the man at the helm had flung down his cap, his coat, and stood propped against the gear-casing in a striped cotton shirt open on his breast. The little brass wheel in his hands had the appearance of a bright and fragile toy. The cords of his neck stood hard and lean, a dark patch lay in the hollow of his throat, and his face was still and sunken as in death.

Captain MacWhirr wiped his eyes. The sea that had nearly taken him overboard had, to his great annoyance, washed his sou'-wester hat off his bald head. The fluffy, fair hair, soaked and darkened, resembled a mean skein of cotton threads festooned round his bare skull. His face, glistening with sea-water, had been made crimson with the wind, with the sting of sprays. He looked as though he had come off sweating from before a furnace.

"You here?" he muttered, heavily.

The second mate had found his way into the wheelhouse some time before. He had fixed himself in a corner with his knees up, a fist pressed against each temple; and this attitude suggested rage, sorrow, resignation, surrender, with a sort of concentrated unforgiveness. He said mournfully and defiantly, "Well, it's my watch below now: ain't it?"

The steam gear clattered, stopped, clattered again; and the helmsman's eyeballs seemed to project out of a hungry face as if the compass card behind the binnacle glass had been meat. God knows how long he had been left there to steer, as if forgotten by all his shipmates. The bells had not been struck; there had been no reliefs; the ship's routine had gone down wind; but he was trying to keep her head north-north-east. The rudder might have been gone for all he knew, the fires out, the engines broken down, the ship ready to roll over like a corpse. He was anxious not to get muddled and lose control of her head, because the compass-card swung far both ways, wriggling on the pivot, and sometimes seemed to whirl right round. He suffered from mental stress. He was horribly afraid, also, of the wheelhouse going. Mountains of water kept on tumbling against it. When the ship took one of her desperate dives the corners of his lips twitched.

Captain MacWhirr looked up at the wheelhouse clock. Screwed to the bulk-head, it had a white face on which the black hands appeared to stand quite still. It was half-past one in the morning.

"Another day," he muttered to himself.

The second mate heard him, and lifting his head as one grieving amongst ruins, "You won't see it break," he exclaimed. His wrists and his knees could be seen to shake violently. "No, by God! You won't. . . ."

He took his face again between his fists.

The body of the helmsman had moved slightly, but his head didn't budge on his neck,—like a stone head fixed to look one way from a column. During a roll that all but took his booted legs from under him, and in the very stagger to save himself, Captain MacWhirr said austerely, "Don't you pay any attention to what that man says." And then, with an indefinable change of tone, very grave, he added, "He isn't on duty."

The sailor said nothing.

The hurricane boomed, shaking the little place, which seemed air-tight; and the light of the binnacle flickered all the time.

"You haven't been relieved," Captain MacWhirr went on, looking down. "I want you to stick to the helm, though, as long as you can. You've got the hang of her. Another man coming here might make a mess of it. Wouldn't do. No child's play. And the hands are probably busy with a job down below. . . . Think you can?"

The steering-gear leaped into an abrupt short clatter, stopped smouldering like an ember; and the still man, with a motionless gaze, burst out, as if all the passion in him had gone into his lips: "By Heavens, sir! I can steer for ever if nobody talks to me."

"Oh! aye! All right. . . ." The Captain lifted his eyes for the first time to the man, ". . . Hackett."

And he seemed to dismiss this matter from his mind. He stooped to the engine-room speaking-tube, blew in, and bent his head. Mr. Rout below answered, and at once Captain MacWhirr put his lips to the mouthpiece.

With the uproar of the gale around him he applied alternately his lips and his ear, and the engineer's voice mounted to him, harsh and as if out of the heat of an engagement. One of the stokers was disabled, the others had given in, the second engineer and the donkey-man were firing-up. The third engineer was standing by the steam-valve. The engines were being tended by hand. How was it above?

"Bad enough. It mostly rests with you," said Captain MacWhirr. Was the mate down there yet? No? Well, he would be presently. Would Mr. Rout let him talk through the speaking-tube?—through the deck speaking-tube, because he—the Captain—was going out again on the bridge directly. There was some trouble amongst the Chinamen. They were fighting, it seemed. Couldn't allow fighting anyhow. . . .

Mr. Rout had gone away, and Captain MacWhirr could feel against his ear the pulsation of the engines, like the beat of the ship's heart. Mr. Rout's voice down there shouted something distantly. The ship pitched head-long, the pulsation leaped with a hissing tumult, and stopped dead. Captain MacWhirr's face was impassive, and his eyes were fixed aimlessly on the crouching shape of the second mate. Again Mr. Rout's voice cried out in the depths, and the pulsating beats recommenced, with slow strokes—growing swifter.

Mr. Rout had returned to the tube. "It don't matter much what they do," he said, hastily; and then, with irritation, "She takes these dives as if she never meant to come up again."

"Awful sea," said the Captain's voice from above.

"Don't let me drive her under," barked Solomon Rout up the pipe.

"Dark and rain. Can't see what's coming," uttered the voice. "Must—keep—her—moving—enough to steer—and chance it," it went on to state distinctly.

"I am doing as much as I dare."

"We are—getting—smashed up—a good deal up here," proceeded the voice mildly. "Doing—fairly well—though. Of course, if the wheelhouse should go. . . ."

Mr. Rout, bending an attentive ear, muttered peevishly something under his breath.

But the deliberate voice up there became animated to ask: "Jukes turned up yet?" Then, after a short wait, "I wish he would bear a hand. I want him to be done and come up here in case of anything. To look after the ship. I am all alone. The second mate's lost. . . ."

"What?" shouted Mr. Rout into the engine-room, taking his head away. Then up the tube he cried, "Gone overboard?" and clapped his ear to.

"Lost his nerve," the voice from above continued in a matter-of-fact tone. "Damned awkward circumstance."

Mr. Rout, listening with bowed neck, opened his eyes wide at this. However, he heard something like the sounds of a scuffle and broken exclamations coming down to him. He strained his hearing; and all the time Beale, the third engineer, with his arms uplifted, held between the palms of his hands the rim of a little black wheel projecting at the side of a big copper pipe. He seemed to be poising it above his head, as though it were a correct attitude in some sort of game.

To steady himself, he pressed his shoulder against the white bulkhead, one knee bent, and a sweat-rag tucked in his belt hanging on his hip. His smooth cheek was be-grimed and flushed, and the coal dust on his eyelids, like the black pencilling of a make-up, enhanced the liquid brilliance of the whites, giving to his youthful face some-thing of a feminine, exotic and fascinating aspect. When the ship pitched he would with hasty movements of his hands screw hard at the little wheel.

"Gone crazy," began the Captain's voice suddenly in the tube. "Rushed at me. . . . Just now. Had to knock him down. . . . This minute. You heard, Mr. Rout?"

"The devil!" muttered Mr. Rout. "Look out, Beale!"

His shout rang out like the blast of a warning trum-pet, between the iron walls of the engine-room. Painted white, they rose high into the dusk of the skylight, slop-ing like a roof; and the whole lofty space resembled the interior of a monument, divided by floors of iron grating, with lights flickering at different levels, and a mass of gloom lingering in the middle, within the columnar stir of machinery under the motionless swelling of the cylin-ders. A loud and wild resonance, made up of all the noises of the hurricane, dwelt in the still warmth of the air. There was in it the smell of hot metal, of oil, and a slight mist of steam. The blows of the sea seemed to traverse it in an unringing, stunning shock, from side to side.

Gleams, like pale long flames, trembled upon the polish of metal; from the flooring below the enormous crank-heads emerged in their turns with a flash of brass and steel—going over; while the connecting-rods, big-jointed, like skeleton limbs, seemed to thrust them down and pull them up again with an irresistible precision. And deep in the half-light other rods dodged deliberately to and fro, crossheads nodded, discs of metal rubbed smoothly against each other, slow and gentle, in a commingling of shadows and gleams.

Sometimes all those powerful and unerring movements would slow down simultaneously, as if they had been the functions of a living organism, stricken suddenly by the blight of languor; and Mr. Rout's eyes would blaze darker in his long sallow face. He was fighting this fight in a pair of carpet slippers. A short shiny jacket barely covered his loins, and his white wrists protruded far out of the tight sleeves, as though the emergency had added to his stature, had lengthened his limbs, augmented his pallor, hollowed his eyes.

He moved, climbing high up, disappearing low down, with a restless, purposeful industry, and when he stood still, holding the guard-rail in front of the starting-gear, he would keep glancing to the right at the steam-gauge, at the water-gauge, fixed upon the white wall in the light of a swaying lamp. The mouths of two speaking-tubes gaped stupidly at his elbow, and the dial of the engine-room telegraph resembled a clock of large diameter, bearing on its face curt words instead of figures. The grouped letters stood out heavily black, around the pivot-head of the indicator, emphatically symbolic of loud exclamations: AHEAD, ASTERN, SLOW, HALF, STAND BY; and the fat black hand pointed downwards to the word FULL, which, thus singled out, captured the eye as a sharp cry secures attention.

The wood-encased bulk of the low-pressure cylinder, frowning portly from above, emitted a faint wheeze at every thrust, and except for that low hiss the engines worked their steel limbs headlong or slow with a silent, determined smoothness. And all this, the white walls, the moving steel, the floor plates under Solomon Rout's feet, the floors of iron grating above his head, the dusk and the gleams, uprose and sank continuously, with one accord, upon the harsh wash of the waves against the ship's side. The whole loftiness of the place, booming hollow to the great voice of the wind, swayed at the top like a tree, would go over bodily, as if borne down this way and that by the tremendous blasts.

"You've got to hurry up," shouted Mr. Rout, as soon as he saw Jukes appear in the stokehold doorway.

Jukes' glance was wandering and tipsy; his red face was puffy, as though he had overslept himself. He had had an arduous road, and had travelled over it with immense vivacity, the agitation of his mind corresponding to the exertions of his body. He had rushed up out of the bunker, stumbling in the dark alleyway amongst a lot of bewildered men who, trod upon, asked "What's up, sir?" in awed mutters all round him;—down the stokehold ladder, missing many iron rungs in his hurry, down into a place deep as a well, black as Tophet, tipping over back and forth like a see-saw. The water in the bilges thundered at each roll, and lumps of coal skipped to and fro, from end to end, rattling like an avalanche of pebbles on a slope of iron.

Somebody in there moaned with pain, and somebody else could be seen crouching over what seemed the prone body of a dead man; a lusty voice blasphemed; and the glow under each fire-door was like a pool of flaming blood radiating quietly in a velvety blackness.

A gust of wind struck upon the nape of Jukes' neck and next moment he felt it streaming about his wet ankles. The stokehold ventilators hummed: in front of the six fire-doors two wild figures, stripped to the waist, staggered and stooped, wrestling with two shovels.

"Hallo! Plenty of draught now," yelled the second engineer at once, as though he had been all the time looking out for Jukes. The donkeyman, a dapper little chap with a dazzling fair skin and a tiny, gingery moustache, worked in a sort of mute transport. They were keeping a full head of steam, and a profound rumbling, as of an empty furniture van trotting over a bridge, made a sustained bass to all the other noises of the place.

"Blowing off all the time," went on yelling the second. With a sound as of a hundred scoured saucepans, the orifice of a ventilator spat upon his shoulder a sudden gush of salt water, and he volleyed a stream of curses upon all things on earth including his own soul, ripping and raving, and all the time attending to his business. With a sharp clash of metal the ardent pale glare of the fire opened upon his bullet head, showing his spluttering lips, his insolent face, and with another clang closed like the white-hot wink of an iron eye.

"Where's the blooming ship? Can you tell me? blast my eyes! Under water—or what? It's coming down here in tons. Are the condemned cowls gone to Hades? Hey? Don't you know anything—you jolly sailor-man you . . . ?"

Jukes, after a bewildered moment, had been helped by a roll to dart through; and as soon as his eyes took in the comparative vastness, peace and brilliance of the engine-room, the ship, setting her stern heavily in the water, sent him charging head down upon Mr. Rout.

The chief's arm, long like a tentacle, and straightening as if worked by a spring, went out to meet him, and deflected his rush into a spin towards the speaking-tubes. At the same time Mr. Rout repeated earnestly:

"You've got to hurry up, whatever it is."

Jukes yelled "Are you there, sir?" and listened. Nothing. Suddenly the roar of the wind fell straight into his ear, but presently a small voice shoved aside the shouting hurricane quietly.

"You, Jukes?—Well?"

Jukes was ready to talk: it was only time that seemed to be wanting. It was easy enough to account for everything. He could perfectly imagine the coolies battened down in the reeking 'tween-deck, lying sick and scared between the rows of chests. Then one of these chests—or perhaps several at once—breaking loose open, and all these clumsy Chinamen rising up in a body to save their property. Afterwards every fling of the ship would hurl that tramping, yelling mob here and there, from side to side, in a whirl of smashed wood, torn clothing, rolling dollars. A struggle once started, they would be unable to stop themselves. Nothing could stop them now except main force. It was a disaster. He had seen it, and that was all he could say. Some of them must be dead, he believed. The rest would go on fighting. . . .

He sent up his words, tripping over each other, crowding the narrow tube. They mounted as if into a silence of an enlightened comprehension dwelling alone up there with a storm. And Jukes wanted to be dismissed from the face of that odious trouble intruding on the great need of the ship.

V

He waited. Before his eyes the engines turned with slow labour, that in the moment of going off into a mad fling would stop dead at Mr. Rout's shout, "Look out, Beale!" They paused in an intelligent immobility, stilled in mid-stroke, a heavy crank arrested on the cant, as if conscious of danger and the passage of time. Then, with a "Now, then!" from the chief, and the sound of a breath expelled through clenched teeth, they would accomplish the interrupted revolution and begin another.

There was the prudent sagacity of wisdom and the deliberation of enormous strength in their movements. This was their work—this patient coaxing of a distracted ship over the fury of the waves and into the very eye of the wind. At times Mr. Rout's chin would sink on his breast, and he watched them with knitted eyebrows as if lost in thought.

The voice that kept the hurricane out of Jukes' ear began: "Take the hands with you . . . ," and left off unexpectedly.

"What could I do with them, sir?"

A harsh, abrupt, imperious clang exploded suddenly. The three pairs of eyes flew up to the telegraph dial to see the hand jump from FULL to STOP, as if snatched by a devil. And then these three men in the engine-room had the intimate sensation of a check upon the ship, of a strange shrinking, as if she had gathered herself for a desperate leap.

"Stop her!" bellowed Mr. Rout.

Nobody—not even Captain MacWhirr, who alone on deck had caught sight of a white line of foam coming on at such a height that he couldn't believe his eyes—nobody was to know the steepness of that sea and the awful depth of the hollow the hurricane had scooped out behind the running wall of water.

It raced to meet the ship, and, with a pause, as of girding the loins, the *Nan-Shan* lifted her bows and leaped. The flames in all the lamps sank, darkening the engine-room. One went out. With a tearing crash and a swirling, raving tumult, tons of water fell upon the deck, as though the ship had darted under the foot of a cataract.

Down there they looked at each other, stunned.

"Swept from end to end, by God!" bawled Jukes.

She dipped into the hollow straight down, as if going over the edge of the world. The engine-room toppled forward menacingly, like the inside of a tower nodding in an earthquake. An awful racket, of iron things falling, came from the stokehold. She hung on this appalling slant long enough for Beale to drop on his hands and knees and begin to crawl as if he meant to fly on all fours out of the engine-room, and for Mr. Rout to turn his head slowly, rigid, cavernous, with the lower jaw dropping. Jukes had shut his eyes, and his face in a moment became hopelessly blank and gentle, like the face of a blind man.

At last she rose slowly, staggering, as if she had to lift a mountain with her bows.

Mr. Rout shut his mouth; Jukes blinked; and little Beale stood up hastily.

"Another one like this, and that's the last of her," cried the chief.

He and Jukes looked at each other, and the same thought came into their heads. The Captain! Everything must have been swept away. Steering-gear gone—ship like a log. All over directly.

"Rush!" ejaculated Mr. Rout thickly, glaring with enlarged, doubtful eyes at Jukes, who answered him by an irresolute glance.

The clang of the telegraph gong soothed them instantly. The black hand dropped in a flash from STOP to FULL.

"Now then, Beale!" cried Mr. Rout.

The steam hissed low. The piston-rods slid in and out. Jukes put his ear to the tube. The voice was ready for him. It said: "Pick up all the money. Bear a hand now. I'll want you up here." And that was all.

"Sir?" called up Jukes. There was no answer.

He staggered away like a defeated man from the field of battle. He had got, in some way or other, a cut above his left eyebrow—a cut to the bone. He was not aware of it in the least: quantities of the China Sea, large enough to break his neck for him, had gone over his head, had cleaned, washed, and salted that wound. It did not bleed, but only gaped red; and this gash over the eye, his dishevelled hair, the disorder of his clothes, gave him the aspect of a man worsted in a fight with fists.

"Got to pick up the dollars." He appealed to Mr. Rout, smiling pitifully at random.

"What's that?" asked Mr. Rout, wildly. "Pick up . . . ? I don't care. . . ." Then, quivering in every muscle, but with an exaggeration of paternal tone, "Go away now, for God's sake. You deck people'll drive me silly. There's that second mate been going for the old man. Don't you know? You fellows are going wrong for want of something to do. . . ."

At these words Jukes discovered in himself the beginnings of anger. Want of something to do—indeed. . . . Full of hot scorn against the chief, he turned to go the way he had come. In the stokehold the plump donkeyman toiled with his shovel mutely, as if his tongue had been cut out; but the second was carrying on like a noisy, undaunted maniac, who had preserved his skill in the art of stoking under a marine boiler.

"Hallo, you wandering officer! Hey! Can't you get some of your slush-slingers to wind up a few of them ashes? I am getting choked with them here. Curse it! Hallo! Hey!

Remember the articles: *Sailors and firemen to assist each other*. Hey! D'ye hear?"

Jukes was climbing out frantically, and the other, lifting up his face after him, howled, "Can't you speak? What are you poking about here for? What's your game, anyhow?"

A frenzy possessed Jukes. By the time he was back amongst the men in the darkness of the alleyway, he felt ready to wring all their necks at the slightest sign of hanging back. The very thought of it exasperated him. *He* couldn't hang back. They shouldn't.

The impetuosity with which he came amongst them carried them along. They had already been excited and startled at all his comings and goings—by the fierceness and rapidity of his movements; and more felt than seen in his rushes, he appeared formidable—busied with matters of life and death that brooked no delay. At his first word he heard them drop into the bunker one after another obediently, with heavy thumps.

They were not clear as to what would have to be done. "What is it? What is it?" they were asking each other. The boatswain tried to explain; the sounds of a great scuffle surprised them: and the mighty shocks, reverberating awfully in the black bunker, kept them in mind of their danger. When the boatswain threw open the door it seemed that an eddy of the hurricane, stealing through the iron sides of the ship, had set all these bodies whirling like dust: there came to them a confused uproar, a tempestuous tumult, a fierce mutter, gusts of screams dying away, and the tramping of feet mingling with the blows of the sea.

For a moment they glared amazed, blocking the doorway. Jukes pushed through them brutally. He said nothing, and simply darted in. Another lot of coolies on the ladder, struggling suicidally to break through the battened hatch to a swamped deck, fell off as before, and he disappeared under them like a man overtaken by a landslide.

The boatswain yelled excitedly: "Come along. Get the mate out. He'll be trampled to death. Come on."

They charged in, stamping on breasts, on fingers, on faces, catching their feet in heaps of clothing, kicking broken wood; but before they could get hold of him Jukes emerged waist deep in a multitude of clawing hands. In the instant he had been lost to view, all the buttons of his jacket had gone, its back had got split up to the collar, his waistcoat had been torn open. The central struggling mass of Chinamen went over to the roll, dark, indistinct, helpless, with a wild gleam of many eyes in the dim light of the lamps.

"Leave me alone—damn you. I am all right," screeched Jukes. "Drive them forward. Watch your chance when she pitches. Forward with 'em. Drive them against the bulkhead. Jam 'em up."

The rush of the sailors into the seething 'tween-deck was like a splash of cold water into a boiling cauldron. The commotion sank for a moment.

The bulk of Chinamen were locked in such a compact scrimmage that, linking their arms and aided by an appalling dive of the ship, the seamen sent it forward in one great shove, like a solid block. Behind their backs small clusters and loose bodies tumbled from side to side.

The boatswain performed prodigious feats of strength. With his long arms open, and each great paw clutching at a stanchion, he stopped the rush of seven entwined Chinamen rolling like a boulder. His joints cracked; he said, "Ha!" and they flew apart. But the carpenter showed the greater intelligence. Without saying a word to anybody he went back into the alleyway, to fetch several coils of cargo gear he had seen there—chain and rope. With these life-lines were rigged.

There was really no resistance. The struggle, however it began, had turned into a scramble of blind panic. If the coolies had started up after their scattered dollars they were by that time fighting only for their footing. They took each other by the throat merely to save themselves from being hurled about. Whoever got a hold anywhere would kick at the others who caught at his legs and hung on, till a roll sent them flying together across the deck.

The coming of the white devils was a terror. Had they come to kill? The individuals torn out of the ruck became very limp in the seamen's hands: some, dragged aside by the heels, were passive, like dead bodies, with open, fixed eyes. Here and there a coolie would fall on his knees as if begging for mercy; several, whom the excess of fear made unruly, were hit with hard fists between the eyes, and cowered; while those who were hurt submitted to rough handling, blinking rapidly without a plaint. Faces streamed with blood; there were raw places on the shaven heads, scratches, bruises, torn wounds, gashes. The broken porcelain out of the chests was mostly responsible for the latter. Here and there a Chinaman, wild-eyed, with his tail unplaited, nursed a bleeding sole.

They had been ranged closely, after having been shaken into submission, cuffed a little to allay excitement, addressed in gruff words of encouragement that sounded like promises of evil. They sat on the deck in ghastly, drooping rows, and at the end the carpenter, with two hands to help him, moved busily from place to place, setting taut and hitching the life-lines. The boatswain, with one leg and one arm embracing a stanchion, struggled with a lamp pressed to his breast, trying to get a light, and growling all the time like an industrious gorilla. The figures of seamen stooped repeatedly, with the movements of gleaners, and everything was being flung into the bunker: clothing, smashed wood, broken china, and the dollars, too, gathered up in men's jackets. Now and then a sailor would stagger towards the doorway with his arms full of rubbish; and dolorous, slanting eyes followed his movements.

With every roll of the ship the long rows of sitting Celestials would sway forward brokenly, and her headlong dives knocked together the line of shaven polls from end to end. When the wash of water rolling on the deck died away for a moment, it seemed to Jukes, yet quiver-

ing from his exertions, that in his mad struggle down
there he had overcome the wind somehow: that a silence
had fallen upon the ship, a silence in which the sea struck
thunderously at her sides.

Everything had been cleared out of the 'tween-deck—
all the wreckage, as the men said. They stood erect and
tottering above the level of heads and drooping shoulders. Here and there a coolie sobbed for his breath. Where
the high light fell, Jukes could see the salient ribs of one,
the yellow, wistful face of another; bowed necks; or would
meet a dull stare directed at his face. He was amazed
that there had been no corpses; but the lot of them seemed
at their last gasp, and they appeared to him more pitiful
than if they had been all dead.

Suddenly one of the coolies began to speak. The light
came and went on his lean, straining face; he threw his
head up like a baying hound. From the bunker came the
sounds of knocking and the tinkle of some dollars rolling
loose; he stretched out his arm, his mouth yawned black,
and the incomprehensible guttural hooting sounds, that
did not seem to belong to a human language, penetrated
Jukes with a strange emotion as if a brute had tried to be
eloquent.

Two more started mouthing what seemed to Jukes
fierce denunciations; the others stirred with grunts and
growls. Jukes ordered the hands out of the 'tween-decks
hurriedly. He left last himself, backing through the door,
while the grunts rose to a loud murmur and hands were
extended after him as after a malefactor. The boatswain
shot the bolt, and remarked uneasily, "Seems as if the
wind had dropped, sir."

The seamen were glad to get back into the alleyway.
Secretly each of them thought that at the last moment
he could rush out on deck—and that was a comfort. There
is something horribly repugnant in the idea of being
drowned under a deck. Now they had done with the Chinamen, they again became conscious of the ship's position.

Jukes on coming out of the alleyway found himself up
to the neck in the noisy water. He gained the bridge, and

discovered he could detect obscure shapes as if his sight
had become preternaturally acute. He saw faint outlines.
They recalled not the familiar aspect of the *Nan-Shan*,
but something remembered—an old dismantled steamer
he had seen years ago rotting on a mudbank. She recalled
that wreck.

There was no wind, not a breath, except the faint currents created by the lurches of the ship. The smoke tossed
out of the funnel was settling down upon her deck. He
breathed it as he passed forward. He felt the deliberate
throb of the engines, and heard small sounds that seemed
to have survived the great uproar: the knocking of broken
fittings, the rapid tumbling of some piece of wreckage on
the bridge. He perceived dimly the squat shape of his
captain holding on to a twisted bridge-rail, motionless
and swaying as if rooted to the planks. The unexpected
stillness of the air oppressed Jukes.

"We have done it, sir," he gasped.

"Thought you would," said Captain MacWhirr.

"Did you?" murmured Jukes to himself.

"Wind fell all at once," went on the Captain.

Jukes burst out: "If you think it was an easy job——"

But his captain, clinging to the rail, paid no attention.
"According to the books the worst is not over yet."

"If most of them hadn't been half dead with seasick-
ness and fright, not one of us would come out of that
'tween-deck alive," said Jukes.

"Had to do what's fair by them," mumbled MacWhirr,
stolidly. "You don't find everything in books."

"Why, I believe they would have risen on us if I hadn't
ordered the hands out of that pretty quick," continued
Jukes with warmth.

After the whisper of their shouts, their ordinary tones,
so distinct, rang out very loud to their ears in the amazing stillness of the air. It seemed to them they were talking in a dark and echoing vault.

Through a jagged aperture in the dome of clouds the
light of a few stars fell upon the black sea, rising and
falling confusedly. Sometimes the head of a watery cone

would topple on board and mingle with the rolling flurry of foam on the swamped deck; and the *Nan-Shan* wallowed heavily at the bottom of a circular cistern of clouds. This ring of dense vapours, gyrating madly round the calm of the centre, encompassed the ship like a motionless and unbroken wall of an aspect inconceivably sinister. Within, the sea, as if agitated by an internal commotion, leaped in peaked mounds that jostled each other, slapping heavily against her sides; and a low moaning sound, the infinite plaint of the storm's fury, came from beyond the limits of the menacing calm. Captain MacWhirr remained silent, and Jukes' ready ear caught suddenly the faint, long-drawn roar of some immense wave rushing unseen under that thick blackness, which made the appalling boundary of his vision.

"Of course," he started resentfully, "they thought we had caught at the chance to plunder them. Of course! You said—pick up the money. Easier said than done. They couldn't tell what was in our heads. We came in, smash—right into the middle of them. Had to do it by a rush."

"As long as it's done . . . ," mumbled the Captain, without attempting to look at Jukes. "Had to do what's fair."

"We shall find yet there's the devil to pay when this is over," said Jukes, feeling very sore. "Let them only recover a bit, and you'll see. They will fly at our throats, sir. Don't forget, sir, she isn't a British ship now. These brutes know it well, too. The damned Siamese flag."

"We are on board, all the same," remarked Captain MacWhirr.

"The trouble's not over yet," insisted Jukes, prophetically, reeling and catching on. "She's a wreck," he added, faintly.

"The trouble's not over yet," assented Captain MacWhirr, half aloud. . . . "Look out for her a minute."

"Are you going off the deck, sir?" asked Jukes, hurriedly, as if the storm were sure to pounce upon him as soon as he had been left alone with the ship.

He watched her, battered and solitary, labouring heavily in a wild scene of mountainous black waters lit by the gleams of distant worlds. She moved slowly, breathing into the still core of the hurricane the excess of her strength in a white cloud of steam—and the deep-toned vibration of the escape was like the defiant trumpeting of a living creature of the sea impatient for the renewal of the contest. It ceased suddenly. The still air moaned. Above Jukes' head a few stars shone into a pit of black vapours. The inky edge of the cloud-disc frowned upon the ship under the patch of glittering sky. The stars, too, seemed to look at her intently, as if for the last time, and the cluster of their splendour sat like a diadem on a lowering brow.

Captain MacWhirr had gone into the chart-room. There was no light there; but he could feel the disorder of that place where he used to live tidily. His armchair was upset. The books had tumbled out on the floor: he scrunched a piece of glass under his boot. He groped for the matches, and found a box on a shelf with a deep ledge. He struck one, and puckering the corners of his eyes, held out the little flame towards the barometer whose glittering top of glass and metals nodded at him continuously.

It stood very low—incredibly low, so low that Captain MacWhirr grunted. The match went out, and hurriedly he extracted another, with thick, stiff fingers.

Again a little flame flared up before the nodding glass and metal of the top. His eyes looked at it, narrowed with attention, as if expecting an imperceptible sign. With his grave face he resembled a booted and misshapen pagan burning incense before the oracle of a Joss. There was no mistake. It was the lowest reading he had ever seen in his life.

Captain MacWhirr emitted a low whistle. He forgot himself till the flame diminished to a blue spark, burnt his fingers and vanished. Perhaps something had gone wrong with the thing!

There was an aneroid glass screwed above the couch. He turned that way, struck another match, and discovered the white face of the other instrument looking at him from the bulkhead, meaningly, not to be gainsaid, as though the wisdom of men were made unerring by the indifference of matter. There was no room for doubt now. Captain MacWhirr pshawed at it, and threw the match down.

The worst was to come, then—and if the books were right this worst would be very bad. The experience of the last six hours had enlarged his conception of what heavy weather could be like. "It'll be terrific," he pronounced, mentally. He had not consciously looked at anything by the light of the matches except at the barometer; and yet somehow he had seen that his water-bottle and the two tumblers had been flung out of their stand. It seemed to give him a more intimate knowledge of the tossing the ship had gone through. "I wouldn't have believed it," he thought. And his table had been cleared, too; his rulers, his pencils, the inkstand—all the things that had their safe appointed places—they were gone, as if a mischievous hand had plucked them out one by one and flung them on the wet floor. The hurricane had broken in upon the orderly arrangements of his privacy. This had never happened before, and the feeling of dismay reached the very seat of his composure. And the worst was to come yet! He was glad the trouble in the 'tween-deck had been discovered in time. If the ship had to go after all, then, at least, she wouldn't be going to the bottom with a lot of people in her fighting teeth and claw. That would have been odious. And in that feeling there was a humane intention and a vague sense of the fitness of things.

These instantaneous thoughts were yet in their essence heavy and slow, partaking of the nature of the man. He extended his hand to put back the matchbox in its corner of the shelf. There were always matches there—by his order. The steward had his instructions impressed upon him long before. "A box . . . just there, see? Not so very full . . . where I can put my hand on it, steward. Might want a light in a hurry. Can't tell on board ship *what* you might want in a hurry. Mind, now."

And of course on his side he would be careful to put it back in its place scrupulously. He did so now, but before he removed his hand it occurred to him that perhaps he would never have occasion to use that box any more. The vividness of the thought checked him and for an infinitesimal fraction of a second his fingers closed again on the small object as though it had been the symbol of all these little habits that chain us to the weary round of life. He released it at last, and letting himself fall on the settee, listened for the first sounds of returning wind.

Not yet. He heard only the wash of water, the heavy splashes, the dull shocks of the confused seas boarding his ship from all sides. She would never have a chance to clear her decks.

But the quietude of the air was startlingly tense and unsafe, like a slender hair holding a sword suspended over his head. By this awful pause the storm penetrated the defences of the man and unsealed his lips. He spoke out in the solitude and the pitch darkness of the cabin, as if addressing another being awakened within his breast.

"I shouldn't like to lose her," he said half aloud.

He sat unseen, apart from the sea, from his ship, isolated, as if withdrawn from the very current of his own existence, where such freaks as talking to himself surely had no place. His palms reposed on his knees, he bowed his short neck and puffed heavily, surrendering to a strange sensation of weariness he was not enlightened enough to recognize for the fatigue of mental stress.

From where he sat he could reach the door of a wash-stand locker. There should have been a towel there. There was. Good. . . . He took it out, wiped his face, and afterwards went on rubbing his wet head. He towelled himself with energy in the dark, and then remained motionless with the towel on his knees. A moment passed, of a stillness so profound that no one could have guessed there was a man sitting in that cabin. Then a murmur arose.

"She may come out of it yet."

When Captain MacWhirr came out on deck, which he did brusquely, as though he had suddenly become conscious of having stayed away too long, the calm had lasted already more than fifteen minutes—long enough to make itself intolerable even to his imagination. Jukes, motionless on the forepart of the bridge, began to speak at once. His voice, blank and forced as though he were talking through hard-set teeth, seemed to flow away on all sides into the darkness, deepening again upon the sea.

"I had the wheel relieved. Hackett began to sing out that he was done. He's lying in there alongside the steering-gear with a face like death. At first I couldn't get anybody to crawl out and relieve the poor devil. That boss'en's worse than no good, I always said. Thought I would have had to go myself and haul out one of them by the neck."

"Ah, well," muttered the Captain. He stood watchful by Jukes' side.

"The second mate's in there, too, holding his head. Is he hurt, sir?"

"No—crazy," said Captain MacWhirr, curtly.

"Looks as if he had a tumble, though."

"I had to give him a push," explained the Captain.

Jukes gave an impatient sigh.

"It will come very sudden," said Captain MacWhirr, "and from over there, I fancy. God only knows though. These books are only good to muddle your head and make you jumpy. It will be bad, and there's an end. If we only can steam her round in time to meet it. . . ."

A minute passed. Some of the stars winked rapidly and vanished.

"You left them pretty safe?" began the Captain abruptly, as though the silence were unbearable.

"Are you thinking of the coolies, sir? I rigged lifelines all ways across that 'tween-deck."

"Did you? Good idea, Mr. Jukes."

"I didn't . . . think you cared to . . . know," said Jukes—the lurching of the ship cut his speech as though somebody had been jerking him around while he talked— "how I got on with . . . that infernal job. We did it. And it may not matter in the end."

"Had to do what's fair, for all—they are only China-men. Give them the same chance with ourselves—hang it all. She isn't lost yet. Bad enough to be shut up below in a gale——"

"That's what I thought when you gave me the job, sir," interjected Jukes, moodily.

"——without being battered to pieces," pursued Captain MacWhirr with rising vehemence. "Couldn't let that go on in my ship, if I knew she hadn't five minutes to live. Couldn't bear it, Mr. Jukes."

A hollow echoing noise, like that of a shout rolling in a rocky chasm, approached the ship and went away again. The last star, blurred, enlarged, as if returning to the fiery mist of its beginning, struggled with the colossal depth of blackness hanging over the ship—and went out.

"Now for it!" muttered Captain MacWhirr. "Mr. Jukes."

"Here, sir."

The two men were growing indistinct to each other.

"We must trust her to go through it and come out on the other side. That's plain and straight. There's no room for Captain Wilson's storm-strategy here."

"No, sir."

"She will be smothered and swept again for hours," mumbled the Captain. "There's not much left by this time above deck for the sea to take away—unless you or me."

"Both, sir," whispered Jukes, breathlessly.

"You are always meeting trouble half way, Jukes," Captain MacWhirr remonstrated quaintly. "Though it's a fact that the second mate is no good. D'ye hear, Mr. Jukes? You would be left alone if. . . ."

Captain MacWhirr interrupted himself, and Jukes, glancing on all sides, remained silent.

"Don't you be put out by anything," the Captain continued, mumbling rather fast. "Keep her facing it. They may say what they like, but the heaviest seas run with the wind. Facing it—always facing it—that's the way to get through. You are a young sailor. Face it. That's enough for any man. Keep a cool head."

"Yes, sir," said Jukes, with a flutter of the heart.

In the next few seconds the Captain spoke to the engine-room and got an answer.

For some reason Jukes experienced an access of confidence, a sensation that came from outside like a warm breath, and made him feel equal to every demand. The distant muttering of the darkness stole into his ears. He noted it unmoved, out of that sudden belief in himself, as a man safe in a shirt of mail would watch a point.

The ship laboured without intermission amongst the black hills of water, paying with this hard tumbling the price of her life. She rumbled in her depths, shaking a white plummet of steam into the night, and Jukes' thought skimmed like a bird through the engine-room, where Mr. Rout—good man—was ready. When the rumbling ceased it seemed to him that there was a pause of every sound, a dead pause in which Captain Mac-Whirr's voice rang out startlingly.

"What's that? A puff of wind?"—it spoke much louder than Jukes had ever heard it before—"On the bow. That's right. She may come out of it yet."

The mutter of the winds drew near apace. In the forefront could be distinguished a drowsy waking plaint passing on, and far off the growth of a multiple clamour, marching and expanding. There was the throb as of many drums in it, a vicious rushing note, and like the chant of a tramping multitude.

Jukes could no longer see his captain distinctly. The darkness was absolutely piling itself upon the ship. At most he made out movements, a hint of elbows spread out, of a head thrown up.

Captain MacWhirr was trying to do up the top button of his oilskin coat with unwonted haste. The hurricane, with its power to madden the seas, to sink ships, to uproot trees, to overturn strong walls and dash the very birds of the air to the ground, had found this taciturn man in its path, and, doing its utmost, had managed to wring out a few words. Before the renewed wrath of winds swooped on his ship, Captain MacWhirr was moved to declare, in a tone of vexation, as it were: "I wouldn't like to lose her."

He was spared that annoyance.

VI

On a bright sunshiny day, with the breeze chasing her smoke far ahead, the *Nan-Shan* came into Fu-chau. Her arrival was at once noticed on shore, and the seamen in harbour said: "Look! Look at that steamer. What's that? Siamese—isn't she? Just look at her!"

She seemed, indeed, to have been used as a running target for the secondary batteries of a cruiser. A hail of minor shells could not have given her upper works a more broken, torn, and devastated aspect: and she had about her the worn, weary air of ships coming from the far ends of the world—and indeed with truth, for in her short passage she had been very far; sighting, verily, even the coast of the Great Beyond, whence no ship ever returns to give up her crew to the dust of the earth. She was incrusted and gray with salt to the trucks of her masts and to the top of her funnel; as though (as some facetious seaman said) "the crowd on board had fished her out somewhere from the bottom of the sea and brought her in here for salvage." And further, excited by the felicity of his own wit, he offered to give five pounds for her—"as she stands."

Before she had been quite an hour at rest, a meagre little man, with a red-tipped nose and a face cast in an angry mould, landed from a sampan on the quay of the Foreign Concession, and incontinently turned to shake his fist at her.

A tall individual, with legs much too thin for a rotund stomach, and with watery eyes, strolled up and remarked, "Just left her—eh? Quick work."

He wore a soiled suit of blue flannel with a pair of dirty

cricketing shoes; a dingy gray moustache drooped from his lip, and daylight could be seen in two places between the rim and the crown of his hat.

"Hallo! what are you doing here?" asked the ex-second-mate of the *Nan-Shan*, shaking hands hurriedly.

"Standing by for a job—chance worth taking—got a quiet hint," explained the man with the broken hat, in jerky, apathetic wheezes.

The second shook his fist again at the *Nan-Shan*. "There's a fellow there that ain't fit to have the command of a scow," he declared, quivering with passion, while the other looked about listlessly.

"Is there?"

But he caught sight on the quay of a heavy seaman's chest, painted brown under a fringed sailcloth cover, and lashed with new manila line. He eyed it with awakened interest.

"I would talk and raise trouble if it wasn't for that damned Siamese flag. Nobody to go to—or I would make it hot for him. The fraud! Told his chief engineer—that's another fraud for you—I had lost my nerve. The greatest lot of ignorant fools that ever sailed the seas. No! You can't think . . ."

"Got your money all right?" inquired his seedy acquaintance suddenly.

"Yes. Paid me off on board," raged the second mate. " 'Get your breakfast on shore,' says he."

"Mean skunk!" commented the tall man, vaguely, and passed his tongue on his lips. "What about having a drink of some sort?"

"He struck me," hissed the second mate.

"No! Struck! You don't say? The man in blue began to bustle about sympahetically. "Can't possibly talk here. I want to know all about it. Struck—eh? Let's get a fellow to carry your chest. I know a quiet place where they have some bottled beer. . . ."

Mr. Jukes, who had been scanning the shore through a pair of glasses, informed the chief engineer afterwards that "our late second mate hasn't been long in finding a

friend. A chap looking uncommonly like a bummer. I saw
them walk away together from the quay."

The hammering and banging of the needful repairs did
not disturb Captain MacWhirr. The steward found in
the letter he wrote, in a tidy chart-room, passages of such
absorbing interest that twice he was nearly caught in the
act. But Mrs. MacWhirr, in the drawing-room of the
forty-pound house, stifled a yawn—perhaps out of self-
respect—for she was alone.

She reclined in a plush-bottomed and gilt hammock-
chair near a tiled fireplace, with Japanese fans on the
mantel and a glow of coals in the grate. Lifting her hands,
she glanced wearily here and there into the many pages.
It was not her fault they were so posy, so completely
uninteresting—from "My darling wife" at the beginning,
to "Your loving husband" at the end. She couldn't be
really expected to understand all these ship affairs. She
was glad, of course, to hear from him, but she had never
asked herself why, precisely.

". . . They are called typhoons . . . The mate did
not seem to like it . . . Not in books . . . Couldn't think
of letting it go on. . . ."

The paper rustled sharply. ". . . A calm that lasted
more than twenty minutes," she read perfunctorily; and
the next words her thoughtless eyes caught, on the top of
another page, were: "see you and the children again.
. . ." She had a movement of impatience. He was always
thinking of coming home. He had never had such a good
salary before. What was the matter now?

It did not occur to her to turn back overleaf to look.
She would have found it recorded there that between 4
and 6 A. M. on December 25th, Captain MacWhirr did
actually think that his ship could not possibly live another hour in such a sea, and that he would never see his
wife and children again. Nobody was to know this (his
letters got mislaid so quickly)—nobody whatever but the
steward, who had been greatly impressed by that disclosure. So much so, that he tried to give the cook some
idea of the "narrow squeak we all had" by saying sol-

emnly, "The old man himself had a dam' poor opinion of our chance."

"How do you know?" asked, contemptuously, the cook, an old soldier. "He hasn't told you, maybe?"

"Well, he did give me a hint to that effect," the steward brazened it out.

"Get along with you! He will be coming to tell *me* next," jeered the old cook, over his shoulder.

Mrs. MacWhirr glanced farther, on the alert. ". . . Do what's fair. . . . Miserable objects . . . Only three, with a broken leg each, and one . . . Thought had better keep the matter quiet . . . hope to have done the fair thing. . . ."

She let fall her hands. No: there was nothing more about coming home. Must have been merely expressing a pious wish. Mrs. MacWhirr's mind was set at ease, and a black marble clock, priced by the local jeweller at £3 18*s.* 6*d.*, had a discreet stealthy tick.

The door flew open, and a girl in the long-legged, short-frocked period of existence, flung into the room. A lot of colourless, rather lanky hair was scattered over her shoulders. Seeing her mother, she stood still, and directed her pale prying eyes upon the letter.

"From father," murmured Mrs. MacWhirr. "What have you done with your ribbon?"

The girl put her hands up to her head and pouted.

"He's well," continued Mrs. MacWhirr, languidly. "At least I think so. He never says." She had a little laugh. The girl's face expressed a wandering indifference, and Mrs. MacWhirr surveyed her with fond pride.

"Go and get your hat," she said after a while. "I am going out to do some shopping. There is a sale at Linom's."

"Oh, how jolly!" uttered the child, impressively, in unexpectedly grave vibrating tones, and bounded out of the room.

It was a fine afternoon, with a gray sky and dry sidewalks. Outside the draper's Mrs. MacWhirr smiled upon a woman in a black mantle of generous proportions armoured in jet and crowned with flowers blooming falsely above a bilious matronly countenance. They broke into a swift little babble of greetings and exclamations both together, very hurried, as if the street were ready to yawn open and swallow all that pleasure before it could be expressed.

Behind them the high glass doors were kept on the swing. People couldn't pass, men stood aside waiting patiently, and Lydia was absorbed in poking the end of her parasol between the stone flags. Mrs. MacWhirr talked rapidly.

"Thank you very much. He's not coming home yet. Of course it's very sad to have him away, but it's such a comfort to know he keeps so well." Mrs. MacWhirr drew breath. "The climate there agrees with him," she added, beamingly, as if poor MacWhirr had been away touring in China for the sake of his health.

Neither was the chief engineer coming home yet. Mr. Rout knew too well the value of a good billet.

"Solomon says wonders will never cease," cried Mrs. Rout joyously at the old lady in her armchair by the fire. Mr. Rout's mother moved slightly, her withered hands lying in black half-mittens on her lap.

The eyes of the engineer's wife fairly danced on the paper. "That captain of the ship he is in—a rather simple man, you remember, mother?—has done something rather clever, Solomon says."

"Yes, my dear," said the old woman meekly, sitting with bowed silvery head, and that air of inward stillness characteristic of very old people who seem lost in watching the last flickers of life. "I think I remember."

Solomon Rout, Old Sol, Father Sol, the Chief, "Rout, good man"—Mr. Rout, the condescending and paternal friend of youth, had been the baby of her many children —all dead by this time. And she remembered him best as a boy of ten—long before he went away to serve his apprenticeship in some great engineering works in the North. She had seen so little of him since, she had gone through so many years, that she had now to retrace her steps very far back to recognize him plainly in the mist of time. Sometimes it seemed that her daughter-in-law was talking of some strange man.

Mrs. Rout junior was disappointed. "H'm. H'm." She turned the page. "How provoking! He doesn't say what it is. Says I couldn't understand how much there was in it. Fancy! What could it be so very clever? What a wretched man not to tell us!"

She read on without further remark soberly, and at last sat looking into the fire. The chief wrote just a word or two of the typhoon; but something had moved him to express an increased longing for the companionship of the jolly woman. "If it hadn't been that mother must be looked after, I would send you your passage-money to-day. You could set up a small house out here. I would have a chance to see you sometimes then. We are not growing younger. . . ."

"He's well, mother," sighed Mrs. Rout, rousing herself.

"He always was a strong healthy boy," said the old woman, placidly.

But Mr. Jukes' account was really animated and very full. His friend in the Western Ocean trade imparted it freely to the other officers of his liner. "A chap I know writes to me about an extraordinary affair that happened on board his ship in that typhoon—you know— that we read of in the papers two months ago. It's the funniest thing! Just see for yourself what he says. I'll show you his letter."

There were phrases in it calculated to give the impression of light-hearted, indomitable resolution. Jukes had written them in good faith, for he felt thus when he wrote. He described with lurid effect the scenes in the 'tween-deck. ". . . It struck me in a flash that those confounded Chinamen couldn't tell we weren't a desperate kind of robbers. 'Tisn't good to part the Chinaman from his money if he is the stronger party. We need have been desperate indeed to go thieving in such weather, but what could these beggars know of us? So, without thinking of it twice, I got the hands away in a jiffy. Our work was done—that the old man had set his heart on. We cleared out without staying to inquire how they felt. I am convinced that if they had not been so unmercifully shaken, and afraid—each individual one of them—to stand up, we would have been torn to pieces. Oh! It was pretty complete, I can tell you; and you may run to and fro across the Pond to the end of time before you find yourself with such a job on your hands."

After this he alluded professionally to the damage done to the ship, and went on thus:

"It was when the weather quieted down that the situation became confoundedly delicate. It wasn't made any better by us having been lately transferred to the Siamese flag; though the skipper can't see that it makes any difference—'as long as *we* are on board'—he says. There are feelings that this man simply hasn't got—and there's an end of it. You might just as well try to make a bedpost understand. But apart from this it is an infernally lonely state for a ship to be going about the China seas with no proper consuls, not even a gunboat of her own anywhere, nor a body to go to in case of some trouble.

"My notion was to keep these Johnnies under hatches for another fifteen hours or so; as we weren't much farther than that from Fu-chau. We would find there, most likely, some sort of a man-of-war, and once under her guns we were safe enough; for surely any skipper of a man-of-war—English, French or Dutch—would see white men through as far as row on board goes. We could get rid of them and their money afterwards by delivering them to their Mandarin or Taotai, or whatever they call these chaps in goggles you see being carried about in sedan-chairs through their stinking streets.

"The old man wouldn't see it somehow. He wanted to keep the matter quiet. He got that notion into his head, and a steam windlass couldn't drag it out of him. He wanted as little fuss made as possible, for the sake of the ship's name and for the sake of the owners—'for the sake of all concerned,' says he, looking at me very hard. It made me angry hot. Of course you couldn't keep a thing like that quiet; but the chests had been secured in the usual manner and were safe enough for any earthly gale, while this had been an altogether fiendish business I couldn't give you even an idea of.

"Meantime, I could hardly keep on my feet. None of us had a spell of any sort for nearly thirty hours, and there the old man sat rubbing his chin, rubbing the top of his head, and so bothered he didn't even think of pulling his long boots off.

"'I hope, sir,' says I, 'you won't be letting them out on deck before we make ready for them in some shape or other.' Not, mind you, that I felt very sanguine about controlling these beggars if they meant to take charge. A trouble with a cargo of Chinamen is no child's play. I was dam' tired, too. 'I wish,' said I, 'you would let us throw the whole lot of these dollars down to them and leave them to fight it out amongst themselves, while we get a rest.'

"'Now you talk wild, Jukes,' says he, looking up in his slow way that makes you ache all over, somehow. 'We must plan out something that would be fair to all parties.'

"I had no end of work on hand, as you may imagine, so I set the hands going, and then I thought I would turn in a bit. I hadn't been asleep in my bunk ten minutes when in rushes the steward and begins to pull at my leg.

"'For God's sake, Mr. Jukes, come out! Come on deck quick, sir. Oh, do come out!'

"The fellow scared all the sense out of me. I didn't know what had happened: another hurricane—or what. Could hear no wind.

"'The Captain's letting them out. Oh, he is letting them out! Jump on deck, sir, and save us. The chief engineer has just run below for his revolver.'

"That's what I understood the fool to say. However, Father Rout swears he went in there only to get a clean pocket-handkerchief. Anyhow, I made one jump into my trousers and flew on deck aft. There was certainly a good deal of noise going on forward of the bridge. Four of the hands with the boss'en were at work abaft. I passed up to them some of the rifles all the ships on the China coast carry in the cabin, and led them on the bridge. On the way I ran against Old Sol, looking startled and sucking at an unlighted cigar.

" 'Come along,' I shouted to him.

"We charged, the seven of us, up to the chart-room. All was over. There stood the old man with his sea-boots still drawn up to the hips and in shirt-sleeves—got warm thinking it out, I suppose. Bun Hin's dandy clerk at his elbow, as dirty as a sweep, was still green in the face. I could see directly I was in for something.

" 'What the devil are these monkey tricks, Mr. Jukes?' asks the old man, as angry as ever he could be. I tell you frankly it made me lose my tongue. 'For God's sake, Mr. Jukes,' says he, 'do take away these rifles from the men. Somebody's sure to get hurt before long if you don't. Damme, if this ship isn't worse than Bedlam! Look sharp now. I want you up here to help me and Bun Hin's China-man to count that money. You wouldn't mind lending a hand, too, Mr. Rout, now you are here. The more of us the better.'

"He had settled it all in his mind while I was having a snooze. Had we been an English ship, or only going to land our cargo of coolies in an English part, like Hong-Kong, for instance, there would have been no end of in-quiries and bother, claims for damages and so on. But these Chinamen know their officials better than we do.

"The hatches had been taken off already, and they were all on deck after a night and a day down below. It made you feel queer to see so many gaunt, wild faces to-gether. The beggars stared about at the sky, at the sea, at the ship, as though they had expected the whole thing to have been blown to pieces. And no wonder! They had had a doing that would have shaken the soul out of a white man. But then they say a Chinaman has no soul. He has, though, something about him that is deuced tough. There was a fellow (amongst others of the badly hurt) who had had his eye all but knocked out. It stood out of his head the size of half a hen's egg. This would have laid out a white man on his back for a month: and yet there was that

chap elbowing here and there in the crowd and talking to
the others as if nothing had been the matter. They made
a great hubbub amongst themselves, and whenever the
old man showed his bald head on the foreside of the
bridge, they would all leave off jawing and look at him
from below.

"It seems that after he had done his thinking he made
that Bun Hin's fellow go down and explain to them the
only way they could get their money back. He told me
afterwards that, all the coolies having worked in the same
place and for the same length of time, he reckoned he
would be doing the fair thing by them as near as possible
if he shared all the cash we had picked up equally among
the lot. You couldn't tell one man's dollars from another's, he said, and if you asked each man how much money
he brought on board he was afraid they would lie, and he
would find himself a long way short. I think he was right
there. As to giving up the money to any Chinese official
he could scare up in Fu-chau, he said he might just as
well put the lot in his own pocket at once for all the good
it would be to them. I suppose they thought so, too.

"We finished the distribution before dark. It was rather
a sight: the sea running high, the ship a wreck to look at,
these Chinamen staggering up on the bridge one by one
for their share, and the old man still booted, and in his
shirt-sleeves, busy paying out at the chart-room door, per-
spiring like anything, and now and then coming down
sharp on myself or Father Rout about one thing or another not quite to his mind. He took the share of those
who were disabled himself to them on the No. 2 hatch.
There were three dollars left over, and these went to the
three most damaged coolies, one to each. We turned-to
afterwards, and shovelled out on deck heaps of wet rags,
all sorts of fragments of things without shape, and that
you couldn't give a name to, and let them settle the ownership themselves.

"This certainly is coming as near as can be to keeping
the thing quiet for the benefit of all concerned. What's
your opinion, you pampered mail-boat swell? The old

chief says that this was plainly the only thing that could be done. The skipper remarked to me the other day, 'There are things you find nothing about in books.' I think that he got out of it very well for such a stupid man."

Ogden Nash

IT'S ALL WRONG

(The office of Dr. Durfee, the eminent psychiatrist. Mr. Herkimer, a patient, has just entered. Dr. Durfee is somewhat taken aback at the sight of a male patient, but prepares to make the best of his plight)

DR. DURFEE—Well, sir, what seems to be the trouble?

MR. HERKIMER—I get things mixed up.

DR. DURFEE—Come, come! That will never do.

MR. HERKIMER—That's what I say.

DR. DURFEE—We must look into this. What kind of things do you get mixed up?

MR. HERKIMER—Different things.

DR. DURFEE—Be more frank, please, if you want me to help you.

MR. HERKIMER—Well, mostly names.

DR. DURFEE—Any particular kind of names? Names of ladies? Very embarrassing, ha ha!

MR. HERKIMER—Literary names. You know. Books. Authors. Heroes. Heroines.

DR. DURFEE—Well, well. Are you a writer, Mr. Herkimer?

MR. HERKIMER—No. A reader.

DR. DURFEE—You read?

MR. HERKIMER—Always. And I get mixed up.

DR. DURFEE—Give me an example, please.

MR. HERKIMER—Well, it began with Jack the Giant-Killer.

DR. DURFEE—Hmm, Jack the Giant-Killer.

MR. HERKIMER—I got him mixed up with Jack and the Beanstalk.

DR. DURFEE—Because the names were similar, I daresay.

MR. HERKIMER—Sure you'd daresay. Coolidge would daresay that.

Dr. Durfee—Never mind Coolidge. Continue, please.

Mr. Herkimer—Then there was Snow White and Rose Red. I got them mixed up, too. Mixed up with each other and with the Wars of the Roses. York, Snow White; Lancaster, Rose Red. Gee, Dr. Durfee, it was terrible.

Dr. Durfee—How about Bluebeard and Blackbeard?

Mr. Herkimer—To this day I couldn't tell you which was which. And who wrote the Odyssey? Was it Homer, or James Joyce? I don't know.

Dr. Durfee—You can't be much of a reader.

Mr. Herkimer—Sure I'm a reader, but I get mixed up. And why not? Look at Winston Churchill.

Dr. Durfee—What about Winston Churchill?

Mr. Herkimer—There's two of him: that's what about him.

Dr. Durfee—No, no, surely not two of him.

Mr. Herkimer—Yes sir: one, two. A novelist and a prime minister.

Dr. Durfee—Which is the novelist?

Mr. Herkimer—Winston Churchill.

Dr. Durfee—And the prime minister?

Mr. Herkimer—Winston Churchill.

Dr. Durfee— I fail to see your problem, Mr. Herkimer. If they're both Winston Churchill—

Mr. Herkimer—They're *not!* They're different Winston Churchills.

Dr. Durfee—A Winston Churchill is a Winston Churchill. (*He opens a book which is lying before him.*) See? Science says so.

Mr. Herkimer—Oh, if you want to start getting scientific—tracking me down like the Hound of the d'Urbervilles—

Dr. Durfee—You mean Tess of the Baskervilles—

Mr. Herkimer—You mean Lady Chatterley's Fan—

Dr. Durfee—You mean Lady Windermere's Lover—

Mr. Herkimer—You mean Sinclair Lewis—

Dr. Durfee—You mean Upton Sinclair—

Mr. Herkimer—You mean "Æ"—

Dr. Durfee—You mean "H. D."—

Mr. Herkimer—You mean John Vassos—

Dr. Durfee—You mean John Dos Passos—

Mr. Herkimer—You mean Maxwell Anderson—

Dr. Durfee—You mean Sherwood Bodenheim—

Mr. Herkimer—You mean Zoë Gale—

Dr. Durfee—You mean Zona Akins—

Mr. Herkimer—You mean Miss Lulu Belle—

Dr. Durfee—You mean Lulu Bett—

Mr. Herkimer—You mean Wallace Irwin—

Dr. Durfee—You mean Will Irvin—

Mr. Herkimer—You mean Irwin S. Cobb—

Dr. Durfee—Shut up, you!

Mr. Herkimer—I will not shut up. You're a fine doctor. You're a credit to your profession. You're a real help, you are! I'll bet you can't tell the Gibbses apart. I'll bet you can't tell the Bensons apart. I'll bet you can't even tell the Powyses apart!

Dr. Durfee—Anyway, I can tell the Sitwells apart.

Mr. Herkimer—Yaah! now I *know* you're lying. Nobody can tell the Sitwells apart.

Dr. Durfee—Well, Mr. Herkimer, I guess the game's up. You've got me. What are you going to do about it?

Mr. Herkimer—You seem a decent sort of chap at heart, Dr. Durfee. Tell you what: I'll give you one chance. Do you know Ben Hecht?

Dr. Durfee—You mean Abou Ben Hecht—

Mr. Herkimer (*seizing the telephone*)—Operance, Operance, I want an ambulator!

A. Conan Doyle

THE HORROR OF THE HEIGHTS

(WHICH INCLUDES THE MANUSCRIPT KNOWN AS THE
JOYCE-ARMSTRONG FRAGMENT)

THE idea that the extraordinary narrative which has
been called the Joyce-Armstrong Fragment is an elaborate practical joke evolved by some unknown person,
cursed by a perverted and sinister sense of humour, has
now been abandoned by all who have examined the matter. The most *macabre* and imaginative of plotters would
hesitate before linking his morbid fancies with the unquestioned and tragic facts which reinforced the statement. Though the assertions contained in it are amazing
and even monstrous, it is none the less forcing itself upon
the general intelligence that they are true, and that we
must readjust our ideas to the new situation. This world
of ours appears to be separated by a slight and precari-
ous margin of safety from a most singular and unexpected danger. I will endeavour in this narrative, which
reproduces the original document in its necessarily somewhat fragmentary form, to lay before the reader the
whole of the facts up to date, prefacing my statement by
saying that, if there be any who doubt the narrative of
Joyce-Armstrong, there can be no question at all as to
the facts concerning Lieutenant Myrtle, R.N., and Mr.
Hay Connor, who undoubtedly met their end in the manner described.

The Joyce-Armstrong Fragment was found in the field
which is called Lower Haycock, lying one mile to the
westward of the village of Withyham, upon the Kent and
Sussex border. It was on the fifteenth of September last
that an agricultural labourer, James Flynn, in the employment of Mathew Dodd, farmer, of the Chauntry
Farm, Withyham, perceived a briar pipe lying near the

footpath which skirts the hedge in Lower Haycock. A few paces farther on he picked up a pair of broken binocular glasses. Finally, among some nettles in the ditch, he caught sight of a flat, canvas-backed book, which proved to be a note-book with detachable leaves, some of which had come loose and were fluttering along the base of the hedge. These he collected, but some, including the first, were never recovered, and leave a deplorable hiatus in this all-important statement. The note-book was taken by the labourer to his master, who in turn showed it to Dr. J. H. Atherton, of Hartfield. This gentleman at once recognised the need for an expert examination, and the manuscript was forwarded to the Aero Club in London, where it now lies.

The first two pages of the manuscript are missing. There is also one torn away at the end of the narrative, though none of these affect the general coherence of the story. It is conjectured that the missing opening is concerned with the record of Mr. Joyce-Armstrong's qualifications as an aeronaut, which can be gathered from other sources and are admitted to be unsurpassed among the air-pilots of England. For many years he has been looked upon as among the most daring and the most intellectual of flying men, a combination which has enabled him to both invent and test several new devices, including the common gyroscopic attachment which is known by his name. The main body of the manuscript is written neatly in ink, but the last few lines are in pencil and are so ragged as to be hardly legible—exactly, in fact, as they might be expected to appear if they were scribbled off hurriedly from the seat of a moving aeroplane. There are, it may be added, several stains, both on the last page and on the outside cover which have been pronounced by the Home Office experts to be blood—probably human and certainly mammalian. The fact that something closely resembling the organism of malaria was discovered in this blood, and that Joyce-Armstrong is known to have suffered from intermittent fever, is a remarkable example of the new weapons which modern science has placed in the hands of our detectives.

And now a word as to the personality of the author of this epoch-making statement. Joyce-Armstrong, according to the few friends who really knew something of the man, was a poet and a dreamer, as well as a mechanic and an inventor. He was a man of considerable wealth, much of which he had spent in the pursuit of his aeronautical hobby. He had four private aeroplanes in his hangars near Devizes, and is said to have made no fewer than one hundred and seventy ascents in the course of last year. He was a retiring man with dark moods, in which he would avoid the society of his fellows. Captain Dangerfield, who knew him better than any one, says that there were times when his eccentricity threatened to develop into something more serious. His habit of carrying a shotgun with him in his aeroplane was one manifestation of it.

Another was the morbid effect which the fall of Lieutenant Myrtle had upon his mind. Myrtle, who was attempting the height record, fell from an altitude of something over thirty thousand feet. Horrible to narrate, his head was entirely obliterated, though his body and limbs preserved their configuration. At every gathering of airmen, Joyce-Armstrong, according to Dangerfield, would ask, with an enigmatic smile: "And where, pray, is Myrtle's head?"

On another occasion after dinner, at the mess of the Flying School on Salisbury Plain, he started a debate as to what will be the most permanent danger which airmen will have to encounter. Having listened to successive opinions as to air-pockets, faulty construction, and over-banking, he ended by shrugging his shoulders and refusing to put forward his own views, though he gave the impression that they differed from any advanced by his companions.

It is worth remarking that after his own complete disappearance it was found that his private affairs were arranged with a precision which may show that he had a

strong premonition of disaster. With these essential ex-
planations I will now give the narrative exactly as it
stands, beginning at page three of the blood-soaked note-
book:—

"Nevertheless, when I dined at Rheims with Coselli and
Gustav Raymond I found that neither of them was
aware of any particular danger in the higher layers of
the atmosphere. I did not actually say what was in my
thoughts, but I got so near to it that if they had any corresponding idea they could not have failed to express it.
But then they are two empty, vainglorious fellows with
no thought beyond seeing their silly names in the newspaper. It is interesting to note that neither of them had
ever been much beyond the twenty-thousand-foot level. Of
course, men have been higher than this both in balloons
and in the ascent of mountains. It must be well above that
point that the aeroplane enters the danger zone—always
presuming that my premonitions are correct.

"Aeroplaning has been with us now for more than
twenty years, and one might well ask: Why should this
peril be only revealing itself in our day? The answer is
obvious. In the old days of weak engines, when a hundred
horse-power Gnome or Green was considered ample for
every need, the flights were very restricted. Now that
three hundred horse-power is the rule rather than the
exception, visits to the upper layers have become easier
and more common. Some of us can remember how, in our
youth, Garros made a world-wide reputation by attain-
ing nineteen thousand feet, and it was considered a remarkable achievement to fly over the Alps. Our standard
now has been immeasurably raised, and there are twenty
high flights for one in former years. Many of them have
been undertaken with impunity. The thirty-thousand-
foot level has been reached time after time with no discomfort beyond cold and asthma. What does this prove?
A visitor might descend upon this planet a thousand
times and never see a tiger. Yet tigers exist, and if he
chanced to come down into a jungle he might be de-

voured. There are jungles of the upper air, and there are worse things than tigers which inhabit them. I believe in time they will map these jungles accurately out. Even at the present moment I could name two of them. One of them lies over the Pau-Biarritz district of France. Another is just over my head as I write here in my house in Wiltshire. I rather think there is a third in the Homburg-Wiesbaden district.

"It was the disappearance of the airmen that first set me thinking. Of course, every one said that they had fallen into the sea, but that did not satisfy me at all. First, there was Verrier in France; his machine was found near Bayonne, but they never got his body. There was the case of Baxter also, who vanished, though his engine and some of the iron fixings were found in a wood in Leicestershire. In that case, Dr. Middleton, of Amesbury, who was watching the flight with a telescope, declares that just before the clouds obscured the view he saw the machine, which was at an enormous height, suddenly rise perpendicularly upwards in a succession of jerks in a manner that he would have thought to be impossible. That was the last seen of Baxter. There was a correspondence in the papers, but it never led to anything. There were several other similar cases, and then there was the death of Hay Connor. What a cackle there was about an un-solved mystery of the air, and what columns in the half-penny papers, and yet how little was ever done to get to the bottom of the business! He came down in a tre-mendous vol-plane from an unknown height. He never got off his machine and died in his pilot's seat. Died of what? 'Heart disease,' said the doctors. Rubbish! Hay Connor's heart was as sound as mine is. What did Venables say? Venables was the only man who was at his side when he died. He said that he was shivering and looked like a man who had been badly scared. 'Died of fright,' said Vena-bles, but could not imagine what he was frightened about. Only said one word to Venables, which sounded like 'Mon-strous.' They could make nothing of that at the inquest. But I could make something of it. Monsters! That was the last word of poor Harry Hay Connor. And he *did* die of fright, just as Venables thought.

"And then there was Myrtle's head. Do you really believe—does anybody really believe—that a man's head could be driven clean into his body by the force of a fall? Well, perhaps it may be possible, but I, for one, have never believed that it was so with Myrtle. And the grease upon his clothes—'all slimy with grease,' said somebody at the inquest. Queer that nobody got thinking after that! I did—but, then, I had been thinking for a good long time. I've made three ascents—how Dangerfield used to chaff me about my shot-gun—but I've never been high enough. Now, with this new light Paul Veroner machine and its one hundred and seventy-five Robur, I should easily touch the thirty thousand to-morrow. I'll have a shot at the record. Maybe I shall have a shot at something else as well. Of course, it's dangerous. If a fellow wants to avoid danger he had best keep out of flying altogether and subside finally into flannel slippers and a dressing-gown. But I'll visit the air-jungle to-morrow—and if there's anything there I shall know it. If I return, I'll find myself a bit of a celebrity. If I don't, this note-book may explain what I am trying to do, and how I lost my life in doing it. But no drivel about accidents or mysteries, if *you* please.

"I chose my Paul Veroner monoplane for the job. There's nothing like a monoplane when real work is to be done. Beaumont found that out in very early days. For one thing, it doesn't mind damp, and the weather looks as if we should be in the clouds all the time. It's a bonny little model and answers my hand like a tender-mouthed horse. The engine is a ten-cylinder rotary Robur working up to one hundred and seventy-five. It has all the modern improvements—enclosed fuselage, high-curved landing skids, brakes, gyroscopic steadiers, and three speeds, worked by an alteration of the angle of the planes upon the Venetian-blind principle. I took a shot-gun with me and a dozen cartridges filled with buck-shot. You should have seen the face of Perkins, my old mechanic, when I directed him to put them in. I was dressed like an Arctic explorer, with two jerseys under my overalls, thick socks inside my padded boots, a storm-cap with flaps, and my talc goggles. It was stifling outside the hangars, but I was going for the summit of the Himalayas, and had to dress for the part. Perkins knew there was something on and implored me to take him with me. Perhaps I should if I were using the biplane, but a monoplane is a one-man show—if you want to get the last foot of lift out of it. Of course, I took an oxygen bag; the man who goes for the altitude record without one will either be frozen or smothered—or both.

"I had a good look at the planes, the rudder-bar, and the elevating lever before I got in. Everything was in order so far as I could see. Then I switched on my engine and found that she was running sweetly. When they let her go she rose almost at once upon the lowest speed. I circled my home field once or twice just to warm her up, and then, with a wave to Perkins and the others, I flattened out my planes and put her on her highest. She skimmed like a swallow down wind for eight or ten miles until I turned her nose up a little and she began to climb in a great spiral for the cloud-bank above me. It's all-important to rise slowly and adapt yourself to the pressure as you go.

"It was a close, warm day for an English September, and there was the hush and heaviness of impending rain. Now and then there came sudden puffs of wind from the south-west—one of them so gusty and unexpected that it caught me napping and turned me half-round for an instant. I remember the time when gusts and whirls and air-pockets used to be things of danger—before we learned to put an over-mastering power into our engines. Just as I reached the cloud-banks, with the altimeter marking three thousand, down came the rain. My word, how it poured! It drummed upon my wings and lashed against my face, blurring my glasses so that I could hardly see. I got down on to a low speed, for it was painful to travel against it. As I got higher it became hail, and I had to turn tail to it. One of my cylinders was out of action—a dirty plug, I should imagine, but still I was rising steadily with plenty of power. After a bit the trouble passed, whatever it was, and I heard the full deep-throated purr—the ten singing as one. That's where the beauty of our modern silencers comes in. We can at last control our engines by ear. How they squeal and squeak and sob when they are in trouble! All those cries for help were wasted in the old days, when every sound was swallowed up by the monstrous racket of the machine. If only the early aviators could come back to see the beauty and perfection of the mechanism which have been bought at the cost of their lives!

"About nine-thirty I was nearing the clouds. Down below me, all blurred and shadowed with rain, lay the vast expanse of Salisbury Plain. Half-a-dozen flying machines were doing hack-work at the thousand-foot level, looking like little black swallows against the green back-ground. I dare say they were wondering what I was doing up in cloud-land. Suddenly a grey curtain drew across beneath me and the wet folds of vapour were swirling round my face. It was clammily cold and miserable. But I was above the hailstorm, and that was something gained. The cloud was as dark and thick as a London fog. In my anxiety to get clear, I cocked her nose up until the automatic alarm-bell rang, and I actually began to slide backwards. My sopped and dripping wings had made me heavier than I thought, but presently I was in lighter cloud, and soon had cleared the first layer. There was a second—opal-coloured and fleecy—at a great height above my head, a white unbroken ceiling above, and a dark unbroken floor below, with the monoplane labouring upwards upon a vast spiral between them. It is deadly lonely in these cloud-spaces. Once a great flight of some small water-birds went past me, flying very fast to the westwards. The quick whirr of their wings and their musical cry were cheery to my ear. I fancy that they were teal, but I am a wretched zoologist. Now that we humans have become birds we must really learn to know our brethren by sight.

"The wind down beneath me whirled and swayed the broad cloud-plain. Once a great eddy formed in it, a whirlpool of vapour, and through it, as down a funnel, I caught sight of the distant world. A large white biplane was passing at a vast depth beneath me. I fancy it was the morning mail service betwixt Bristol and London. Then the drift swirled inwards again and the great solitude was unbroken.

"Just after ten I touched the lower edge of the upper cloud-stratum. It consisted of fine diaphanous vapour drifting swiftly from the westward. The wind had been steadily rising all this time and it was now blowing a sharp breeze—twenty-eight an hour by my gauge. Already it was very cold, though my altimeter only marked nine thousand. The engines were working beautifully, and we went droning steadily upwards. The cloud-bank was thicker than I had expected, but at last it thinned out into a golden mist before me, and then in an instant I had shot out from it, and there was an unclouded sky and a brilliant sun above my head—all blue and gold above, all shining silver below, one vast glimmering plain as far as my eyes could reach. It was a quarter past ten o'clock, and the barograph needle pointed to twelve thousand eight hundred. Up I went and up, my ears concentrated upon the deep purring of my motor, my eyes busy always with the watch, the revolution indicator, the petrol lever, and the oil pump. No wonder aviators are said to be a fearless race. With so many things to think of there is no time to trouble about oneself. About this time I noted how unreliable is the compass when above a certain height from earth. At fifteen thousand feet mine was pointing east and a point south. The sun and the wind gave me my true bearings.

"I had hoped to reach an eternal stillness in these high altitudes, but with every thousand feet of ascent the gale grew stronger. My machine groaned and trembled in every joint and rivet as she faced it, and swept away like a sheet of paper when I banked her on the turn, skimming down wind at a greater pace, perhaps, than ever mortal man has moved. Yet I had always to turn again and tack up in the wind's eye, for it was not merely a height record that I was after. By all my calculations it was above little Wiltshire that my air-jungle lay, and all my labour might be lost if I struck the outer layers at some farther point.

"When I reached the nineteen-thousand-foot level, which was about midday, the wind was so severe that I looked with some anxiety to the stays of my wings, expecting momentarily to see them snap or slacken. I even cast loose the parachute behind me, and fastened its hook into the ring of my leathern belt, so as to be ready for the worst. Now was the time when a bit of scamped work by the mechanic is paid for by the life of the aeronaut. But she held together bravely. Every cord and strut was humming and vibrating like so many harpstrings, but it was glorious to see how, for all the beating and the buffeting, she was still the conqueror of Nature and the mistress of the sky. There is surely something divine in man himself that he should rise so superior to the limitations which Creation seemed to impose—rise, too, by such unselfish, heroic devotion as this air-conquest has shown. Talk of human degeneration! When has such a story as this been written in the annals of our race?

"These were the thoughts in my head as I climbed that monstrous inclined plane with the wind sometimes beating in my face and sometimes whistling behind my ears, while the cloud-land beneath me fell away to such a distance that the folds and hummocks of silver had all smoothed out into one flat, shining plain. But suddenly I had a horrible and unprecedented experience. I have known before what it is to be in what our neighbours have called a *tourbillon*, but never on such a scale as this. That huge, sweeping river of wind of which I have spoken had, as it appears, whirlpools within it which were as monstrous as itself. Without a moment's warning I was dragged suddenly into the heart of one. I spun round for a minute or two with such velocity that I almost lost my senses, and then fell suddenly, left wing foremost, down the vacuum funnel in the centre. I dropped like a stone, and lost nearly a thousand feet. It was only my belt that kept me in my seat, and the shock and breathlessness left me hanging half-insensible over the side of the fuselage. But I am always capable of a supreme effort—it is my one great merit as an aviator. I was conscious that the descent was slower. The whirlpool was a cone rather than a funnel, and I had come to the apex. With a terrific wrench, throwing my weight all to one side, I levelled my planes and brought her head away from the wind. In an instant I had shot out of the eddies and was skimming down the sky. Then, shaken but victorious, I turned her nose up and began once more my steady grind on the upward spiral. I took a large sweep to avoid the danger-spot of the whirlpool, and soon I was safely above it. Just after one o'clock I was twenty-one thousand feet above the sea-level. To my great joy I had topped the gale, and with every hundred feet of ascent the air grew stiller. On the other hand, it was very cold, and I was conscious of that peculiar nausea which goes with rarefication of the air. For the first time I unscrewed the mouth of my oxygen bag and took an occasional whiff of the glorious gas. I could feel it running like a cordial through my veins, and I was exhilarated almost to the point of drunkenness. I shouted and sang as I roared upwards into the cold, still outer world.

"It is very clear to me that the insensibility which came upon Glaisher, and in a lesser degree upon Coxwell, when, in 1862, they ascended in a balloon to the height of thirty thousand feet, was due to the extreme speed with which a perpendicular ascent is made. Doing it at an easy gradient and accustoming oneself to the lessened barometric pressure by slow degrees, there are no such dreadful symptoms. At the same great height I found that even without my oxygen inhaler I could breathe without undue distress. It was bitterly cold, however, and my thermometer was at zero, Fahrenheit. At one-thirty I was nearly seven miles above the surface of the earth, and still ascending steadily. I found, however, that the rarefied air was giving markedly less support to my planes, and that my angle of ascent had to be considerably lowered in consequence. It was already clear that even with my light weight and strong engine-power there was a point in front of me where I should be held. To make matters worse, one of my sparking-plugs was in trouble again and there was intermittent misfiring in the engine. My heart was heavy with the fear of failure.

"It was about that time that I had a most extraordinary experience. Something whizzed past me in a trail of smoke and exploded with a loud, hissing sound, sending forth a cloud of steam. For the instant I could not imagine what had happened. Then I remembered that the earth is for ever being bombarded by meteor stones, and would be hardly inhabitable were they not in nearly every case turned to vapour in the outer layers of the atmosphere. Here is a new danger for the high-altitude man, for two others passed me when I was nearing the forty-thousand-foot mark. I cannot doubt that at the edge of the earth's envelope the risk would be a very real one.

"My barograph needle marked forty-one thousand three hundred when I became aware that I could go no farther. Physically, the strain was not as yet greater than I could bear, but my machine had reached its limit. The attenuated air gave no firm support to the wings, and the least tilt developed into side-slip, while she seemed sluggish on her controls. Possibly, had the engine been at its best, another thousand feet might have been within our capacity, but it was still misfiring, and two out of the ten cylinders appeared to be out of action. If I had not already reached the zone for which I was searching then I should never see it upon this journey. But was it not possible that I had attained it? Soaring in circles like a monstrous hawk upon the forty-thousand-foot level I let the monoplane guide herself, and with my Mannheim glass I made a careful observation of my surroundings.

The heavens were perfectly clear; there was no indication of those dangers which I had imagined.

"I have said that I was soaring in circles. It struck me suddenly that I would do well to take a wider sweep and open up a new air-tract. If the hunter entered an earth-jungle he would drive through it if he wished to find his game. My reasoning had led me to believe that the air-jungle which I had imagined lay somewhere over Wiltshire. This should be to the south and west of me. I took my bearings from the sun, for the compass was hopeless and no trace of earth was to be seen—nothing but the distant silver cloud-plain. However, I got my direction as best I might and kept her head straight to the mark. I reckoned that my petrol supply would not last for more than another hour or so, but I could afford to use it to the last drop, since a single magnificent vol-plane could at any time take me to the earth.

"Suddenly I was aware of something new. The air in front of me had lost its crystal clearness. It was full of long, ragged wisps of something which I can only compare to very fine cigarette-smoke. It hung about in wreaths and coils, turning and twisting slowly in the sunlight. As the monoplane shot through it, I was aware of a faint taste of oil upon my lips, and there was a greasy scum upon the wood-work of the machine. Some infinitely fine organic matter appeared to be suspended in the atmosphere. There was no life there. It was inchoate and diffuse, extending for many square acres and then fringing off into the void. No, it was not life. But might it not be the remains of life? Above all, might it not be the food of life, of monstrous life, even as the humble grease of the ocean is the food for the mighty whale? The thought was in my mind when my eyes looked upwards and I saw the most wonderful vision that ever man has seen. Can I hope to convey it to you even as I saw it myself last Thursday?

"Conceive a jelly-fish such as sails our summer seas, bell-shaped and of enormous size—far larger, I should judge, than the dome of St. Paul's. It was of a light pink colour veined with a delicate green, but the whole huge fabric so tenuous that it was but a fairy outline against the dark blue sky. It pulsated with a delicate and regular rhythm. From it there depended two long, dripping green tentacles, which swayed slowly backwards and forwards. This gorgeous vision passed gently with noiseless dignity over my head, as light and fragile as a soap-bubble, and drifted upon its stately way.

"I had half-turned my monoplane, that I might look after this beautiful creature, when, in a moment, I found myself amidst a perfect fleet of them, of all sizes, but none so large as the first. Some were quite small, but the majority about as big as an average balloon, and with much the same curvature at the top. There was in them a delicacy of texture and colouring which reminded me of the finest Venetian glass. Pale shades of pink and green were the prevailing tints, but all had a lovely iridescence where the sun shimmered through their dainty forms. Some hundreds of them drifted past me, a wonderful fairy squadron of strange, unknown argosies of the sky—creatures whose forms and substance were so attuned to these pure heights that one could not conceive anything so delicate within actual sight or sound of earth.

"But soon my attention was drawn to a new phenomenon—the serpents of the outer air. These were long, thin, fantastic coils of vapour-like material, which turned and twisted with great speed, flying round and round at such a pace that the eyes could hardly follow them. Some of these ghost-like creatures were twenty or thirty feet long, but it was difficult to tell their girth, for their outline was so hazy that it seemed to fade away into the air around them. These air-snakes were of very light grey or smoke colour, with some darker lines within, which gave the impression of a definite organism. One of them whisked past my very face, and I was conscious of a cold, clammy contact, but their composition was so unsubstantial that I could not connect them with any thought of physical danger, any more than the beautiful bell-like creatures which had preceded them. There was no more solidity in their frames than in the floating spume from a broken wave.

"But a more terrible experience was in store for me. Floating downwards from a great height there came a purplish patch of vapour, small as I saw it first, but rapidly enlarging as it approached me, until it appeared to be hundreds of square feet in size. Though fashioned of some transparent, jelly-like substance, it was none the less of much more definite outline and solid consistence than anything which I had seen before. There were more traces, too, of a physical organisation, especially two vast shadowy, circular plates upon either side, which may have been eyes, and a perfectly solid white projection between them which was as curved and cruel as the beak of a vulture.

"The whole aspect of this monster was formidable and threatening, and it kept changing its colour from a very light mauve to a dark, angry purple so thick that it cast a shadow as it drifted between my monoplane and the sun. On the upper curve of its huge body there were three great projections which I can only describe as enormous bubbles, and I was convinced as I looked as them that they were charged with some extremely light gas which served to buoy up the misshapen and semi-solid mass in the rarefied air. The creature moved swiftly along, keeping pace easily with the monoplane, and for twenty miles or more it formed my horrible escort, hovering over me like a bird of prey which is waiting to pounce. Its method of progression—done so swiftly that it was not easy to follow—was to throw out a long, glutinous streamer in front of it, which in turn seemed to draw forward the rest of the writhing body. So elastic and gelatinous was it that never for two successive minutes was it the same shape, and yet each change made it more threatening and loathsome than the last.

"I knew that it meant mischief. Every purple flush of its hideous body told me so. The vague, goggling eyes which were turned always upon me were cold and merciless in their viscid hatred. I dipped the nose of my monoplane downwards to escape it. As I did so, as quick as a flash there shot out a long tentacle from this mass of floating blubber, and it fell as light and sinuous as a whip-lash across the front of my machine. There was a loud hiss as it lay for a moment across the hot engine, and it whisked itself into the air again, while the huge flat body drew itself together as if in sudden pain. I dipped to a volpiqué, but again a tentacle fell over the monoplane and was shorn off by the propeller as easily as it might have cut through a smoke wreath. A long, gliding, sticky, serpent-like coil came from behind and caught me round the waist, dragging me out of the fuselage. I tore at it, my fingers sinking into the smooth, glue-like surface, and for an instant I disengaged myself, but only to be caught round the boot by another coil, which gave me a jerk that tilted me almost on to my back.

"As I fell over I blazed both barrels of my gun, though, indeed, it was like attacking an elephant with a pea-shooter to imagine that any human weapon could cripple that mighty bulk. And yet I aimed better than I knew, for, with a loud report, one of the great blisters upon the creature's back exploded with the puncture of the buck-shot. It was very clear that my conjecture was right, and that these vast clear bladders were distended with some lifting gas, for in an instant the huge cloud-like body turned sideways, writhing desperately to find its balance, while the white beak snapped and gaped in horrible fury. But already I had shot away on the steepest glide that I dared to attempt, my engine still full on, the flying propeller and the force of gravity shooting me downwards like an aerolite. Far behind me I saw a dull, purplish smudge growing swiftly smaller and merging into the blue sky behind it. I was safe out of the deadly jungle of the outer air.

"Once out of danger I throttled my engine, for nothing tears a machine to pieces quicker than running on full power from a height. It was a glorious spiral vol-plane from nearly eight miles of altitude—first, to the level of the silver cloud-bank, then to that of the storm-cloud beneath it, and finally, in beating rain, to the surface of the earth. I saw the Bristol Channel beneath me as I broke from the clouds, but, having still some petrol in my tanks, I got twenty miles inland before I found myself stranded in a field half a mile from the village of Ashcombe. There I got three tins of petrol from a passing motor-car, and at ten minutes past six that evening I alighted gently in my own home meadow at Devizes, after such a journey as no mortal upon earth has ever yet taken and lived to tell the tale. I have seen the beauty and I have seen the horror of the heights—and greater beauty or greater horror than that is not within the ken of man.

"And now it is my plan to go once again before I give my results to the world. My reason for this is that I must surely have something to show by way of proof before I lay such a tale before my fellow-men. It is true that others will soon follow and will confirm what I have said, and yet I should wish to carry conviction from the first. Those lovely iridescent bubbles of the air should not be hard to capture. They drift slowly upon their way, and the swift monoplane could intercept their leisurely course. It is likely enough that they would dissolve in the heavier layers of the atmosphere, and that some small heap of amorphous jelly might be all that I should bring to earth with me. And yet something there would surely be by which I could substantiate my story. Yes, I will go, even if I run a risk by doing so. These purple horrors would not seem to be numerous. It is probable that I shall not see one. If I do I shall dive at once. At the worst there is always the shot-gun and my knowledge of . . ."

Here a page of the manuscript is unfortunately missing. On the next page is written, in large, straggling writing:—

"Forty-three thousand feet. I shall never see earth again. They are beneath me, three of them. God help me; it is a dreadful death to die!"

Such in its entirety is the Joyce-Armstrong Statement. Of the man nothing has since been seen. Pieces of his shattered monoplane have been picked up in the preserves of Mr. Budd-Lushington upon the borders of Kent and Sussex, within a few miles of the spot where the note-book was discovered. If the unfortunate aviator's theory is correct that this air-jungle, as he called it, existed only over the south-west of England, then it would seem that he had fled from it at the full speed of his monoplane, but had been overtaken and devoured by these horrible creatures at some spot in the outer atmosphere above the place where the grim relics were found. The picture of that monoplane skimming down the sky, with the nameless terrors flying as swiftly beneath it and cutting it off always from the earth while they gradually closed in upon their victim, is one upon which a man who valued his sanity would prefer not to dwell. There are many, as I am aware, who still jeer at the facts which I have here set down, but even they must admit that Joyce-Armstrong has disappeared, and I would commend to them his own words: "This note-book may explain what I am trying to do, and how I lost my life in doing it. But no drivel about accidents or mysteries, if *you* please."

Pearl S. Buck

THE FRILL

MY DEAR, the only way to manage these native tailors is to be firm!"

Mrs. Lowe, the postmaster's wife, settled herself with some difficulty into the wicker rocking-chair upon the wide veranda of her house. She was a large woman, red-faced from more food than necessary and little exercise over the ten-odd years she had spent in a port town on the China coast. Now as she looked at her caller and thus spoke, her square hard-fleshed face grew a little redder. Beside her stood a Chinese manservant who had just announced in a mild voice:

"Tailor have come, missy."

Little Mrs. Newman looked at her hostess with vague admiration.

"I'm sure I wish I had your way with them, Adeline," she murmured, fanning herself slowly with a palm-leaf fan. She went on in a plaintive complaining way: "Sometimes I think it is scarcely worth while to bother with new clothes, although they are so cheap here, especially if you buy the native silks. But it is so much trouble to have them made, and these tailors say—my dear, my tailor promises me faithfully he will make a dress in three days and then he doesn't come for a week or two!" Her weak voice dwindled and ended in a sigh and she fanned herself a trifle more quickly.

"Watch me, now," said Mrs. Lowe commandingly. She had a deep firm voice and round hard gray eyes set a little near together beneath closely waved dead brown hair. She turned these eyes upon the Chinese manservant as he stood looking decorously down to the floor, his head drooping slightly, and said, "Boy, talkee tailor come this side!"

"Yes, missy," murmured the servant and disappeared. Almost instantly there was the sound of soft steady footsteps through the open doors, and from the back of the house through the hall following the manservant there came the tailor. He was a tall man, taller than the servant, middle-aged, his face quiet with a sort of closed tranquillity. He wore a long robe of faded blue grasscloth, patched neatly at the elbows and very clean. Under his arm he carried a bundle wrapped in a white cloth. He bowed to the two white women and then squatting down put this bundle upon the floor of the veranda and untied its knots. Inside was a worn and frayed fashion book from some American company and a half-finished dress of a spotted blue and white silk. This dress he shook out carefully and held up for Mrs. Lowe to see. From its generous proportions it could be seen that it was made for her. She surveyed it coldly and with hostility, searching its details.

Suddenly she spoke in a loud voice: "No wantchee that collar, tailor! I have talkee you wantchee frill—see, so fashion!" She turned the pages of the book rapidly to a section devoted to garments for ample women. "See, all same fashion this lady. What for you makee flat collar? No wantchee—no wantchee—take it away!"

Upon the tailor's calm patient face a perspiration broke forth. "Yes, missy," he said faintly. And then he pressed his lips together slightly and took a breath and began: "Missy, you first talkee frill, then you say no frill. Other day you say wantchee flat collar, frill too fat."

He looked imploringly at the white woman. But Mrs. Lowe waved him away with a fat ringed hand.

"No, you talkee lie, tailor," she cried sternly. "I know how I talkee. I never say I wantchee flat collar—never! No lady have flat collar now. What for you talkee so fashion?"

"Yes, missy," said the tailor. Then brightening somewhat he suggested, "Have more cloth, missy. Suppose I makee frill, never mind."

But Mrs. Lowe was not to be thus easily appeased. "Yes, never mind you, but you have spoil so much my cloth. What you think, I buy this cloth no money? Plenty money you make me lose." She turned to her guest. "I have been counting on that dress, Minnie, and now look at it! I wanted to wear it to the garden party at the consulate day after tomorrow. I told him a frill—just look at that silly collar!"

"Yes, I know. It's just what I was saying," said Mrs. Newman in her tired peevish voice. "What I want to know is how will you manage it?"

"Oh, I'll manage it," replied Mrs. Lowe grimly.

She ignored the tailor for a while and stared out over her trim garden. In the hot sunshine a blue-coated coolie squatted over a border of zinnias, glittering in the September noon. A narrow sanded path ran about a square of green lawn. She said nothing, and the tailor stood acutely uncomfortable, the dress still held delicately by the shoulders. A small trickle of perspiration ran down each side of his face. He wet his lips and began in a trembling voice:

"Missy wantchee try?"

"No, I do not," snapped Mrs. Lowe. "What for wantchee try? All wrong—collar all wrong—what for try?" She continued to stare out into the shining garden.

"Can makee all same frill," said the tailor eagerly, persuasively. "Yes, yes, missy, I makee all same you say. What time you want?"

"I want it tomorrow," replied the white woman. "You bring tomorrow twelve o'clock. Suppose you no bring, then I no pay—savee? All time you talkee what time you bring and you never bring."

"Can do, missy," said the tailor quietly. He squatted gracefully, folded the dress into the cloth again and tied it tenderly, careful to crush nothing. Then he rose and stood waiting, upon his face some agony of supplication. His whole soul rose in this silent supplication, so that it was written upon his quiet high-cheeked face, upon his close-set lips. Sweat broke out upon him afresh. Even Mrs. Lowe could feel dimly that imploring soul. She paused in her rocking, and looked up.

"What is it?" she asked sharply. "What more thing?"

The tailor wet his lips again and spoke in a faint voice. "Missy, can you give me litty money—one dollar, two dollar——" Before her outraged look his voice dropped yet lower. "My brother's son he die today, I think—he have three piecee baby, one woman—no money buy coffin —no nothing—he very ill today——"

Mrs. Lowe looked at her caller. "Well, of all the nerve!" she breathed, genuinely aghast. Mrs. Newman answered her look.

"It's just what I said," she replied. "They are more trouble than they are worth—and the way they *cut*—and then they think about nothing but money!"

Mrs. Lowe turned her rolling gray eyes upon the tailor. He did not look up, but he wiped his lip furtively with his sleeve. She stared at him an instant and then her voice came forth filled with righteous anger.

"No," she said. "No. You finish dress all proper with frill, I pay you. No finish dress, no pay. Never. You savee, tailor?"

"Yes, missy," sighed the tailor. All vestige of hope had now disappeared from his face. The atmosphere of supplication died away. A look of cold despair came over his face like a curtain. "I finish tomorrow twelve o'clock, missy," he said and turned away.

"See that you do," shouted Mrs. Lowe triumphantly after him and she watched his figure with contempt as it disappeared into the hall. Then she turned to her caller. "If I say tomorrow," she explained, "perhaps it will be ready by the day after." She thought of something and reaching forward in her chair pressed a bell firmly. The servant appeared.

"Boy," she said, "look see tailor—see he no takee something."

Her loud voice penetrated into the house, and the tailor's body, still visible at the end of the hall, straightened itself somewhat and then passed out of sight.

"You never can tell," said Mrs. Lowe. "You can't tell whether they are making up these stories or not. If they need money—but they always do need money. I never saw such people. They must make a lot, though, sewing for all these foreigners here in the port. But this tailor is worse than most. He is forever wanting money before his work is done. Three separate times he has come and said a child was dying or something. I don't believe a word of it. Probably smokes opium or gambles. They all gamble —you can't believe a word they say!"

"Oh, I know——" sighed Mrs. Newman rising to depart. Mrs. Lowe rose also.

"After all, one simply has to be firm," she said again.

Outside the big white foreign house the tailor went silently and swiftly through the hot street. Well, he had asked her, and she would not give him anything. After all his dread and fear of her refusal, all his summoning of courage, she would not give him anything. The dress was more than half done, except for the frill, too. She had given him the silk two days ago, and he had been glad because it would bring him in a few dollars for this nephew of his who was like his own son now that the gods had taken away his own little children, three of them.

He had therefore clung the more to this only son of his dead younger brother, a young man apprenticed to an ironsmith, and he had three little children now too. Such a strong young man—who could have thought he would have been seized for death like this? Two months ago it was that the long piece of red-hot iron he was beating into the shape of a plowshare had slipped somehow from his pincers and had fallen upon his leg and foot and seared the flesh away almost to the bone. It had fallen on his naked flesh, for it was summer and the little shop was hot and he had only his thin cotton trousers on rolled to his thighs.

Well, and they had tried every sort of ointment, but what ointment will grow sound flesh again, and what balm is there for such a wound? The whole leg had swollen and now on this hot day in the ninth moon the young man lay dying. There were black plasters on his leg from hip to foot, but they were of no avail.

Yes, the tailor had seen that for himself this morning when he went to see his nephew—he had seen death there plainly. The young wife sat weeping in the doorway of the one room that was their home and the two elder children stared at her gravely, too stricken for play. The third was but a babe she held in her bosom.

The tailor turned down an alleyway and into a door in a wall. He passed through a court filled with naked children screaming and quarreling and shouting at play.

Above his head were stretched bamboo poles upon which were hung ragged garments washed in too scanty water and without any soap. Here about these courts a family lived in every room and poured its waste into the court so that even though it was a dry day—and the days had been dry for a moon or more—yet the court was slimy and running with waste water.

But he did not notice this. He passed through three more courts like the first and turned to an open door at the right and went into the dark windowless room. There was a different odor here. It was the odor of dying rotten flesh. The sound of a woman's wailing rose from beside the curtained bed and thither the tailor went, his face not changed from the look it had borne away from the white woman's house. The young wife did not look up at his coming. She sat crouched on the ground beside the bed and her face was wet with tears. Her long black hair had come uncoiled and stretched over her shoulder and hung to the earth. Over and over she moaned: "Oh, my husband —oh, my man—I am left alone—oh, my husband——"

The babe lay on the ground beside her crying feebly now and again. The two elder children sat close to their mother, each of them holding fast to a corner of her coat. They had been weeping too but now they were silent, their streaked faces upturned to look at their uncle.

But the tailor paid no heed to them now. He looked into the hempen curtains of the bed and said gently:

"Are you still living, my son?"

The dying man turned his eyes with difficulty. He was horribly swollen, his hands, his naked upper body, his neck, his face. But these were nothing to the immense log-like swelling of his burned leg. It lay there so huge it seemed he was attached to it, rather than it to him. His glazed eyes fixed themselves upon his uncle. He opened his puffed lips and after a long time and a mighty effort of concentration his voice came forth in a hoarse whisper:

"These children——"

The tailor's face was suddenly convulsed with suffering. He sat down upon the edge of the bed and began to speak earnestly:

"You need not grieve for your children, my son. Die peacefully. Your wife and your children shall come to my house. They shall take the place of my own three. Your wife shall be daughter to me and to my wife, and your children shall be our grandchildren. Are you not my own brother's son? And he dead too, and only I left now."

He began to weep quietly, and it could be seen that the lines upon his face were set there by other hours of this repressed silent weeping, for as he wept his face hardly changed at all, only the tears rolled down his cheeks.

After a long time the dying man's voice came again with the same rending effort, as though he tore himself out of some heavy stupor to say what must be said:

"You—are poor—too——"

But the uncle answered quickly, bending toward the dying man, for the swollen eyes were now closed and he could not be sure he was heard: "You're not to worry. Rest your heart. I have work—these white women are always wanting new dresses. I have a silk dress now nearly finished for the postmaster's wife—nearly done, except for a frill, and then she will give me money for it and perhaps more sewing. We shall do very well——"

But the young man made no further reply. He had gone into that stupor forever and he could rouse himself no more.

Nevertheless, he still breathed slightly throughout that long hot day. The tailor rose once to place his bundle in a corner and to remove his robe, and then he took his place again beside the dying man and remained immovable through the hours. The woman wailed on and on, but at last she was exhausted and sat leaning against the end of the bed, her eyes closed, sobbing now and again softly. But the children grew used to it. They grew used even to their father's dying, and they ran out into the court to play. Once or twice a kindly neighbor woman came and put her head into the door and the last time she picked up the babe and carried him away, holding him to her own full breast to comfort him. Outside her voice could be heard shouting in cheerful pity:

"Well, his hour is come, and he is foul already as though he had been dead a month!"

So the hot day drew on at last to its end and when twilight came the young man ceased breathing and was dead.

Only then did the tailor rise. He rose and put on his gown and took his bundle and he said to the crouching woman, "He is dead. Have you any money at all?"

Then the young woman rose also and looked at him anxiously, smoothing the hair back from her face. It could now be seen that she was still very young—not more than twenty years of age—a young common creature such as may be seen anywhere on any street in any day, neither pretty nor ugly, slight, and somewhat slovenly even on ordinary occasions, and now unwashed for many days. Her grimy face was round, the mouth full and projecting, the eyes a little stupid. It was clear that she had lived from day to day, never foreseeing the catastrophe that had now befallen her. She looked at the tailor humbly and anxiously.

"We have nothing left," she said. "I pawned his clothes and my winter clothes and the table and stools and we have only that bed on which he lies."

The look of despair deepened on the man's face. "Is there anyone of whom you might borrow?" he asked.

She shook her head. "I do not know anyone except these people in the court. And what have they?" Then as the full terror of her position came upon her she cried out shrilly, "Uncle, we have no one but you in the world!"

"I know," he said simply. He looked once more at the

bed. "Cover him," he said in a low voice. "Cover him against the flies."

He passed through the courts quickly then and the neighbor woman, who was still holding the babe, bawled at him as he went, "Is he dead yet?"

"He is dead," said the tailor and went through the gate into the street and turned to the west where his own home was.

It seemed to him that this was the most hot day of that whole summer. So is the ninth moon hot sometimes, and so does summer often pass burning fiercely into autumn. The evening had brought no coolness and thunderous clouds towered over the city. The streets were filled with half-naked men and with women in thinnest garb, sitting upon little low bamboo couches they had moved out of their houses. Some lay flat upon the street on mats of reed or strips of woven matting. Children wailed everywhere and mothers fanned their babies wearily, dreading the night.

Through this crowd the tailor passed swiftly, his head bent down. He was now very weary but still not hungry although he had fasted the whole day. He could not eat— no, not even when he reached the one room in a court which was his home, and he could not eat even when his poor stupid old wife, who could not keep her babies alive, came shuffling and panting out of the street and placed a bowl of cold rice gruel on the table for him to eat. There was that smell about his clothes—it filled his nostrils still. He thought suddenly of the silk dress. Suppose the white woman noticed the odor there! He rose suddenly and opened the bundle and shook out the dress, and turning it carefully inside out he hung it to air upon a decrepit dressmaker's form that stood by the bed.

But it could not hang there long. He must finish it and have the money. He took off his robe and his undershirt and his shoes and stockings and sat in his trousers. He must be careful in this heat that his sweat did not stain the dress. He found a gray towel and wrapped it about his head to catch the drops of sweat and put a rag upon the table on which to wipe his hands from time to time.

While he sewed swiftly, not daring to hasten beyond what he was able to do well lest she be not pleased, he pondered on what he could do. He had had one apprentice last year, but the times were so evil he had had to let the lad go, and so had now but his own ten fingers to use. But that was not altogether ill because the lad had made so many mistakes and the white woman said insistently, "You must makee yourself, tailor—no give small boy makee spoil." Yes, but with just these ten fingers of his could he hope to make another dress in three days—suppose she had another silk dress—that would be ten dollars for the two. He could buy a coffin for ten dollars down and the promise of more later.

But supposing she had no more work to give him now—then what could he do? What indeed, but go to a usurer? And yet that he did not dare to do. A man was lost if he went to a usurer for the interest ran faster than a tiger upon him—in a few months double and triple what he had borrowed. Then when the coffin was buried he must bring the young wife and the three babies here. There was only this one room for them all, too. His heart warmed somewhat at the thought of the babies and then stopped in terror at the thought that he must feed them.

Midnight drew on and he was not finished. There was the worst of all yet to be made—the frill. He fetched his fashion book and pored over it beneath the flickering light of the small tin kerosene lamp. So the frill went, here it turned, a long wide frill, closely pleated. He folded the small pleats, his hands trembling with fatigue. His wife lay snoring in the bed now. Nothing would wake her, not even the rackety noisy sewing machine with which he set fast the carefully basted frill. At dawn there remained but the edge to whip by hand and the irons to heat on the charcoal brazier. Well, he would sleep a little and rest his aching eyes and then get up to finish it. He hung the dress upon the form, and then he lay down beside his wife and fell instantly into deep sleep.

But not for long could he sleep. At seven he rose and went to his work again and worked until nearly noon, stopping only for a mouthful of the food he could not eat the night before. Then he was finished. It had taken him longer than he hoped it would. He squinted up at the sun. Yes, he could just get to the house by noon. He must hasten. He must not make her angry so that she would perhaps refuse him the other dress. No, somehow he must have the other dress. Then if he sewed this afternoon and tonight he could finish it in another day. He smelled the finished dress anxiously. A little odor, perhaps—would she notice it?

But fortunately she did not notice it. She was sitting in that strange moving chair she had on the veranda, and she looked at the dress critically.

"All finish?" she asked in her loud sudden way.

"Yes, missy," he answered humbly.

"All right, I go try."

She had gone into her room, then and he held his breath, waiting. Perhaps there was some odor to it yet? But she came back wearing the dress, a satisfied look upon her face; but not too satisfied.

"How much?" she said abruptly.

He hesitated. "Five dollar, missy, please." Then seeing her angry eyes he added hastily. "Silk dress, five dollar, please, missy. Any tailor five dollar."

"Too much—too much," she declared. "You spoil my cloth too!" But she paid the money to him grudgingly, and he took it from her, delicately careful not to touch her hand.

"Thank you, missy," he said gently.

He dropped to his heels and began to tie up his bundle, his fingers trembling. He must ask her now. But how could he? What would he do if she refused? He gathered his courage together desperately.

"Missy," he said looking up humbly but avoiding her eyes. "You have more dress I can do?"

He waited, hanging on her answer, staring into the shining garden. But she had already turned to go into the house again to take off the dress. She called back at him carelessly:

"No—no more! You makee too muchee trouble. You spoil my cloth—plenty more tailor more cheap and not so muchee trouble!"

The next day at the garden party she met little Mrs. Newman, sitting languidly in a wicker chair, watching white figures move about the lawn intent upon a game of croquet. Mrs. Newman's faded blue eyes brightened somewhat at the sight of the new dress.

"You really did get your dress after all," she said with faint interest. "I didn't think you really would. He did that frill nicely, didn't he?"

Mrs. Lowe looked down upon her large bosom. There the frill lay, beautifully pleated, perfectly ironed. She said with satisfaction, "Yes, it is nice, isn't it? I am glad I decided to have the frill, after all. And so cheap! My dear, with all this frill the dress cost only five dollars to be made—that's less than two dollars at home! . . . What's that—oh yes, he brought it punctually at twelve, as I told him he must. It's as I said—you simply have to be firm with these native tailors!"

John Masefield

THE SEEKERS

Friends and loves we have none, nor wealth nor blessed
abode,
But the hope of the City of God at the other end of the
road.

Not for us are content, and quiet, and peace of mind,
For we go seeking a city that we shall never find.

There is no solace on earth for us—for such as we—
Who search for a hidden city that we shall never see.

Only the road and the dawn, the sun, the wind, and the
rain,
And the watch fire under stars, and sleep, and the road
again.

We seek the City of God, and the haunt where beauty
dwells,
And we find the noisy mart and the sound of burial bells.

Never the golden city, where radiant people meet,
But the dolorous town where mourners are going about
the street.

We travel the dusty road till the light of the day is dim,
And sunset shows us spires away on the world's rim.

We travel from dawn to dusk, till the day is past and oy,
Seeking the Holy City beyond the rim of the sky.

Friends and loves we have none, nor wealth nor blest abode,
But the hope of the City of God at the other end of the
road.

Stefan Zweig

AMOK

In march 1912, when a big mail-boat was unloading at Naples, there was an accident about which extremely inaccurate reports appeared in the newspapers. I myself saw nothing of the affair, for (in common with many of the passengers), wishing to escape the noise and discomfort of coaling, I had gone to spend the evening ashore. As it happens, however, I am in a position to know what really occurred, and to explain the cause. So many years have now elapsed since the incidents about to be related, that there is no reason why I should not break the silence I have hitherto maintained.

I had been travelling in the Federated Malay States. Recalled home by cable on urgent private affairs, I joined the *Wotan* at Singapore, and had to put up with very poor accommodation. My cabin was a hole of a place squeezed into a corner close to the engine-room, small, hot, and dark. The fusty, stagnant air reeked of oil. I had to keep the electric fan running, with the result that a fetid draught crawled over my face reminding me of the fluttering of a crazy bat. From beneath came the persistent rattle and groans of the engines, which sounded like a coal-porter tramping and wheezing as he climbed an unending flight of iron stairs; from above came the no less persistent tread of feet upon the promenade deck. As soon as I had had my cabin baggage properly stowed away, I fled from the place to the upper deck, where with delight I inhaled deep breaths of the balmy south wind.

But on this crowded ship the promenade deck, too, was full of bustle and disquiet. It was thronged with passengers, nervously irritable in their enforced idleness and unavoidable proximity, chattering without pause as they prowled to and fro. The light laughter of the women who reclined in deck-chairs, the twists and turns of those who were taking a constitutional on the encumbered deck, the general hubbub, were uncongenial. In Malaysia, and before that in Burma and Siam, I had been visiting an unfamiliar world. My mind was filled with new impressions, with lively images which chased one another in rapid succession. I wanted to contemplate them at leisure, to sort and arrange them, to digest and assimilate; but in this noisy boulevard, humming with life of a very different kind, there was no chance of finding the necessary repose. If I tried to read, the lines in the printed page ran together before my tired eyes when the shadows of the passers-by flickered over the white page. I could never be alone with myself and my thoughts in this thickly peopled alley.

For three days I did my utmost to possess my soul in patience, resigned to my fellow-passengers, staring at the sea. The sea was always the same, blue and void, except that at nightfall for a brief space it became resplendent with a play of varied colours. As for the people, I had grown sick of their faces before the three days were up. I knew every detail of them all. I was surfeited with them, and equally surfeited with the giggling of the women and with the windy argumentativeness of some Dutch officers coming home on leave. I took refuge in the saloon; though from this haven, too, I was speedily driven away because a group of English girls from Shanghai spent their time between meals hammering out waltzes on the piano. There was nothing for it but my cabin. I turned in after luncheon, having drugged myself with a couple of bottles of beer, resolved to escape dinner and the dance that was to follow, hoping to sleep the clock round and more, and thus to spend the better part of a day in oblivion.

When I awoke it was dark, and stuffier than ever in the little coffin. I had switched off the fan, and was dripping with sweat. I felt heavy after my prolonged slumber, and some minutes slipped by before I fully realized where I was. It must certainly be past midnight, for there was no music to be heard, and the tramp-tramp of feet overhead had ceased. The only sound was that of the machinery, the beating heart of the leviathan, who wheezed and groaned as he bore his living fright onward through the darkness.

I groped my way to the deck, where there was not a soul to be seen. Looking first at the smoking funnels and the ghostlike spars, I then turned my eyes upward and saw that the sky was clear; dark velvet, sprinkled with stars. It looked as if a curtain had been drawn across a vast source of light, and as if the stars were tiny rents in the curtain, through which that indescribable radiance poured. Never had I seen such a sky.

The night was refreshingly cool, as so often at this hour on a moving ship even at the equator. I breathed the fragrant air, charged with the aroma of distant isles. For the first time since I had come on board I was seized with a longing to dream, conjoined with another desire, more sensuous, to surrender my body—womanlike—to the night's soft embrace, I wanted to lie down somewhere, and gaze at the white hieroglyphs in the starry expanse. But the long chairs were all stacked and inaccessible. Nowhere on the empty deck was there a place for a dreamer to rest.

I made for the forecastle, stumbling over ropes and past iron windlasses to the bow, where I leaned over the rail watching the stem as it rose and fell, rhythmically, cutting its way through the phosphorescent waters. Did I stand there for an hour, or only for a few minutes? Who can tell? Rocked in that giant cradle, I took no note of the passing of time. All I was conscious of was a gentle lassitude, which was wellnigh voluptuous. I wanted to sleep, to dream; yet I was loath to quit this wizard's world, to return to my 'tween-decks coffin. Moving a pace or two, I felt with one foot a coil of rope. I sat down, and, closing my eyes, abandoned myself to the drowsy intoxication of the night. Soon the frontiers of consciousness became obscured; I was not sure whether the sound I heard was that of my own breathing or that of the mechanical heart of the ship; I gave myself up more and more completely, more and more passively, to the environing charm of this midnight world.

A dry cough near at hand recalled me to my senses with a start. Opening eyes that were now attuned to the darkness, I saw close beside me the faint gleam of a pair of spectacles, and a few inches below this a fitful glow which obviously came from a pipe. Before I sat down I had been intent on the stars and the sea, and had thus overlooked this neighbour, who must have been sitting here motionless all the while. Still a little hazy as to my whereabouts, but feeling as if somehow I was an intruder, I murmured apologetically in my native German: "Excuse me!" The answer came promptly, "Not at all!" in the same language, and with an unmistakably German intonation.

It was strange and eerie, this darkling juxtaposition to an unseen and unknown person. I had the sensation that he was staring vainly at me just as I was staring vainly at him. Neither of us could see more than a dim silhouette, black against a dusky background. I could just hear his breathing and the faint gurgle of his pipe.

The silence became unbearable. I should have liked to get up and go away, but was restrained by the conviction that to do this without a word would be unpardonably rude. In my embarrassment I took out a cigarette and struck a match. For a second or two there was light, and we could see one another. What I saw was the face of a stranger, a man I had never yet seen in the dining saloon or on the promenade deck; a face which (was it only because the lineaments were caricatured in that momentary illumination?) seemed extraordinarily sinister and suggestive of a hob-goblin. Before I had been able to note details accurately, the darkness closed in again, so that once more all that was visible was the fitful glow from the pipe, and above it the occasional glint of the glasses. Neither of us spoke. The silence was sultry and oppressive, like tropical heat.

At length I could bear it no longer. Standing up, I said a civil "Good night."

"Good night!" came the answer, in a harsh and raucous voice.

As I stumbled aft amid the encumbrances on the foredeck, I heard footsteps behind me, hasty and uncertain. My neighbour on the coil of rope was following me with unsteady gait. He did not come quite close, but through the darkness I could sense his anxiety and uneasiness.

He was speaking hurriedly.

"You'll forgive me if I ask you a favour. I . . . I," he hesitated, "I . . . I have private, extremely private reasons for keeping to myself on board. . . . In mourning. . . . That's why I have made no acquaintances during the voyage. You expected, of course. . . . What I want is . . . I mean I should be very greatly obliged if you would refrain from telling any one that you have seen me here. It is, let me repeat, strictly private grounds that prevent my joining in the life of the ship, and it would be most distressing to me were you to let fall a word about my frequenting this forecastle alone at night. I . . ."

He paused, and I was prompt in assuring him that his wishes should be respected. I was but a casual traveller, I said, and had no friends on board. We shook hands. I went back to my cabin to sleep out the night. But my slumbers were uneasy, for I had troublous dreams.

I kept my promise to say nothing to any one about my strange encounter, though the temptation to indiscretion was considerable. On a sea voyage the veriest trifle is an event—a sail on the horizon, a shoal of porpoises, a new flirtation, a practical joke. Besides, I was full of curiosity about this remarkable fellow-passenger. I scanned the list of bookings in search of a name which might fit him; and I looked at this person and that, wondering if they knew anything about him. All day I suffered from nervous impatience, waiting for nightfall when I hoped I might meet him again. Psychological enigmas have invariably fascinated me. An encounter with an inscrutable character makes me thrill with longing to pluck the heart out of the mystery, the urge of this desire being hardly less vehement than that of a man's desire to possess a woman. The day seemed insufferably long. I went to bed early, certain that an internal alarum would awaken me in the small hours.

Thus it was. I awoke at about the same time as on the previous night. Looking at my watch, whose figures and hands stood out luminous from the dial, I saw that the hour had just gone two. Quickly I made for the deck.

In the tropics the weather is less changeable than in our northern climes. The night was as before: dark, clear, and lit with brilliant stars. But in myself there was a difference. I no longer felt dreamy and easeful, was no longer agreeably lulled by the gentle swaying of the ship. An intangible something confused and disturbed me, drew me irresistibly to the foredeck. I wanted to know whether the mysterious stranger would again be sitting there, solitary, on the coil of rope. Reluctant and yet eager, I yielded to the impulse. As I neared the place, I caught sight of what looked like a red and glowing eye—his pipe. He was there!

Involuntarily I stopped short, and was about to retreat, when the dark figure rose, took two steps forward, and, coming close to me, said in an apologetic and lifeless voice:

"Sorry! I'm sure you were coming back to your old place, and it seems to me that you were about to turn away because you saw me. Won't you sit down? I'm just off."

I hastened to rejoin that I was only on the point of withdrawing because I was afraid of disturbing him, and that I hoped he would stay.

"You won't disturb me!" he said with some bitterness. "Far from it; I am glad not to be alone once in a while. For days upon days I have hardly spoken to a soul; years, it seems; and I find it almost more than I can bear to have to bottle everything up in myself. I can't sit in the cabin any longer, the place is like a prison-cell; and yet I can't stand the passengers either, for they chatter and laugh all day. Their perpetual frivolling drives me frantic. The silly noise they make finds its way into my cabin, so that I have to stop my ears. Of course, they don't know I can hear them, or how they exasperate me. Not that they'd care if they did, for they're only a pack of foreigners."

He suddenly pulled himself up, saying: "But I know I must be boring you. I didn't mean to be so loquacious."

He bowed, and moved to depart, but I pressed him to stay.

"You are not boring me in the least. Far from it, for I too am glad to have a quiet talk up here under the stars. Won't you have a cigarette?"

As he lighted it, I again got a glimpse of his face, the face which was now that of an acquaintance. In the momentary glare, before he threw away the match, he looked earnestly, searchingly at me, appealingly it almost seemed, as his spectacled eyes fixed themselves on mine.

I felt a thrill akin to horror. This man, so it seemed to me, had a tale to tell, was on fire to tell it, but some inward hindrance held him back. Only by silence, a silence that invited confidence, could I help him to throw off his restraint.

We sat down on the coil of rope, half facing one another, leaning against the top rail. His nervousness was betrayed by the shaking of the hand which held the cigarette. We smoked, and still I said never a word. At length he broke the silence.

"Are you tired?"

"Not an atom!"

"I should rather like to ask you something." He hesitated. "It would be more straightforward to say I want to tell you something. I know how ridiculous it is of me to begin babbling like this to the first comer; but, mentally speaking, I'm in a tight place. I've got to the point where I simply must tell some one, or else go clean off my head. You'll understand why, as soon as I've told you. Of course, you can do nothing to help me, but keeping my trouble to myself is making me very ill, and you know what fools sick folk are—or what fools they seem to healthy people."

I interrupted him, and begged him not to distress himself with fancies of that sort, but to go ahead with his story. "Naturally there would be no meaning in my giving you unlimited promises of help, when I don't know the situation. Still, I can at least assure you of my willingness to give you what help I may. That's one's plain duty, isn't it, to show that one's ready to pull a fellow-mortal out of a hole? One can try to help, at least."

"Duty to offer help? Duty to try, at least? Duty to show that one's ready to pull a fellow-mortal out of a hole?"

Thus did he repeat what I had said, staccato, in a tone of unwonted bitterness flavoured with mockery, whose significance was to become plain to me later. For the moment, there was something in his scanning iteration of my words which made me wonder whether he was mad, or drunk.

As if guessing my thoughts, he went on in a more ordinary voice: "You'll perhaps think me queer in the head, or that I've been imbibing too freely in my loneliness. That's not what's the matter, and I'm sane enough—so far! What set me off was one word you used, and the connexion in which you happened to use it, the word 'duty.' It touched me on the raw, and I'm raw all over, for the strange thing is that what torments me all the time is a question of duty, duty, duty."

He pulled himself up with a jerk. Without further circumlocution, he began to explain himself clearly.

"I'm a doctor, you must know. That's a vital point in my story. Now in medical practice one often has to deal with cases in which duty is not so plain as you might think. Fateful cases; you can call them borderline cases, if you like. In these cases there's not just one obvious duty; there are conflicting duties: one duty of the ordinary kind, which runs counter to a duty to the State, and perhaps on the other side runs counter to a duty to science. Help pull a fellow-mortal out of a hole? Of course one should. That's what one's there for. But such maxims are purely theoretical. In a practical instance, how far is help to go? Here you turn up, a nocturnal visitant, and,

though you've never seen me before, and I've no claim
on you, I ask you not to tell any one you've seen me. Well,
you hold your tongue, because you feel it your duty to
help me in the way I ask. Then you turn up again, and I
beg you to let me talk to you because silence is eating my
heart out. You are good enough to listen. After all, that's
easy enough. I haven't asked you anything very difficult.
But suppose I were to say: 'Catch hold of me and throw
me overboard!' You would quickly reach the limit of your
complaisance, wouldn't you? You would no longer regard
it as a 'duty to help,' I suppose! There must be a limit
somewhere. This duty of which you speak, surely it comes
to an end before the point is reached at which one's own
life is gravely imperilled, or one's own responsibility to
accepted public institutions is affected? Or perhaps this
duty to help has no limits at all, where a doctor is concerned? Should a doctor be a universal saviour, simply
because he has a diploma couched in Latin? Has he for
that reason to fling away his life when some one happens
along and implores him to be helpful and kindhearted?
There is a limit to one's duty, and one reaches it when
one is at the end of one's tether!"

He went off at a tangent once more.

"I'm sorry to show so much excitement. It's not because I'm drunk. I'm not drunk—yet. True, I'm drinking
heavily here on board; and I've got drunk now and again
of late, for my life has been so damnably lonely in the
East. Just think, for seven years I've been living almost
exclusively among natives and animals; and in such conditions one naturally forgets how to talk sanely and
calmly. When, at last, one gets a chance of talking to a
man of one's own people, one's tongue runs away with
one. Where was I? I was going to put a question to you,
was going to place a problem before you, to ask you
whether it was really incumbent on one to help, no matter in what circumstances, as an angel from heaven might
help. . . . But I'm afraid it will be rather a long business. You're really not tired?"

"Not the least bit in the world!"

He was groping behind him in the darkness. I heard something clink, and could make out the forms of a couple of bottles. He poured from one of them into a glass, and handed it to me—a large peg of neat whisky.

"Won't you have a drink?"

To keep him company, I sipped, while he, for lack of another glass, took a bountiful swig from the bottle. There was a moment's silence, during which came five strokes on the ship's bell. It was half-past two in the morning.

"Well, I want to put a case before you. Suppose there was a doctor practising in a little town—in the country, really. A doctor who . . ."

He broke off, hesitated a while, and then made a fresh start.

"No, that won't do. I must tell you the whole thing exactly as it happened, and as it happened to myself. A direct narrative from first to last. Otherwise you'll never be able to understand. There must be no false shame, no concealment. When people come to consult me, they have to strip to the buff, have to show me their excreta. If I am to help them, they must make no bones about informing me as to the most private matters. It will be of no use for me to tell you of something that happened to some one else, to a mythical Doctor Somebody, somewhere and somewhen. I shall strip naked, as if I were your patient. Anyway, I have forgotten all decency in that horrible place where I have been living, in that hideous solitude, in a land which eats the soul out of one's body and sucks the marrow out of one's bones."

I must have made some slight movement of protest, for he went off on a side issue.

"Ah, I can see you are an enthusiast for the East, an admirer of the temples and the palm trees, filled full with the romance of the regions where you have been travelling for your pleasure, to wile away a month or two. No doubt the tropics are charming to one who hurries or saunters through them by rail, in a motor car, or in a rickshaw. I felt the same when I first came out here seven years ago. I was full of dreams about what I was going to do : 'learn the native tongue; read the Sacred Books in the original; study tropical diseases; do original scientific work; master the psychology of the indigenes (thus do we phrase it in our European jargon); become a missionary of civilization. . . .

"But life out there is like living in a hot-house with invisible walls. It saps the energies. You get fever, though you swallow quinine by the teaspoonful; and fever takes all the guts out of you, you become limp and lazy, as soft as a jellyfish. A European is cut adrift from his moorings if he has to leave the big towns and is sent to one of those accursed settlements in a jungle or a swamp. Sooner or later he will lose his poise. Some take to drink; others learn opium-smoking from the Chinese; others find relief in brutality, sadism, or what not—they all go off the rails. How one longs for home! To walk along a street with proper buildings in it! To sit in a solidly constructed room with glass windows, and among white men and women. So it goes on year after year, until at length the time for home leave comes round—and a man finds he has grown too inert even to take his furlough. What would be the use? He knows he has been forgotten, and that, if he did go home, there would be no welcome awaiting him or (worse still) his coming might be utterly ignored. So he stays where he is, in a mangrove swamp, or in a steaming forest. It was a sad day for me when I sold myself into servitude on the equator.

"Besides, forgoing my home leave was not quite so voluntary an affair as I have implied. I had studied medicine in Germany, where I was born, and, soon after I was qualified, I got a good post at the Leipzig Clinic. If you were to look up the files of the medical papers of that date, you would find that a new method of treatment I advocated for one of the commoner diseases made some little stir, so that I had been a good deal talked about for so young a man.

"Then came a love affair which ruined my chances. It was with a woman whose acquaintance I made at the hos-

pital. She'd been living with a man she'd driven so crazy
that he tried to shoot himself and failed to make a clean
job of it. Soon I was as crazy as he. She had a sort of cold
pride about her which I found irresistible. Women that
are domineering and rather impudent can always do anything they like with me, but this woman reduced me to
pulp. I did whatever she wanted and in the end (it seems
hard to tell you, though the story's an old one now, dating
from eight years ago) for her sake I stole some money
from the hospital safe. The thing came out, of course, and
there was the devil to pay. An uncle of mine made the loss
good, but there was no more career for me in Leipzig.

"Just at this time I heard that the Dutch Government
was short of doctors in the colonial service, would take
Germans, and was actually offering a premium. That told
me there must be a catch in it somewhere, and I knew well
enough that in these tropical plantations tombstones grow
as luxuriantly as the vegetation. But when one is young
one is always ready to believe that fever and death will
strike some other fellow down and give one's self the go-
by.

"After all, I hadn't much choice. I made my way to
Rotterdam, signed on for ten years, and got a fine, thick
wad of banknotes. I sent half of them to my uncle. A girl
of the town got the rest—the half of the premium and any
other money I could raise—all because she was so like the
young woman to whom I owed my downfall. Without
money, without even a watch, without illusions, I steamed
away from Europe, and was by no means sad at heart
when the vessel cleared the port. I sat on deck much as
you are sitting now; ready to take delight in the East, in
the palm trees under new skies; dreaming of the wonderful forests, of solitude, and of peace.

"I soon had my fill of solitude. They did not station me
in Batavia or in Surabaya, in one of the big towns where
there are human beings with white skins, a club and a golf-
course, books and newspapers. They sent me to—well,
never mind the name! A god-forgotten place up country,
a day's journey from the nearest town. The 'society' con-

sisted of two or three dull-witted and sun-dried officials
and one or two half-castes. The settlement was encircled
by interminable forests, plantations, jungles, and swamps.

"Still, it was tolerable at first. There was the charm of
novelty. I studied hard for a time. Then the Vice-Resident was making a tour of inspection through the district,
and had a motor smash. Compound fracture of the leg,
no other doctor within hail, an operation needed, followed
by a good recovery—and a considerable amount of kudos
for me, since the patient was a big gun. I did some an-
thropological work, on the poisons and weapons used by
the primitives. Until the freshness had worn off, I found
a hundred and one things which helped to keep me alive.

"This lasted just as long as the vigour I had brought
with me from Europe. Then the climate got hold of me.
The other white man in the settlement bored me to death.
I shunned their company, began to drink rather heavily,
and to browse on my own weary thoughts. After all, I had
only to stick it for another two years. Then I could retire
on a pension, and start life afresh in Europe. Nothing to
do but wait till the time was up. And there I should still
be waiting, but for the unexpected happening I am going
to tell you about."

The voice in the darkness ceased. So still was the night
that once more I could hear the sound of the ship's stem
clearing the water, and the distant pulsing of the machinery. I should have been glad to light a cigarette, but I
was afraid I might startle the narrator by any sudden
movement and by the unexpected glare.

For a time the silence was unbroken. Had he changed
his mind, and decided it would be indiscreet to tell me any
more? Had he dropped off into a doze?

While I was thus meditating, six bells struck. It was
three in the morning. He stirred, and I heard a faint clink
as he picked up the whisky bottle. He was priming himself
again. Then he resumed, with a fresh access of tense passion.

"Well, so things went with me. Month after month, I

had been sitting inactive in that detestable spot, as motionless as a spider in the centre of its web. The rainy season was over. For weeks I had been listening to the downpour on the roof, and not a soul had come near me —no European, that is to say. I had been alone in the house with my native servants and my whisky. Being even more homesick than usual, when I read in a novel about lighted streets and white women, my fingers would begin to tremble. You are only what we call a globe-trotter; you don't know the country as those who live there know it. A white man is seized at times by what might be accounted one of the tropical diseases, a nostalgia so acute as to drive him almost into delirium. Well, in some such paroxysm I was poring over an atlas, dreaming of journeys possible and impossible. At this moment two of my servants came, open-mouthed with astonishment, to say that a lady had called to see me—a white lady.

"I, too, was amazed. I had heard no sound of carriage or of car. What the devil was a white woman doing in this wilderness?

"I was sitting in the upstairs veranda of my two-storied house, and not dressed for white company. In the minute or two that were needed for me to make myself presentable, I was able to pull myself together a little; but I was still nervous, uneasy, filled with disagreeable forebodings, when at length I went downstairs. Who on earth could it be? I was friendless. Why should a white woman come to visit me in the wilds?

"The lady was sitting in the ante-room, and behind her chair was standing a China boy, obviously her servant. As she jumped up to greet me, I saw that her face was hidden by a thick motor-veil. She began to speak before I could say a word.

" 'Good morning, Doctor,' she said in English. 'You'll excuse my dropping in like this without an appointment, won't you?' She spoke rather rapidly, almost as if repeating a speech which had been mentally rehearsed. 'When we were driving through the settlement, and had to stop the car for a moment, I remembered that you lived here.'

This was puzzling! If she had come in a car, why hadn't she driven up to the house? 'I've heard so much about you —what a wonder you worked when the Vice-Resident had that accident. I saw him the other day playing golf as well as ever. Your name is in every one's mouth down there, and we'd all gladly give away our grumpy old senior surgeon and his two assistants if we could but get you in exchange. Besides, why do you never come to headquarters? You live up here like a yogi!'

"She ran on and on, without giving me a chance to get in a word edgewise. Manifestly her loquacity was the outcome of nervousness, and it made me nervous in my turn. 'Why does she go on chattering like this?' I wondered. 'Why doesn't she tell me who she is? Why doesn't she take off her veil? Has she got fever? Is she a madwoman?' I grew more and more distrait, feeling like a fool as I stood there mumchance, while she overwhelmed me with her babble. At length the stream ran dry, so that I was able to invite her upstairs. She made a sign to the boy to stay where he was, and swept up the stairway in front of me.

" 'Pleasant quarters here,' she exclaimed, letting her gaze roam over my sitting-room. 'Ah, what lovely books. How I should like to read them all!' She strolled to the bookcase and began to con the titles. For the first time since she had said good-morning to me, she was silent for a space.

" 'May I offer you a cup of tea?' I inquired.

"She answered without turning round.

" 'No, thank you, Doctor. I've only a few minutes to spare. Hullo, there's Flaubert's *Education sentimentale*. What a book! So you read French, too. Wonderful people, you Germans—they teach you so many languages at school. It must be splendid to be able to speak them as you do. The Vice-Resident swears he would never allow any one but you to use a knife on him. That senior surgeon of ours, all he's fit for is bridge. But you—well, it came into my head today that I should like to consult you, and, as I was driving through the settlement, I thought to myself, "There's no time like the present!" But'—all this she said without looking at me, for she kept her face towards the books—'I expect you're frightfully busy. Perhaps I'd better call another day?'

" 'Are you going to show your cards at last?' I wondered. Of course I gave no sign of this, but assured her that I was at her service, now or later, as she preferred.

" 'Oh, well, since I'm here!' She turned half round towards me, but did not look up, continuing to flutter the pages of a book she had taken from the shelf. "It's nothing serious. The sort of troubles women often have. Giddiness, fainting-fits, nausea. This morning in the car, when we were rounding a curve, I suddenly lost my senses completely. The boy had to hold me up, or I should have slipped on to the floor. He got me some water, and then I felt better. I suppose the chauffeur must have been driving too fast. Don't you think so, Doctor?'

" 'I can't answer that offhand. Have you had many such fainting-fits?'

" 'No. Not until recently, that is. During the last few weeks, pretty often. And I've been feeling so sick in the mornings.'

"She was back at the bookcase, had taken down another volume, and was fluttering the pages as before. Why did she behave so strangely? Why didn't she lift her veil and look me in the face? Purposely I made no answer. It pleased me to let her wait. If she could behave queerly, so could I! At length she went on, in her nonchalant, detached way.

" 'You agree, don't you, Doctor? It can't be anything serious. Not one of those horrid tropical diseases, surely? Nothing dangerous.'

" 'I must see if you have any fever. Let me feel your pulse.'

"I moved towards her, but she evaded me.

" 'No, Doctor, I'm sure I have no fever. I've taken my temperature every day since . . . since I began to be troubled with this faintness. Never above normal. And my digestion's all right, too.'

"I hesitated for a little. The visitor's strange manner had aroused my suspicions. Obviously she wanted to get something out of me. She had not driven a couple of hundred miles into this remote corner in order to discuss Flaubert! I kept her waiting for a minute or two before saying: 'Excuse me, but may I ask you a few plain questions?'

" 'Of course, of course. One comes to a doctor for that,' she said lightly. But she had turned her back on me again, and was fiddling with the books.

" 'Have you had any children?'

" 'Yes, one, a boy.'

" 'Well, did you have the same sort of symptoms then, in the early months, when you were pregnant?'

" 'Yes.'

"The answer was decisive, blunt, and no longer in the tone of mere prattle which had characterized her previous utterances.

" 'Well, isn't it possible that that's what's the matter with you now?'

" 'Yes.'

"Again the response was sharp and decisive.

" 'You'd better come into my consulting-room. An examination will settle the question in a moment.'

"At length she turned to face me squarely, and I could almost feel her eyes piercing me through her veil.

" 'No need for that, Doctor. I haven't a shadow of doubt as to my condition.' "

A pause.
I heard the narrator take another dose of his favourite stimulant. Then he resumed:
"Think the matter over for yourself. I had been rotting away there in my loneliness, and then this woman turned up from nowhere, the first white woman I had seen for years—and I felt as if something evil, something dangerous, had come into my room. Her iron determination made my flesh creep. She had come, it seemed, for idle

chatter; and then without warning she voiced a demand
as if she were throwing a knife at me. For what she wanted
of me was plain enough. That was not the first time
women had come to me with such a request. But they had
come imploringly, had with tears besought me to help
them in their trouble. Here, however, was a woman of ex-
ceptional, of virile determination. From the outset I had
felt that she was stronger than I, that she could probably
mould me to her will. Yet if there were evil in the room, it
was in me likewise, in me the man. Bitterness had risen in
me, a revolt against her. I had sensed in her an enemy.

"For a time I maintained an obstinate silence. I felt
that she was eyeing me from behind her veil, that she was
challenging me; that she wanted to force me to speak.
But I was not ready to comply. When I did answer, I
spoke beside the point, as if unconsciously mimicking her
discursive and indifferent manner. I pretended that I had
not understood her; tried to compel her to be candid. I
was unwilling to meet her half way. I wanted her to implore me, as the others had done—wanted it for the very
reason that she had approached me so imperiously, and
precisely because I knew myself to be a weakling in face
of such arrogance as hers.

"Consequently, I talked all round the subject, saying
that her symptoms were of trifling importance, that such
fainting-fits were common form in early pregnancy, and
that, far from being ominous, they generally meant that
things would go well. I quoted cases I had seen and cases
I had read of; I treated the whole affair as a bagatelle; I
talked and talked, waiting for her to interrupt me. For I
knew she would have to cut me short.

"She did so with a wave of the hand, as if sweeping my
words of reassurance into the void.

" 'That's not what worries me, Doctor. I'm not so well
as I was the time before. My heart troubles me.'

" 'Heart trouble, you say?' I rejoined, feigning an
anxiety I did not feel. 'Well, I'd better go into that at
once.' I made a movement as if to reach for my stetho-
scope.

"Once more she was recalcitrant. She spoke commandingly, almost like a drill-sergeant.

"'You may take my word for it that I have heart trouble. I don't want to waste my time and yours with examinations that are quite unnecessary. Besides, I think you might show a little more confidence in what I tell you. I have trusted you to the full!'

"This was a declaration of war. She had thrown down the glove, and I did not hesitate to lift it.

"'Trust implies frankness, perfect frankness. Please speak to me straightforwardly. But, above all, take off your veil and sit down. Let the books alone and put your cards on the table. One doesn't keep a veil on when one comes to consult a medical man.'

"In her turn she accepted the challenge. Sitting down in front of me, she lifted her veil. The face thus disclosed was the sort of face I had dreaded; it was controlled and inscrutable; one of those exceptionally beautiful English faces which age cannot wither; but this lovely woman was still quite young, this woman with grey eyes that seemed so full of self-confident repose, and yet to hint at depths of passion. Her lips were firmly set, and would betray nothing she wished to keep to herself. For a full minute we gazed at one another; she imperiously and yet questioningly, with a look almost cruelly cold, so that in the end I had to lower my eyes.

"Her knuckles rattled against the table. She could not shake off her nervousness. Suddenly she said:

"'Doctor, do you or do you not know what I want of you?'

"'I can make a shrewd guess, I fancy! Let us speak plainly. You want to put an end to your present condition. You want me to free you from the fainting-fits, the nausea, and so on—by removing the cause. Is that it?'

"'Yes.'

"The word was as decisive as the fall of the knife in a guillotine.

"'Are you aware that such things are dangerous—to both the persons concerned?'

" 'Yes.'

" 'That the operation is illegal?'

" 'I know that there are circumstances in which it is not prohibited; nay, in which it is regarded as essential.'

" 'Yes, when there are good medical grounds for undertaking it.'

" 'Well, you can find such grounds. You are a doctor.'

"She looked at me without a quiver, as if issuing an order; and I, the weakling, trembled in my amazement at the elemental power of her resolve. Yet I still resisted. I would not let her see that she was too strong for me. 'Not so fast,' I thought. 'Make difficulties! Compel her to sue!'

" 'A doctor cannot always find sufficient reasons. Still, I don't mind having a consultation with one of my colleagues. . . .'

" 'I don't want one of your colleagues. It is you I have come to consult.'

" 'Why me, may I ask?'

"She regarded me coldly, and said:

" 'I don't mind telling you that! I came to you because you live in an out-of-the-way place, because you have never met me before, because of your known ability, and because' . . . she hesitated for the first time, 'because . . . you are not likely to stay in Java much longer—especially if you have a large sum of money in hand to go home with.'

"A shiver ran through me. This mercantile calculation made my flesh creep. No tears, no beseeching. She had taken my measure, had reckoned up my price, and had sought me out in full confidence that she could mould me to her will. In truth I was almost overpowered; but her attitude towards me filled me with gall, and I constrained myself to reply with a chilly, almost sarcastic inflexion:

" 'This large sum of money you speak of, you offer it me for . . . ?'

" 'For your help now, to be followed by your immediate departure from the Dutch Indies.'

" 'Surely you must know that that would cost me my pension?'

" 'The fee I propose would more than compensate you.'

" 'You are good enough to use plain terms, but I should like you to be even more explicit. What fee were you thinking of?'

" 'One hundred thousand gulden, in a draft on Amsterdam.'

"I trembled, both with anger and surprise. She had reckoned it all out, had calculated my price, and offered me this preposterous fee upon the condition that I should break my contract with the Dutch Government; she had bought me before seeing me; she had counted on my compliance. I felt like slapping her face, so angered was I by this contumelious treatment. But when I rose up in my wrath (she, too, was standing once more), the sight of that proud, cold mouth of hers which would not beg a favour, the flash of her arrogant eyes, aroused the brute in me, and of a sudden I burned with desire. Something in my expression must have betrayed my feeling, for she raised her eyebrows as one does when a beggar is importunate. In that instant we hated one another, and were aware of our mutual detestation. She hated me because she had to make use of me, and I hated her because she demanded my help instead of imploring it. In this moment of silence we were for the first time speaking frankly to one another. As if a venomous serpent had bitten me, a terrible thought entered my mind, and I said to her . . . I said to her . . .

"But I go too fast, and you will misunderstand me. I must first of all explain to you whence this crazy notion came."

He paused. More whisky. His voice was stronger when he resumed.

"I'm not trying to make excuses for myself. But I don't want you to misunderstand me. I suppose I've never been what is called a 'good' man, and yet I think I've always been ready to help people whenever I could. In the rotten sort of life I had to live out there, my one pleasure was to use the knowledge I had scraped together, and thus to give poor sick wretches new hopes of health. That's a creative pleasure, you know; makes a man feel as if, for once, he were a god. It was pure delight to me when a brown-skinned Javanese was brought in, foot swollen to the size of his head from snake-bite, shrieking with terror lest the only thing that would save him might be an amputation—and I was able to save both life and leg. I have driven hours into the jungle to help a native woman laid up with fever. At Leipzig, in the clinic, I was ready enough, sometimes, to help women in just the same plight as my lady here. But in those cases, at least, one felt that one's patient had come to one in bitter need, asking to be rescued from death or from despair. It was the feeling of another's need that made me ready to help.

"But this particular woman—how can I make you understand? She had irritated me from the first moment when she dropped in with the pretence that she was on a casual excursion. Her arrogance had set my back up. Her manner had aroused the slumbering demon, the Caliban that lies hidden in us all. I was furious that she should come to me with her fine-lady airs, with her assumption of dispassionateness in what was really a life-or-death matter. Besides, a woman does not get in the family way from playing golf, or some such trifle. I pictured to myself with exasperating plainness that this imperious creature, so cold, so aloof—for whom I was to be a mere instrument, and, apart from that, of no more significance to her than the dirt beneath her feet—must, only two or three months before, have been passionate enough when clasped in the arms of the father of this unborn child she now wished me to destroy. Such was the thought which obsessed me. She had approached me with supercilious contempt; but I would make her mine with all the virile masterfulness and impetus and ardour of that unknown man. This is what I want you to grasp. Never before had I tried to take advantage of my position as doctor. If I did so now, it was not from lust, not from an animal longing for sexual possession. I assure you it was not. I was moved by the craving to master her pride, to prove myself a dominant male, and thus to assert the supremacy of my ego over hers.

"I have already told you that arrogant, seemingly cold women have always exercised a peculiar power over me. Superadded to this, on the present occasion, was the fact that for seven years I had not had a white woman in my arms, had never encountered resistance in my wooing. Native girls are timorous little creatures who tremble with respectful ecstasy when a 'white lord,' a 'tuan,' deigns to take possession of them. They are overflowing with humility, always ready to give themselves for the asking— with a servility that robs voluptuousness of its tang. The Arab girls are different, I believe, and perhaps even the Chinese and the Malays; but I had been living among the Javanese. You can understand, then, how thrilled I was by this woman, so haughty and fierce and reserved; so brim-full of mystery, and gravid with the fruit of a recent passion. You can realize what it meant to me that such a woman should walk boldly into the cage of such a man as I—a veritable beast, lonely, starved, cut off from human fellowship. I tell you all this that you may understand what follows. Those were the thoughts that coursed through my brain, those were the impulses that stirred me, when, simulating indifference, I said coolly:

" 'One hundred thousand gulden? No, I won't do it for that.

"She looked at me, paling a little. No doubt she felt intuitively that the obstacle was not a matter of money. All she said, however, was:

" 'What fee do you ask, then?'

" 'Let's be frank with one another,' I rejoined. 'I am no trader. You must not look upon me as the poverty-stricken apothecary in *Romeo and Juliet* who vends poison for the "worse poison," gold. You will never get what you want from me if you regard me as a mere man of business.'

" 'You won't do it, then?'

" 'Not for money.'

"For a moment there was silence. The room was so still that I could hear her breathing.

" 'What else can you want?'

"I answered hotly:

" 'I want, first of all, that you should approach me, not as a trader, but as a man. That when you need help you should come to me, not with a parade of your gold "that's poison to men's souls," but with a prayer to me, the human being, that I should help you, the human being. I am not only a doctor. "Hours of Consultation" are not the only hours I have to dispose of. There are other hours as well—and you may have chanced upon me in one of those other hours.'

"A brief silence followed. Then she pursed up her lips, and said:

" 'So you would do it if I were to implore you?'

" 'I did not say so. You are still trying to bargain, and will only plead if you have my implied promise. Plead first, and then I will answer you.'

"She tossed her head defiantly, like a spirited horse.

" 'I will not plead for your help. I would rather die.'

"I saw red, and answered furiously.

" 'If you will not sue, I will demand. I think there is no need of words. You know already what I want. When you have given it, I will help you.'

"She stared at me for a moment. Then (how can I make you realize the horror of it?) the tension of her features relaxed and she burst out laughing. She laughed with a contempt which at once ground me to powder and intoxicated me to madness. It came like an explosion of incredible violence, this disdainful laughter; and its effect on me was such that I wanted to abase myself before her, longed to kiss her feet. The energy of her scorn blasted me like lightning—and in that instant she turned, and made for the door.

"Involuntarily I pursued her to mumble excuses, to pray forgiveness, so crushed was I in spirit. But she faced me before leaving, to say, to command:

" 'Do not dare to follow me, or try to find out who I
am. If you do, you will repent it.'

"In a flash, she was gone."

Further hesitation. Another silence. Then the voice
issued from the darkness once more.

"She vanished through the doorway, and I stood rooted
to the spot. I was, as it were, hypnotized by her prohibition. I heard her going downstairs; I heard the house-
door close; I heard everything. I longed to follow her.
Why? I don't know whether it was to call her back, to
strike her, to strangle her. Anyhow, I wanted to follow
her—and could not. It was as if her fierce answer had
paralysed me. I know this will sound absurd; such, however, was the fact. Minutes passed—five, ten, it may be—
before I could stir.

"But as soon as I made the first movement, the spell
was broken. I rushed down the stairs. There was only one
road by which she could have gone, first to the settlement,
and thence back to civilization. I hastened to the shed to
get my bicycle, only to find that I had forgotten the key.
Without waiting to fetch it I dragged the frail bamboo
door from its hinges and seized the wheel. Next moment I
was pedalling madly down the road in pursuit. I must
catch her up; I must overtake her before she could get to
her car; I must speak to her.

"The dusty track unrolled itself in front of me, and the
distance I had to ride before I caught sight of her showed
me how long I must have stood entranced after she left.
There she was at last, where the road curved round the
forest just before entering the settlement. She was walking quickly; behind her strode the China boy. She must
have become aware of my pursuit the instant I saw her,
for she stopped to speak to the boy and then went on
alone, while he stood waiting. Why did she go on alone?
Did she want to speak to me where no one could listen? I
put on a spurt, when suddenly the boy, as I was about to
pass him, leapt in front of me. I swerved to avoid him,
ran up the bank, and fell.

"I was on my feet again in an instant, cursing the boy, and I raised my fist to deal him a blow, but he evaded it. Not bothering about him any more, I picked up my bicycle and was about to remount when the rascal sprang forward and seized the handle-bar, saying in pidgin-English:

" 'Master stoppee here.'

"You haven't lived in the tropics. You can hardly realize the intolerable impudence of such an action on the part of a native, and a servant at that. A yellow beast of a China boy actually presumed to catch hold of my bicycle and to tell me, a white 'tuan,' to stay where I was! My natural answer was to give him one between the eyes. He staggered, but maintained his grip on the cycle. His slit-like, slanting eyes were full of slavish fear, but for all that he was stout of heart, and would not let go.

" 'Master stoppee here!' he repeated.

"It was lucky I had not brought my automatic pistol. Had I had it with me, I should infallibly have shot him then and there.

" 'Let go, you dog!' I shouted.

"He stared at me, panic-stricken, but would not obey. In a fury, and feeling sure that further delay would enable her to escape me, I gave him a knock-out blow on the chin, which crumpled him up in the road.

"Now the cycle was free; but, when I tried to mount, I found that the front wheel had been buckled in the fall and would not turn. After a vain attempt to straighten the wheel, I flung the machine in the dust beside the China boy (who, bleeding from my violence, was coming to his senses) and ran along the road into the settlement.

"Yes, I ran; and here again, you, who have not lived in the tropics, will find it hard to realize all that this implies. For a white man, a European, thus to forget his dignity, and to run before a lot of staring natives, is to make himself a laughing-stock. Well, I was past thinking of my dignity. I ran like a madman in front of the huts, where the inmates gaped to see the settlement doctor, the white lord, running like a rickshaw coolie.

"I was dripping with sweat when I reached the settlement.

" 'Where's the car?' I shouted breathless.

" 'Just gone, Tuan,' came the answer.

"They were staring at me in astonishment. I must have looked like a lunatic, wet and dirty, as I shouted out my question the moment I was within hail. Glancing down the road I saw, no longer the car, but the dust raised by its passing. She had made good her escape. Her device of leaving the boy to hinder me had been successful.

"Yet, after all, her flight availed her nothing. In the tropics the names and the doings of the scattered members of the ruling European caste are known to all. From this outlook, Java is but a big village where gossip is rife. While she had been visiting me, her chauffeur had spent an idle hour in the settlement headquarters. Within a few minutes I knew everything; knew her name, and that she lived in the provincial capital more than a hundred and fifty miles away. She was (as, indeed, I knew already) an Englishwoman. Her husband was a Dutch merchant, fabulously rich. He had been away five months, on a business journey in America, and was expected back in a few days. Then husband and wife were to pay a visit to England.

"Her husband had been five months away. It had been obvious to me that she could not be more than three months pregnant."

"Till now it has been easy enough for me to explain everything to you clearly, for up to this point my motives were plain to myself. As a doctor, a trained observer, I could readily diagnose my own condition. But from now on I was like a man in delirium. I had completely lost self-control. I knew how preposterous were my actions, and yet I went on doing them. Have you ever heard of 'running amuck'?"

"Yes, I think so. It's some sort of drunken frenzy among the Malays, isn't it?"

"More than drunkenness. More than frenzy. It's a condition which makes a man behave like a rabid dog, transforms him into a homicidal maniac. It's a strange and terrible mental disorder. I've seen cases of it and studied them carefully while in the East, without ever being able to clear up its true nature. It's partly an outcome of the climate, of the sultry, damp, oppressive atmosphere, which strains the nerves until at last they snap. Of course a Malay who runs amuck has generally been in trouble of some sort—jealousy, gambling losses, or what. The man will be sitting quietly, as if there were nothing wrong— just as I was sitting in my room before she came to see me.

"Suddenly he will spring to his feet, seize his kris, dash into the street, and run headlong, no matter where. He stabs any who happen to find themselves in his path, and the shedding of blood infuriates him more and more. He foams at the mouth, shouts as he runs, tears on and on, brandishing his blood-stained dagger. Every one knows that nothing but death will stop the madman; they scurry out of his way, shouting 'Amok, Amok,' to warn others. Thus he runs, killing, killing, killing, until he is shot down like the mad dog that he is.

"It is because I have seen Malays running amuck that I know so well what was my condition during those days, those days still so recent, those days about which I am going to tell you. Like such a Malay, I ran my furious course in pursuit of that Englishwoman, looking neither to the right nor to the left, obsessed with the one thought of seeing her again. I can scarcely remember all I did in the hurried moments before I actually set out on her trail. Within a minute or two of learning her name and where she lived, I had borrowed a bicycle and was racing back to my own quarters. I flung a spare suit or two into a valise, stuffed a bundle of notes into my pocket, and rode off to the nearest railway station. I did not report to the district officer; I made no arrangements about a substitute; I left the house just as it was, paying no heed to the servants who gathered round me asking for instructions. Within an hour from the time when that woman had first called to see me, I had broken with the past and was running amuck into the void.

"In truth I gained nothing by my haste, as I should have known had I been able to think. It was late afternoon when I got to the railway station, and in the Javanese mountains the trains do not run after dark for fear of wash-out. After a sleepless night in the dak-bungalow and a day's journey by rail, at six in the evening I reached the town where she lived, feeling sure that, by car, she would have got there long before me. Within ten minutes I was at her door. 'What could have been more senseless?' you will say. I know, I know; but one who is running amuck runs amuck; he does not look where he is going.

"I sent in my card. The servant (not the China boy—I suppose he had not turned up yet) came back to say that his mistress was not well enough to see any one.

"I stumbled into the street. For an hour or more I hung around the house, in the forlorn hope that perhaps she would relent and would send out for me. Then I took a room at a neighbouring hotel and had a couple of bottles of whisky sent upstairs. With these and a stiff dose of veronal I at length managed to drug myself into unconsciousness—a heavy sleep that was the only interlude in the race from life to death."

Eight bells struck. It was four in the morning. The sudden noise startled the narrator, and he broke off abruptly. In a little while, however, collecting himself, he went on with his story.

"It is hard to describe the hours that followed. I think I must have had fever. Anyhow I was in a state of irritability bordering on madness. I was running amuck. It was on Tuesday evening that I got to the coast town, and, as I learned next morning, her husband was expected on Saturday. There were three clear days during which I might help her out of her trouble. I knew there wasn't a moment to waste—and she wouldn't see me! My longing to help, and my longing (still greater, if possible) to excuse myself for my insane demand, intensified the disorder of my nerves. Every second was precious. The whole thing hung by a hair, and I had behaved so outrageously that she would not let me come near her. Imagine that you are running after some one to warn him again an assassin, and that he takes you for the would-be assassin, so that he flees from you towards destruction. All that she could see in me was the frenzied pursuer who had humiliated her with a base proposal and now wanted to renew it.

"That was the absurdity of the whole thing. My one wish was to help her, and she would not see me. I would have committed any crime to help her, but she did not know.

"Next morning when I called, the China boy was standing at the door. I suppose that he had got back by the same train as myself. He must have been on the look-out; for the instant I appeared he whisked out of sight—though not before I had seen the bruises on his face. Perhaps he had only hurried in to announce my coming. That is one of the things that madden me now, to think that she may have realized that, after all, I wanted to help, and may have been ready to receive me. But the sight of him reminded me of my shame, so that I turned back from the door without venturing to send in my name. I went away; went away in torment, when she, perhaps, in no less torment, was awaiting me.

"I did not know how to pass the weary hours in this unfamiliar town. At length it occurred to me to call on the Vice-Resident, the man whose leg I had set to rights up country after he had had a motor smash. He was at home, and was, of course, delighted to see me. Did I tell you that I can speak Dutch as fluently as any Dutchman? I was at school in Holland for a couple of years. That was one reason why I chose the Dutch colonial service when I had to clear out of Leipzig.

"There must have been something queer about my manner, though. My grateful patient, for all his civility, eyed me askance, as if he divined that I was running amuck! I told him I had come to ask for a transfer. I couldn't live in the wilds any longer. I wanted an instant remove to the provincial capital. He looked at me questioningly, and in a noncommittal way—much as a medical man looks at a patient.

" 'A nervous break-down, Doctor?' he inquired. 'I understand that only too well. We can arrange matters for you, but you'll have to wait for a little while; three or four weeks, let us say, while we're finding some one to relieve you at your present post.'

" 'Three or four weeks!' I exclaimed. 'I can't wait a single day!'

Again that questioning look.

" 'I'm afraid you'll have to put up with it, Doctor. We mustn't leave your station unattended. Still, I promise you I'll set matters in train this very day.'

"I stood there biting my lips and realizing for the first time how completely I had sold myself into slavery. It was in my mind to defy him and his regulations; but he was tactful, he was indebted to me, and he did not want an open breach. Forestalling my determination to reply angrily, he went on:

" 'You've been living like a hermit, you know, and that's enough to put any one's nerves on edge. We've all been wondering why you never asked for leave, why you never came to see us down here. Some cheerful company, now and then, would have done you all the good in the world. This evening, by the way, there's a reception at Government House. Won't you join us? The whole colony will be there, including a good many people who have often asked about you, and have wanted very much to make your acquaintance.'

"At this I pricked up my ears. 'Asked about me?' 'Wanted to make my acquaintance?' Was she one of them? The thought was like wine to me. I remembered my manners, thanked him for his invitation, and promised to come early.

"I did go early, too early! Spurred on by impatience, I was the first to appear in the great drawing-room at the Residency. There I had to sit cooling my heels and listening to the soft tread of the bare-footed native servants who went to and fro about their business and (so it seemed to my morbid imagination) were sniggering at me behind my back. For a quarter of an hour I was the only guest amid a silence which, when the servants had finished their preparations, became so profound that I could hear the ticking of my watch in my pocket.

"Then the other guests began to arrive, some government officials with their wives, and the Vice-Resident put in an appearance. He welcomed me most graciously, and entered into a long conversation, in which (I think) I was able to keep my end up all right—until, of a sudden, my nervousness returned, and I began to falter.

"She had entered the room, and it was a good thing that at this moment the Vice-Resident wound up his talk with me and began a conversation with some one else, for otherwise I believe I should simply have turned my back on the man. She was dressed in yellow silk, which set off her ivory shoulders admirably, and was talking brightly amid a group. Yet I, who knew her secret trouble, could read (or fancied I could read) care beneath her smile. I moved nearer, but she did not or would not see me. That smile of hers maddened me once more, for I knew it to be feigned. 'Today is Wednesday,' I thought. 'On Saturday her husband will be back. How can she smile so unconcernedly? How can she toy with her fan, instead of breaking it with a convulsive clutch?'

"I, a stranger, was trembling in face of what awaited her. I, a stranger, had for two days been suffering with her suffering. What could her smile be but a mask to hide the storm that raged within?

"From the next room came the sound of music. Dancing was to begin. A middle-aged officer claimed her as his partner. Excusing herself to those with whom she had been conversing, she took his arm and walked with him towards the ballroom. This brought her close to me, and she could not fail to see me. For a moment she was startled, and then (before I could make up my mind whether or not to claim acquaintance) she nodded in a friendly way, said 'Good evening, Doctor,' and passed on.

"No one could have guessed what lay hidden behind

that casual glance. Indeed, I myself was puzzled. Why
had she openly recognized me? Was she making an advance, an offer of reconciliation? Was she still on the de-
fensive? Had she merely been taken by surprise? How
could I tell? All I knew was that I had been stirred to the
depths.

"I watched her as she waltzed, a smile of enjoyment
playing about her lips, and I knew that all the while she
must be thinking, not of the dance, but of the one thing
of which I was thinking, of the dread secret which she and
I alone shared. The thought intensified (if possible) my
anxiety, my longing, and my bewilderment. I don't know
if any one else was observing me, but I am sure that my
eager scrutiny of her must have been in manifest contrast
to her ostensible unconcern. I simply could not look at
any one but her, for I was watching all the time to see
whether she would not, were it but for a moment, let the
mask fall. The fixity of my stare must have been disagreeable to her. As she came back on her partner's arm, she
flashed a look at me, dictatorial, angry, as if bidding me
to exercise a little more self-control.

"But I, as I have explained to you, was running amuck.
I knew well enough what her glance meant! 'Don't attract
attention to me like this. Keep yourself in hand.' She was
asking me to show some discretion in this place of public
assembly. I felt assured, now, that if I went quietly home
she would receive me should I call on the morrow; that all
she wanted of me was that I should behave decorously;
that she was (with good reason) afraid of my making a
scene. Yes, I understood what she wanted; but I was running amuck, and I had to speak to her there and then. I
moved over to the group amid which she was talking.
They were all strangers to me; yet I rudely shouldered
my way in among them. There I stood my ground listening to her, though I trembled like a whipped cur whenever her eyes rested coldly on mine. I was obviously unwelcome. No one said a word to me, and it must have been
plain that she resented my intrusion.

"I cannot tell how long I should have gone on standing

there. To all eternity, perhaps. I was spellbound. To her, however, the strain became unbearable. Suddenly she broke off, and, with a charming and convincing assumption of indifference, said: 'Well, I'm rather tired, so I shall turn in early. I'll ask you to excuse me. Good night!'

"She gave a friendly nod which included me with the others, and turned away. I watched her smooth, white, well-shaped back above her yellow silk gown, and at first (so dazed was I) I scarcely realized that I was to see her no more that evening, that I was to have no word with her on that last evening to which I had looked forward as the evening of salvation. I stood stock-still until I grasped this. Then . . . then . . .

"I must put the whole picture before you, if I am to make you understand what an idiot I made of myself. The big drawing-room at the Residency was now almost empty, though blazing with light. Most of the guests were dancing in the ballroom, while the older men who had lost taste for pairing off in this way had settled down to cards elsewhere. There were but a few scattered groups talking here and there. Across this huge hall she walked, with that dignity and grace which enthralled me, nodding farewell to one and to another as she passed. By the time I had fully taken in the situation, she was at the other end of the room and about to leave it. At that instant, becoming aware that she would escape me, I started to run after her, yes, to run, my pumps clattering as I sped across the polished floor. Of course every one stared at me, and I was overwhelmed with shame—yet I could not stop. I caught her up as she reached the door, and she turned on me, her eyes blazing, her nostrils quivering with scorn.

"But she had the self-command which in me was so lamentably lacking, and in an instant she had mastered her anger and burst out laughing. With ready wit, speaking loudly so that all could hear, she said:

" 'Ah, Doctor, so you've just remembered that prescription for my little boy, after all! You men of science are apt to be forgetful now and again, aren't you?'

"Two men standing near by grinned good-humouredly. I understood, admired the skill with which she was glossing over my clownishness, and had the sense to take her hint. Pulling out my pocketbook, in which there were some prescription blanks, I tore one off and handed it to her with a muttered apology. Taking the paper from me with a smile and a 'Good night!' she departed.

"She had saved the situation; but I felt that, as far as my position with her was concerned, the case was hopeless, that she loathed me for my insensate folly, hated me more than death; that again and again and again (however often I might come) she would drive me from her door like a dog.

"I stumbled across the room, people staring at me. No doubt there was something strange about my appearance. Making my way to the buffet, I drank four glasses of brandy in brief succession. My nerves were worn to rags, and nothing but this overdose of stimulant would have kept me going. I slipped away by a side door, furtively, as if I had been a burglar. Not for a kingdom would I have crossed the great hall again, have exposed myself to mocking eyes. What did I do next? I can hardly remember. Wandering from one saloon to another, I tried to drink myself into oblivion; but nothing could dull my senses. Still I heard the laugh which had first driven me crazy, and the feigned laughter with which she had covered up my boorishness that evening. Walking on the quays, I looked down into the water, and regretted bitterly that I had not brought my pistol with me, so that I could blow out my brains and drop into the quiet pool. My mind became fixed on this automatic, and I resolved to make an end of myself. I wearily went back to the hotel.

"If I refrained from shooting myself in the small hours, it was not, believe me, from cowardice. Nothing I should have liked better than to press the trigger, in the conviction that thus I could put an end to the torment of my thoughts. After all, I was obsessed by the idea of duty, that accursed notion of duty. It maddened me to think that she might still have need of me, to know that she really did need me. Here was Thursday morning. In two days her husband would be back. I was sure this proud woman would never live to face the shame that must ensue upon discovery. I tramped up and down my room for hours, turning these thoughts over in my mind, cursing the impatience, the blunders, that had made it impossible for me to help her. How was I to approach her now? How was I to convince her that all I asked was to be allowed to serve her? She would not see me, she would not see me. In fancy I heard her fierce laughter, and watched her nostrils twitching with contempt. Up and down, up and down the ten feet of my narrow room, till the tropic day had dawned, and, speedily, the morning sun was glaring into the veranda. As you know, in the tropics every one is up and about by six.

"Flinging myself into a chair, I seized some letter-paper and began to write to her, anything, everything, a cringing letter, in which I implored her forgiveness, proclaimed myself a madman and a villain, besought her to trust me, to put herself in my hands after all. I swore that I would disappear thereafter, from the town, the colony, the world, if she wanted me to. Let her only forgive me and trust me, allow me to help her in this supreme moment.

"I covered twenty pages. It must have been a fantastic letter, like one penned in a lunatic asylum, or by a man in the delirium of fever. When I had finished, I was dripping with sweat, and the room whirled round me as I rose to my feet. Gulping down a glass of water, I tried to read through what I had written, but the words swam before my eyes. I reached for an envelope, and then it occurred to me to add something that might move her. Snatching up the pen once more, I scrawled across the back of the last page: 'Shall await a word of forgiveness here at the hotel. If I don't hear from you before nightfall, I shall shoot myself.'

"Closing the letter, I shouted for one of the boys and

told him to have the chit delivered instantly. There was nothing more for me to do but to await an answer."

As if to mark this interval, it was some minutes before he spoke again. When he did so, the words came with a renewed impetus.

"Christianity has lost its meaning for me. The old myths of heaven and hell no longer influence me. But if there were a hell, I should dread it little, for there could be no hell worse than those hours I spent in the hotel. A little room, baking in the noonday heat. You know these hotel rooms in the tropics—only a bed and a table and a chair. Nothing on the table but a watch and an automatic. Sitting on the chair in front of the table a man staring at the watch and the pistol—a man who ate nothing, drank nothing, did not even smoke, but sat without stirring as he looked at the dial of his watch and saw the second hand making its unending circuit. That was how I spent the day, waiting, waiting, waiting. And yet, for all that I was motionless, I was still like the Malay running amuck, or like a rabid dog, pursuing my frenzied course to destruction.

"Well, I won't make any further attempt to describe those hours. Enough to say that I don't understand how any one can live through such a time and keep reasonably sane.

"At twenty-two minutes past three (my eyes were still glued to the watch) there came a knock at the door. A native youngster with a folded scrap of paper—no envelope. I snatched it from him, and he was gone before I had time to tear open the note. Then, to begin with, I could not read the brief message. Here was her reply at last, and the words ran together before my eyes! They conveyed no meaning to me. I had to dip my head in cold water and calm my agitation before my senses cleared and I could grasp the meaning of the pencilled English.

" 'Too late! Still, you'd better stay at the hotel. Perhaps I shall have to send for you in the end.'

"There was no signature on the crumpled page, a blank

half-sheet torn from a prospectus or something of the kind. The writing was unsteady, perhaps from agitation, perhaps because it had been written in a moving carriage. How could I tell? All I knew was that anxiety, haste, horror, seemed to cling to it; that it gripped me profoundly; and yet that I was glad, for at least she had written to me. I was to keep alive, for she might let me help her after all. I lost myself in the maddest conjectures and hopes. I read the curt words again and again; I kissed them repeatedly; I grew calmer, and passed into a state betwixt sleep and waking when time no longer had any meaning—coma-vigil is what we doctors call it.

"This must have lasted for hours. Dusk was at hand when I came to myself with a start, so it was certainly near six o'clock. Had there been another knock? I listened intently. Then it was unmistakable—a knocking, gentle yet insistent. Unsteadily (for I felt giddy and faint) I sprang to the door. There in the passage stood the China boy. It was still light enough to show me, not only the traces of my rough handling, not only black eyes and a bruised chin, but that his yellow face was ashen pale.

" 'Master come quickly.' That was all.

"I ran downstairs, the boy at my heels. A gharry was waiting, and we jumped in.

" 'What has happened?' I asked, as the man drove off, without further orders.

"The boy looked at me, his lips twitched, but he said never a word. I repeated my questions; still he was silent. I felt angry enough to strike him once more; yet I was touched by his devotion to his mistress, and so I kept myself in hand. If he wouldn't speak, he wouldn't; that was all.

"The gharryman was flogging his ponies, driving so furiously that people had to jump out of the way to avoid being run over. The streets were thronged, for we had left the European settlement, and were on our way through the Javanese and Malay town into the Chinese quarter. Here the gharry drew up in a narrow alley, in front of a tumbledown house. It was a sordid place, a little shop in front, lighted by a tallow candle; the attached dwelling was an unsavoury hotel—one of those opium-dens, brothels, thieves' kitchens, or receivers' stores, such as are run by the worser sort of Chinese in all the big cities of the East.

"The boy knocked at the door. It opened for an inch or two, and a tedious parley ensued. Impatiently I, too, jumped out of the gharry, put my shoulder to the door, forced it open—an elderly Chinese woman fled before me with a shriek. I dashed along a passage, the boy after me, to another door. Opening this, I found myself in a dim interior, reeking of brandy and of blood. Some one was groaning. I could make out nothing in the gloom, but I groped my way towards the sound."

Another pause. When he spoke again, it was with sobs almost as much as with words.

"I groped my way towards the sound—and there she was, lying on a strip of dirty matting, twisted with pain, sighing and groaning. I could not see her face, so dark was the room. Stretching out my hand, I found hers, which was burning hot. She was in a high fever. I shuddered as I realized what had happened. She had come to this foul den in quest of the service I had refused, had sought out a Chinese midwife, hoping in this way to find the secrecy she no longer trusted me to observe. Rather than place herself in my care, she had come to the old witch I had seen in the passage, had had herself mauled by a bungler—because I had behaved like a madman, had so grievously affronted her that she thought it better to take any risks rather than to let me give the aid which, to begin with, I had only been willing to grant on monstrous terms.

"I shouted for light, and that detestable beldame brought a stinking and smoky kerosene lamp. I should have liked to strangle her—but what good would that have done? She put the lamp down on the table; and now, in its yellow glare, I could see the poor, martyred body.

"Then, of a sudden, the fumes were lifted from my brain. No longer half crazed, I forgot my anger, and even for the time forgot the evil mood that had brought us to this pass. Once more I was the doctor, the man of skill and knowledge, to whom there had come an urgent call to use them for the best advantage of a suffering fellow-mortal. I forgot my wretched self; and, with reawakened intelligence, I was ready to do battle with the forces of destruction.

"I passed my hands over the nude body which so recently I had lusted for. Now it had become the body of my patient, and was nothing more. I saw in it only the seat of a life at grips with death, only the form of one writhing in torment. Her blood on my hands was not horrible to me, now that I was again the expert upon whose coolness everything turned. I saw, as an expert, the greatness of her danger. . . .

"I saw, indeed, that all was lost, short of a miracle. She had been so mishandled that her life-blood was rapidly draining away. And what was there, in this filthy hovel, which I could make use of in the hope of stanching the flow? Everything I looked at, everything I touched, was besoiled. Not even a clean basin and clean water!

" 'We must have you removed to hospital instantly,' I said. Thereupon, torture of mind superadded to torture of body, she writhed protestingly.

" 'No,' she whispered, 'no, no. I would rather die. No one must know. No one must know. Take me home, home!'

"I understood. Her reputation was more to her than her life. I understood, and I obeyed. The boy fetched a litter. We lifted her on to it, and then carried her, half dead, home through the night. Ignoring the terrified questions of the servants, we took her to her room. Then began the struggle; the prolonged and futile struggle with death."

He clutched my arm, so that it was hard not to shout from surprise and pain. His face was so close that I could see the white gleam of teeth and the pale sheen of spectacle-glasses in the starlight. He spoke with such intensity, with such fierce wrath, that his voice assailed me like something betwixt a hiss and a shriek.

"You, a stranger I have never glimpsed in the daylight, you who are (I suppose) touring the world at your ease, do you know what it is to see some one die? Have you ever sat by any one in the death agony, seen the body twisting in the last wrestle and the blue fingernails clawing at vacancy; heard the rattle in the throat; watched the inexpressible horror in the eyes of the dying? Have you ever had that terrible experience—you, an idler, a globe-trotter, who can talk so glibly about one's duty to help?

"I have seen it often enough as a doctor, have studied death as a clinical happening. Once only have I experienced it in the full sense of the term. Once only have I lived with another and died with another. Once only, during that ghastly vigil a few nights ago when I sat cudgelling my brains for some way of stopping the flow of blood, some means of cooling the fever which was consuming her before my eyes, some method of staving off imminent death.

"Do you understand what it is to be a doctor, thoroughly trained in the science and practice of medicine, and (as you sagely remark) one whose first duty is to help—and to sit powerless by the bedside of the dying; knowing, for all one's knowledge, only one thing—that one can give no help? To feel the pulse as it flickers and fades? My hands were tied! I could not take her to the hospital, where something might have been done to give her a chance. I could not summon aid. I could only sit and watch her die, mumbling meaningless invocations like an old applewoman at church, and next minute clenching my fists in impotent wrath against a non-existent deity.

"Can you understand? Can you understand? What I cannot understand is how one survives such hours, why one does not die with the dying, how one can get up next morning and clean one's teeth and put on one's necktie;

how one can go on living in the ordinary way after feeling what I had felt, for the first time, that one I would give anything and everything to save was slipping away; somewhither, beyond recall.

"There was an additional torment. As I sat beside the bed (I had given her an injection of morphine to ease the pain, and she lay quiet now, with cheeks ashen pale), I felt the unceasing tension of a fixed gaze boring into my back. The China boy was sitting cross-legged on the floor, murmuring prayers in his own tongue. Whenever I glanced at him, he raised his eyes imploringly to mine, like a hound dumbly beseeching aid. He lifted his hands as if in supplication to a god—lifted them to me, the impotent weakling who knew that all was vain, that I was of no more use in that room than an insect running across the floor.

"It added to my torture, this petitioning of his, this fanatical conviction that my skill would enable me to save the woman whose life was ebbing as he looked on and prayed. I could have screamed at him and have trampled him under foot, so much did his eager expectancy hurt me; and yet I felt that he and I were bound together by our fondness for the dying woman and by the dread secret we shared.

"Like an animal at watch, he sat huddled up behind me; but the instant I wanted anything he was alert, eager to fetch it, hoping I had thought of something that might help even now. He would have given his own blood to save her life. I am sure of it. So would I. But what was the use of thinking of transfusion (even if I had had the instruments) when there was no means of arresting the flow of blood? It would only have prolonged her agony. But this China boy would have died for her, as would I. Such was the power she had. And I had not even the power to save her from bleeding to death!

"Towards daybreak she regained consciousness, awoke from the drugged sleep. She opened her eyes, which were no longer proud and cold. The heat of fever glowed in them as she looked round the room. Catching sight of me, she was puzzled for a moment, and needed an effort to recall who this stranger was. Then she remembered. She regarded me at first with enmity, waving her arms feebly as if to repel me, and showing by her movements that she would have fled from me had she but had the strength. Then, collecting her thoughts, she looked at me more calmly. Her breathing was laboured; she tried to speak; she wanted to sit up, but was too weak. Begging her to desist, I leaned closer to her, so that I should be able to hear her lightest whisper. She regarded me piteously, her lips moved, and faint indeed was the whisper that came from them:

" 'No one will find out? No one?'

" 'No one,' I responded, with heartfelt conviction. 'No one shall ever know.'

"Her eyes were still uneasy. With a great effort she managed to breathe the words:

" 'Swear that no one shall know. Swear it.'

"I raised my hand solemnly and murmured: 'I pledge you my word.'

"She looked at me, weak though she was, cordially, gratefully. Yes, despite all the harm I had done, she was grateful to me at the last, she smiled her thanks. A little later she tried to speak again, but was not equal to the exertion. Then she lay peacefully, with her eyes closed. Before daylight shone clearly into the room, all was over."

A long silence. He had overcome the frenzy which had prompted him to seize me by the arm, and had sunk back exhausted. The stars were paling when three bells struck. A fresh though gentle breeze was blowing as herald of the dawn that comes so quickly in the tropics. Soon I could see him plainly. He had taken off his cap, so that his face was exposed. It was pinched with misery. He scanned me through his spectacles with some interest, to see what sort of a man was this stranger to whom he had been pouring out his heart. Then he went on with his story, speaking with a scornful intonation.

"For her, all was over; but not for me. I was alone with

the corpse, in a strange house; in a town where (as in all such places) gossip runs like wildfire, and I had pledged my word that her secret should be kept! Consider the situation. Here was a woman moving in the best society of the colony, and, to all seeming, in perfect health. She had danced the evening before last at Government House. Now she was dead, and the only doctor who knew anything about the matter, the man who had sat by her while she died, was a chance visitor to the town, summoned to her bedside by one of the servants. This doctor and his servant had brought her home in a litter under cover of darkness and had kept every one else out of the way. Not until morning did they call the other servants, to tell them their mistress was dead. The news would be all over the town within an hour or two, and how was I, the doctor from an up-country station, to account for the sudden death, for what I had done and for what I had failed to do? Why hadn't I sent for one of my colleagues to share the responsibility? Why? . . . Why? . . . Why?

"I knew what lay before me. My only helper was the China boy; but he, at any rate, was a devoted assistant, who realized that there was still a fight to be fought.

"I had said to him: 'You understand, don't you? Your mistress's last wish was that no one shall know what has happened.'

" 'Savvee plenty, Master,' he answered simply; and I knew that I could trust him.

"He washed the blood stains from the floor, set all to rights as quickly as possible, and his fortitude sustained mine.

"Never before have I had so much concentrated energy, nor shall I ever have it again. When one has lost everything but a last remnant, one fights for that last remnant with desperate courage, with fierce resolution. The remnant for which I was fighting was her legacy to me, her secret. I was calm and self-assured in my reception of every one who came, telling them the tale I had decided upon to account for the death. After all, people are used to sudden, grave, and fatal illness in the tropics; and the laity cannot openly question a doctor's authoritative statements. I explained that the China boy, whom she had sent to fetch the doctor when she was taken ill, had chanced to meet me. But while talking thus to all and sundry with apparent composure, I was awaiting the one man who really mattered, the senior surgeon, who would have to inspect the body before burial could take place. It was Thursday morning, and on Saturday the husband was coming back. Speedy burial is the rule in this part of the world; but the senior surgeon, not I, would have to sign the necessary certificates.

"At nine he was announced. I had sent for him, of course. He was my superior in rank, and he bore me a grudge because of the local reputation I had acquired in the little matter of the Vice-Resident's broken leg. This was the doctor of whom she had spoken so contemptuously, as good only for bridge. According to official routine my wish for a transfer would pass through his hands. No doubt the Vice-Resident had already mentioned it to him.

"The instant we met that morning, I guessed his enmity, but this only steeled me to my task.

"As soon as I came into the ante-room where he was waiting, he began the attack:

" 'When did Madame Blank die?'

" 'At six this morning.'

" 'When did she send for you?'

" 'At nightfall yesterday.'

" 'Did you know that I was her regular professional attendant?'

" 'Yes.'

" 'Why didn't you send for me, then?'

" 'There wasn't time—and, besides, Madame Blank had put herself in my hands exclusively. In fact, she expressly forbade me to call in any other doctor.'

"He stared at me. His face flushed. Suppressing an angry retort, he said with assumed indifference:

" 'Well even though you could get on without me so

long as she was alive, you have fulfilled your official duty
in sending for me now, and I must fulfil mine by verify-
ing the death and ascertaining the cause.'

"I made no answer, and let him lead the way to the
death-chamber. As soon as we were there, and before he
could touch the body, I said:

"'It is not a question of ascertaining the cause of
death, but of inventing a cause. Madame Blank sent for
me to save her, if I could, from the consequences of an
abortion, clumsily performed by a Chinese midwife. To
save her life was impossible, but I pledged my word to
save her reputation. I want you to help me.'

"He looked his surprise.

"'You actually want me, the senior surgeon of this
province, to join you in concealing a crime?'

"'Yes, that is what I want you to do.'

"'In fact,' he said with a sneer, 'I am to help in the
hushing-up of a crime you have committed.'

"'I have given you to understand that, as far as Madame Blank is concerned, all I have done is to try to save
her from the consequences of her own indiscretion and
some one else's crime (if you want to insist on the word).
Had I been the culprit, I should not be alive at this hour.
She has herself paid the extreme penalty, and the miserable bungler who procured the abortion really does not
matter one way or the other. You cannot punish the
criminal without tarnishing the dead woman's reputation,
and that I will not suffer.'

"'You will not suffer it? You talk to me as if you were
my official chief, instead of my being yours. You dare to
order me about. I had already surmised there must be
something queer when you were summoned from your
nook in the backwoods. A fine beginning you've made of
it with your attempt to interlope here. Well, all that remains for me is to make my own investigation, and I can
assure you that I shall report exactly what I find. I'm not
going to put my name to a false certificate; you needn't
think so!'

"I was imperturbable.

" 'You'll have to, this once. If you don't, you'll never leave the room alive.'

"I put my hand in my pocket. The pistol was not there (I had left it in my room at the hotel), but the bluff worked. He drew back in alarm; whereupon I made a step forward and said, with a calculated mingling of threat and conciliation:

" 'Look here! I shall be sorry to go to extremes, but you'd better understand that I don't value either my life or yours at a single stiver. I'm so far through that there's only one thing in the world left for me to care about, and that's the keeping of my promise to this dead woman that the manner of her death shall remain secret. I give you my word that if you sign a certificate to the effect that she died of—what shall we say?—a sudden access of malignant tropical fever hyperpyrexia, leading to heart failure—that will sound plausible enough—if you do this, I will leave the Indies within a week. I will, if you like, put a bullet through my head as soon as she is buried and I can be sure that no one (you understand, no one) can make any further examination. That should satisfy you. In fact, it must satisfy you.'

"My voice, my whole aspect, must have been menacing, for he was cowed. Whenever I advanced a little, he retreated, showing that uncontrollable fear with which people flee from a man brandishing a blood-stained kris, a man who is running amuck. He wilted visibly, and changed his tone. He was no longer the adamantine official, standing invincibly upon punctilio.

"Still, with a last vestige of resistance, he murmured:

" 'Never in my life have I signed a false certificate. Perhaps there would be no question raised if I were to word the document as you suggest. It is perfectly clear to me, however, that I ought not to do anything of the kind.'

" 'Of course you "ought not," judging by conventional standards,' I rejoined, wishing to help him to save his face. 'But this is a special case. When you know that the disclosure of the truth can only bring grievous suffering to a living man and blast the reputation of a dead woman, why hesitate?'

"He nodded. We sat down together at the table. Amicable enough now to all seeming, we concocted the certificate which was the basis of the account of the matter published in next day's newspaper. Then he stood up and looked at me searchingly:

" 'You'll sail for Europe by the next boat, won't you?'

" 'Of course! I've pledged you my word.'

"He continued to stare at me. I saw that he wanted to be strict and businesslike, and that the task was hard. It was as much in the endeavour to hide his embarrassment as from any wish to convey information that he said:

" 'Blank was going home with his wife immediately after his arrival from Yokohama. I expect the poor fellow will want to take his wife's body back to her people in England. He's a wealthy man, you know, and the rich can indulge these fancies. I shall order the coffin instantly, and have it lined with sheet lead so that it can be sealed. That will get over immediate difficulties, and he will know that in this sweltering heat there was no possibility of awaiting his appearance on the scene. Even if he thinks we've been precipitate, he won't venture to say so. We're officials, and he's only a merchant after all, though he could buy us both up and never miss the money. Besides, we're acting as we do to save him needless pain.'

"My enemy of a few minutes back was now my acknowledged confederate. Well, he knew he was soon going to be rid of me for ever; and he had to justify himself to himself. But what he did next was utterly unexpected. He shook me warmly by the hand!

" 'I hope you'll soon be all right again,' he said.

"What on earth did he mean? Was I ill? Was I mad? I opened the door for him ceremoniously, and bade him farewell. Therewith my energies ran down. The room swam round me, and I collapsed beside her bed, as the frenzied Malay collapses when he has run his murderous course and is at last shot down.

"I don't know how long I lay on the floor. At length

there was a rustling noise, a movement in the room. I looked up. There stood the China boy, regarding me uneasily.

" 'Some one have come. Wanchee see Mississee,' " he said.

" 'You mustn't let any one in.'

" 'But, Master . . .'

"He hesitated, looked at me timidly, and tried in vain to speak. The poor wretch was obviously suffering.

" 'Who is it?'

"He trembled like a dog in fear of a blow. He did not utter any name. A sense of delicacy rare in a native servant restrained him. He said simply:

" 'B'long that man!'

"He did not need to be explicit. I knew instantly whom he meant. At the word I was all eagerness to see this unknown, whose very existence I had forgotten. For, strange as it may seem to you, after the first disclosure she had made to me and her rejection of my infamous proposal, I had completely put him out of my mind. Amid the hurry and anxiety and stress of what had happened since, it had actually slipped my memory that there was another man concerned in the affair, the man this woman had loved, the man to whom she had passionately given what she had refused to give me. The day before, I should have hated him, should have longed to tear him to pieces. Now I was eager to see him because I loved him—yes, loved the man whom she had loved.

"With a bound I was in the ante-room. A young, very young, fair-haired officer was standing there, awkward and shy. He was pale and slender, looking little more than a boy, and yet touchingly anxious to appear manlike, calm, and composed. His hand was trembling as he raised it in salute. I could have put my arms round him and hugged him, so perfectly did he fulfil my ideal of the man I should have wished to be this woman's lover—not a self-confident seducer, but a tender stripling to whom she had thought fit to give herself.

"He stood before me, abashed. My sudden apparition,

my eager scrutiny, increased his embarrassment. His face puckered slightly, and it was plain that he was on the verge of tears.

" 'I don't want to push in,' he said at length, 'but I should like so much to see Madame Blank once more.'

"Scarcely aware of what I was doing, I put an arm round the young fellow's shoulders and guided him towards the door. He looked at me with astonishment, but with gratitude as well. At this instant we had an indubitable sense of fellowship. We went together to the bedside. She lay there; all but the head, shoulders, and arms hidden by the white linen. Feeling that my closeness must be distasteful to him, I withdrew to a distance. Suddenly he collapsed, as I had done; sank to his knees, and, no longer ashamed to show his emotion, burst into tears.

"What could I say? Nothing!

"What could I do? I raised him to his feet and led him to the sofa. There we sat side by side; and, to soothe him, I gently stroked his soft, blond hair. He took my hand in his and pressed it affectionately. Then he said:

" 'Tell me the whole truth, Doctor. She didn't kill herself, did she?'

" 'No,' I answered.

" 'Then is any one else to blame for her death?'

" 'No, I said once more, although from within was welling up the answer: 'I, I, I—and you. The two of us. We are to blame. We two—and her unhappy pride.'

"But I kept the words unuttered, and was content to say yet again:

" 'No! No one was to blame. It was her doom.'

" 'I can't realize it,' he groaned. 'It seems incredible. The night before last she was at the ball; she nodded to me and smiled. How could it happen? How did she come to die so unexpectedly, so swiftly?'

"I told him a string of falsehoods. Even from her lover I must keep the secret. We spent that day and the next and the next together in brotherly converse, both aware (though we did not give the knowledge voice) that our lives were intertwined by our relationship to the dead

woman. Again and again I found it hard to keep my own
counsel, but I did so. He never learned that she had been
with child by him; that she had come to me to have the
fruit of their love destroyed; and that, after my refusal,
she had taken the step which had ended her own life as
well. Yet we talked of nothing but her during those days
when I was hidden in his quarters. I had forgotten to tell
you that! They were searching for me. Her husband had
arrived after the coffin had been closed. He was suspicious
—all sorts of rumours were afoot—and he wanted my
account of the matter at first hand. But I simply couldn't
endure the thought of meeting him, the man through
whom I knew she had suffered; so I hid myself, and during four days I never left the house. Her lover took a passage for me under a false name, and late at night I went
on board the boat bound for Singapore. I left everything,
all my possessions, the work I had done in the last seven
years. My house stood open to any one who chose to enter
it. No doubt the authorities have already erased my name
from the list of their officials as 'absent without leave.'
But I could not go on living in that house, that town, that
world, where everything reminded me of her. If I fled like
a thief in the night it was to escape her, to forget her.

"Vain was the attempt! When I came on board at midnight, my friend with me to see me off, a great, oblong,
brass-bound chest was being hoisted on board by the
crane. It was her coffin, her coffin! It had followed me,
just as I had followed her down from the hills to the coast.
I could make no sign, I had to look on unheeding, for her
husband was there, too. He was on his way to England.
Perhaps he means to have the coffin opened when he gets
there; to have a post-mortem made; to find out . . .
Anyhow, he has taken her back to him, has snatched her
away from us; she belongs to him now, not to us. At
Singapore, where I transhipped to this German mail-
boat, the coffin was transhipped as well; and he is here,
too, the husband. But I am still watching over her, and
shall watch over her to the end. He shall never learn her
secret. I shall defend her to the last against the man to

escape whom she went to her death. He shall learn nothing, nothing. Her secret belongs to me, and to no one else
in the world.

"Do you understand? Do you understand why I keep
out of the other passengers' way, why I cannot bear to
hear them laugh and chatter, to watch their foolish flirta-
tions—when I know that deep down in the hold, among
the tea-chests and the cases of brazil nuts, her body lies?
I can't get near it, for the hatches are closed; but I feel
its nearness by day and by night, when the passengers
are tramping up and down the promenade deck or dancing merrily in the saloon. It is stupid of me, I know. The
sea ebbs and flows above millions of corpses, and the dead
are rotting beneath every spot where one sets foot on
land. All the same, I cannot bear it. I cannot bear it when
they dance and laugh in this ship which is taking her
body home. I know what she expects of me. There is still
something left for me to do. Her secret is not yet safe;
and, until it is safe, my pledge to her will be unfulfilled."

From midships there came splashing and scraping
noises. The sailors were swabbing the decks. He started
at the sound, and jumped to his feet.

"I must be going," he murmured.

He was a distressing sight, with his careworn expression, and his eyes reddened by weeping and by drink. He
had suddenly become distant in his manner. Obviously he
was regretting his loquacity, was ashamed of himself for
having opened his heart to me as he had done. Wishing
to be friendly, however, I said:

"Won't you let me pay you a visit in your cabin this
afternoon?"

A smile—mocking, harsh, cynical—twisted his lips;
and when he answered, after a momentary hesitation, it
was with appropriate emphasis.

"Ah, yes, 'it's one's duty to help.' That's your favourite maxim, isn't it? Your use of it a few hours ago,
when you caught me in a weak moment, has loosened my

tongue finely! Thank you for your good intentions, but I'd rather be left to myself. Don't imagine, either, that I feel any better for having turned myself inside out before you and for having shown you my very entrails. My life has been torn to shreds, and no one can patch it together again. I have gained nothing by working in the Dutch colonial service for seven years. My pension has gone phut, and I am returning to Germany a pauper—like a dog that slinks behind a coffin. A man cannot run amuck without paying for it. In the end, he is shot down; and I hope that for me the end will come soon. I'm obliged to you for proposing to call, but I've the best of companions to prevent my feeling lonely in my cabin—plenty of bottles of excellent whisky. They're a great consolation. Then there's another old friend, and my only regret is that I didn't make use of it soon instead of late. My automatic, I mean, which will in the end be better for my soul than any amount of open confession. So I won't trouble you to call, if you don't mind. Among the 'rights of man' there is a right which no one can take away, the right to croak when and where and how one pleases, without a 'helping hand.' "

He looked at me scornfully and with a challenging air, but I knew that at bottom his feeling was one of shame, infinite shame. Saying no word of farewell, he turned on his heel, and slouched off in the direction of the cabins. I never saw him again, though I visited the fore-deck several times after midnight. So completely did he vanish that I might have thought myself the victim of hallucination had I not noticed among the other passengers a man wearing a crape armlet, a Dutchman, I was told, whose wife had recently died of tropical fever. He walked apart, holding converse with no one, and was melancholy of mien. Watching him, I was distressed by the feeling that I was aware of his secret trouble. When my path crossed his, I turned my face away, lest he should divine from my expression that I knew more about his fate than he did himself.

*   *   *

In Naples harbour occurred the accident which was explicable to me in the light of the stranger's tale. Most of the passengers were, as I have said, ashore at the time. I had been to the opera, and had then supped in one of the brightly lit cafés in the Via Roma. As I was being rowed back to the steamer, I noticed that there was a commotion going on round the gangway, boats moving to and fro, and men in them holding torches and acetylene lamps as they scanned the water. On deck there were several carabinieri, talking in low tones. I asked one of the deck-hands what was the matter. He answered evasively, so that it was obvious he had been told to be discreet. Next morning, too, when we were steaming towards Genoa, I found it impossible to glean any information. But at Genoa, in an Italian newspaper, I read a high-flown account of what had happened that night at Naples.

Under cover of darkness, it appeared, to avoid disquieting the passengers, a coffin from the Dutch Indies was being lowered into a boat. It contained the body of a lady; and her husband (who was taking it home for burial) was already waiting in the boat. Something heavy had, when the coffin was half-way down the ship's side, dropped on it from the upper deck, carrying it away, so that it fell with a crash into the boat, which instantly capsized. The coffin, being lined with lead, sank. Fortunately there had been no loss of life, for no one had been struck by the falling coffin, and the widower together with the other persons in the boat had been rescued, though not without difficulty.

What had caused the accident? One story, said the reporter, was that a lunatic had jumped overboard, and in his fall had wrenched the coffin from its lashings. Perhaps the story of the falling body had been invented to cover up the remissness of those responsible for lowering the coffin, who had used tackle that was too weak, so that the lead-weighted box had broken away of itself. Anyhow, the officers were extremely reticent.

In another part of the paper was a brief notice to the

effect that the body of an unknown man, apparently about thirty-five years of age, had been picked up in Naples harbour. There was a bullet-wound in the head. No one connected this with the accident which occurred when the coffin was being lowered.

Before my own eyes, however, as I read the brief paragraphs, there loomed from the printed page the ghostly countenance of the unhappy man whose story I have here set down.

William Beebe

THE HOME TOWN OF THE ARMY ANTS

FROM uniform to civilian clothes is a change transcending mere alteration of stuffs and buttons. It is scarcely less sweeping than the shift from civilian clothes to bathing-suit, which so often compels us to concentrate on remembered mental attributes, to avoid demanding a renewed introduction to estranged personality. In the home life of the average soldier, the relaxation from sustained tension and conscious routine results in a gentleness and quietness of mood for which warrior nations are especially remembered.

Army ants have no insignia to lay aside, and their swords are too firmly hafted in their own beings to be hung up as post-bellum mural decorations, or—as is done only in poster-land—metamorphosed into pruning-hooks and plowshares.

I sat at my laboratory table at Kartabo, and looked down river to the pink roof of Kalacoon, and my mind went back to the shambles of Pit Number Five.[1] I was wondering whether I should ever see the army ants in any guise other than that of scouting, battling searchers for living prey, when a voice of the jungle seemed to hear my unexpressed wish. The sharp, high notes of white-fronted antbirds—those white-crested watchers of the ants—came to my ears, and I left my table and followed up the sound. Physically, I merely walked around the bungalow and approached the edge of the jungle at a point where we had erected a small outhouse a day or two before. But this two hundred feet might just as well have been a single step through quicksilver, hand in hand with Alice, for it took me from a world of hyoids and syrinxes, of vials and lenses and clean-smelling xylol, to the home of the army ants.

[1] See *Jungle Peace*, p. 211.

The antbirds were chirping and hopping about on the very edge of the jungle, but I did not have to go that far. As I passed the doorless entrance of the outhouse I looked up, and there was an immense mass of some strange material suspended in the upper corner. It looked like stringy, chocolate-colored tow, studded with hundreds of tiny ivory buttons. I came closer and looked carefully at this mushroom growth which had appeared in a single night, and it was then that my eyes began to perceive and my mind to record, things that my reason besought me to reject. Such phenomena were all right in a dream, or one might imagine them and tell them to children on one's knee, with wind in the eaves—wild tales to be laughed at and forgotten. But this was daylight and I was a scientist; my eyes were in excellent order, and my mind rested after a dreamless sleep; so I had to record what I saw in that little outhouse.

This chocolate-colored mass with its myriad ivory dots was the home, the nest, the hearth, the nursery, the bridal suite, the kitchen, the bed and board of the army ants. It was the focus of all the lines and files which ravaged the jungle for food, of the battalions which attacked every living creature in their path, of the unnumbered rank and file which made them known to every Indian, to every inhabitant of these vast jungles.

Louis Quatorze once said, *"L'Etat, c'est moi!"* but this figure of speech becomes an empty, meaningless phrase beside what an army ant could boast,—*"La maison, c'est moi!"* Every rafter, beam, stringer, window-frame and door-frame, hall-way, room, ceiling, wall and floor, foundation, superstructure and roof, all were ants—living ants, distorted by stress, crowded into the dense walls, spread out to widest stretch across tie-spaces. I had thought it marvelous when I saw them arrange themselves as bridges, walks, hand-rails, buttresses, and sign-boards along the columns; but this new absorption of environment, this usurpation of wood and stone, this insinuation of themselves into the province of the inorganic world, was almost too astounding to credit.

All along the upper rim the sustaining structure was more distinctly visible than elsewhere. Here was a maze of taut brown threads stretching in places across a span of six inches, with here and there a tiny knot. These were actually tie-strings of living ants, their legs stretched almost to the breaking-point, their bodies the inconspicuous knots or nodes. Even at rest and at home, the army ants are always prepared, for every quiescent individual in the swarm was standing as erect as possible, with jaws widespread and ready, whether the great curved mahogany scimitars of the soldiers, or the little black daggers of the smaller workers. And with no eyelids to close, and eyes which were themselves a mockery, the nerve shriveling and never reaching the brain, what could sleep mean to them? Wrapped ever in an impenetrable cloak of darkness and silence, life was yet one great activity, directed, ordered, commanded by scent and odor alone. Hour after hour, as I sat close to the nest, I was aware of this odor, sometimes subtle, again wafted in strong successive waves. It was musty, like something sweet which had begun to mold; not unpleasant, but very difficult to describe; and in vain I strove to realize the importance of this faint essence— taking the place of sound, of language, of color, of motion, of form.

I recovered quickly from my first rapt realization, for a dozen ants had lost no time in ascending my shoes, and, as if at a preconcerted signal, all simultaneously sank their jaws into my person. Thus strongly recalled to the realities of life, I realized the opportunity that was offered and planned for my observation. No living thing could long remain motionless within the sphere of influence of these six-legged Boches, and yet I intended to spend days in close proximity. There was no place to hang a hammock, no over-hanging tree from which I might suspend myself spider-wise. So I sent Sam for an ordinary chair, four tin cans, and a bottle of disinfectant. I filled the tins with the tarry fluid, and in four carefully timed rushes I placed the tins in a chair-leg square. The fifth time I put the chair in place beneath the nest, but I had misjudged my distances and had to retreat with only two tins in place. Another effort, with Spartan-like disregard of the fiery bites, and my haven was ready. I hung a bag of vials, notebook, and lens on the chairback, and, with a final rush, climbed on the seat and curled up as comfortably as possible.

All around the tins, swarming to the very edge of the liquid, were the angry hosts. Close to my face were the lines ascending and descending, while just above me were hundreds of thousands, a bushel-basket of army ants, with only the strength of their thread-like legs as suspension cables. It took some time to get used to my environment, and from first to last I was never wholly relaxed, or quite unconscious of what would happen if a chair-leg broke, or a bamboo fell across the outhouse.

I swiveled round on the chair-seat and counted eight lines of army ants on the ground, converging to the post at my elbow. Each was four or five ranks wide, and the eight lines occasionally divided or coalesced, like a nexus of capillaries. There was a wide expanse of sand and clay, and no apparent reason why the various lines of foragers should not approach the nest in a single large column. The dividing and redividing showed well how completely free were the columns from any individual dominance. There was no control by specific individuals or soldiers, but, the general route once established, the governing factor was the odor of contact.

The law to pass where others have passed is immutable, but freedom of action or individual desire dies with the malleable, plastic ends of the foraging columns. Again and again came to mind the comparison of the entire colony or army with a single organism; and now the home, the nesting swarm, the focus of central control, seemed like the body of this strange amorphous organism —housing the spirit of the army. One thinks of a column of foragers as a tendril with only the tip sensitive and growing and moving, while the corpuscle-like individual ants are driven in the current of blind instinct to and fro, on their chemical errands. And then this whole theory, this most vivid simile, is quite upset by the sights that I watch in the suburbs of this ant home!

The columns were most excellent barometers, and their reaction to passing showers was invariable. The clay surface held water, and after each downfall the pools would be higher, and the contour of the little region altered. At the first few drops, all the ants would hasten, the throbbing corpuscles speeding up. Then, as the rain came down heavier, the column melted away, those near each end hurrying to shelter and those in the center crawling beneath fallen leaves and bits of clod and sticks. A moment before, hundreds of ants were trudging around a tiny pool, the water lined with ant handrails, and in shallow places, veritable formicine pontoons,—large ants which stood up to their bodies in water, with the booty-laden host passing over them. Now, all had vanished, leaving only a bare expanse of splashing drops and wet clay. The sun broke through and the residue rain tinkled from the bamboos.

As gradually as the growth of the rainbow above the jungle, the lines reformed themselves. Scouts crept from the jungle-edge at one side, and from the post at my end, and felt their way, fan-wise, over the rain-scoured surface; for the odor, which was both sight and sound to these ants, had been washed away—a more serious handicap than mere change in contour. Swiftly the wandering individuals found their bearings again. There was deep water where dry land had been, but, as if by long-planned study of the work of sappers and engineers, new pontoon bridges were thrown across, washouts filled in, new cliffs explored, and easy grades established; and by the time the bamboos ceased their own private after-shower, the columns were again running smoothly, battalions of eager light infantry hastening out to battle, and equal hosts of loot-laden warriors hurrying toward the home nest. Four minutes was the average time taken to re-form a column across the ten feet of open clay, with all the road-making and engineering feats which I have mentioned, on the part of ants who had never been over this new route before.

Leaning forward within a few inches of the post, I lost all sense of proportion, forgot my awkward human size, and with a new perspective became an equal of the ants, looking on, watching every passer-by with interest, straining with the bearers of the heavy loads, and breathing more easily when the last obstacle was overcome and home attained. For a period I plucked out every bit of good-sized booty and found that almost all were portions of scorpions from far-distant dead logs in the jungle, creatures whose strength and poisonous stings availed nothing against the attacks of these fierce ants. The loads were adjusted equably, the larger pieces carried by the big, white-headed workers, while the smaller ants transported small eggs and larvæ. Often, when a great mandibled soldier had hold of some insect, he would have five or six tiny workers surrounding him, each grasping any projecting part of the loot, as if they did not trust him in this menial capacity,—as an anxious mother would watch with doubtful confidence a big policeman wheeling her baby across a crowded street. These workers were often diminutive Marcelines, hindering rather than aiding in the progress. But in every phase of activity of these ants there was not an ounce of intentionally lost power, or a moment of time wilfully gone to waste. What a commentary on Bolshevism!

Now that I had the opportunity of quietly watching the long, hurrying columns, I came hour by hour to feel a greater intimacy, a deeper enthusiasm for their vigor of existence, their unfailing life at the highest point of possibility of achievement. In every direction my former desultory observations were discounted by still greater accomplishments. Elsewhere I have recorded the average speed as two and a half feet in ten seconds, estimating this as a mile in three and a half hours. An observant colonel in the American army has laid bare my congenitally hopeless mathematical inaccuracy, and corrected this to five hours and fifty-two seconds. Now, however, I established a wholly new record for the straight-away dash for home of the army ants. With the handicap of gravity pulling them down, the ants, both laden and unburdened, averaged ten feet in twenty seconds, as they raced up the post. I have now called in an artist and an astronomer to verify my results, these two being the only living beings within hailing distance as I write, except a baby red howling monkey curled up in my lap, and a toucan, sloth, and green boa, beyond my laboratory table. Our results are identical, and I can safely announce that the amateur record for speed of army ants is equivalent to a mile in two hours and fifty-six seconds; and this when handicapped by gravity and burdens of food, but with the incentive of approaching the end of their long journey.

As once before, I accidentally disabled a big worker that I was robbing of his load, and his entire abdomen rolled down a slope and disappeared. Hours later in the afternoon, I was summoned to view the same soldier, unconcernedly making his way along an outward-bound column, guarding it as carefully as if he had not lost the major part of his anatomy. His mandibles were ready, and the only difference that I could see was that he could make better speed than others of his caste. That night he joined the general assemblage of cripples quietly awaiting death, halfway up to the nest.

I know of no highway in the world which surpasses that of a big column of army ants in exciting happenings, although I usually had the feeling which inspired Kim as he watched the Great White Road, of understanding so little of all that was going on. Early in the morning there were only outgoing hosts; but soon eddies were seen in the swift current, vortexes made by a single ant here and there forcing its way against the stream. Unlike penguins and human beings, army ants have no rule of the road as to right and left, and there is no lessening of pace or turning aside for a heavily laden drogher. Their blindness caused them to bump squarely into every individual, often sending load and carrier tumbling to the bottom of a vertical path. Another constant loss of energy was a large cockroach leg, or scorpion segment, carried by several ants. Their insistence on trying to carry everything beneath their bodies caused all sorts of comical mishaps. When such a large piece of booty appeared, it was too much of a temptation, and a dozen outgoing ants would rush up and seize hold for a moment, the consequent pulling in all directions reducing progress at once to zero.

Until late afternoon few ants returned without carrying their bit. The exceptions were the cripples, which were numerous and very pitiful. From such fierce strenuousness, such virile activity, as unending as elemental processes, it seemed a very terrible drop to disability, to the utilizing of every atom of remaining strength to return to the temporary home nest—that instinct which drives so many creatures to the same homing, at the approach of death.

Even in their helplessness they were wonderful. To see a big black-headed worker struggling up a post with five short stumps and only one good hind leg, was a lesson in achieving the impossible. I have never seen even a suspicion of aid given to any cripple, no matter how slight or how complete the disability; but frequently a strange thing occurred, which I have often noticed but can never explain. One army ant would carry another, perhaps of its own size and caste, just as if it were a bit of dead provender; and I always wondered if cannibalism was to be added to their habits. I would capture both, and the minute they were in the vial, the dead ant would come to life, and with equal vigor and fury both would rush about their prison, seeking to escape, becoming indistinguishable in the twinkling of an eye.

Very rarely an ant stopped and attempted to clean another which had become partly disabled through an accumulation of gummy sap or other encumbering substance. But when a leg or other organ was broken or missing, the odor of the ant-blood seemed to arouse only suspicion and to banish sympathy, and after a few casual wavings of antennæ, all passed by on the other side. Not only this, but the unfortunates were actually in danger of attack within the very lines of traffic of the legionaries. Several times I noticed small rove-beetles accompanying the ants, who paid little attention to them. Whenever an ant became suspicious and approached with a raised-eyebrow gesture of antennæ, the beetles turned their backs quickly and raised threatening tails. But I did not suspect the vampire or thug-like character of these guests—tolerated where any other insect would have been torn to pieces at once. A large crippled worker, hobbling along, had slipped a little away from the main line, when I was astonished to see two rove-beetles rush at him and bite him viciously, a third coming up at once and joining in. The poor worker had no possible chance against this combination, and he went down after a short, futile struggle. Two small army ants now happened to pass, and after a preliminary whiffing with waving antennæ, rushed joyously into the *mêlée*. The beetles had a cowardly weapon, and raising their tails, ejected a drop or two of liquid, utterly confusing the ants, which turned and hastened back to the column. For the next few minutes until the scent wore off, they aroused suspicion wherever they went. Meanwhile, the hyena-like rove-beetles, having hedged themselves within a barricade of their malodor, proceeded to feast, quarreling with one another as such cowards are wont to do.

Thus I thought, having identified myself with the army ants. From a broader, less biased point of view, I realized that credit should be given to the rove-beetles for having established themselves in a zone of such constant danger, and for being able to live and thrive in it.

The columns converged at the foot of the post, and up its surface ran the main artery of the nest. Halfway up, a flat board projected, and here the column divided for the last time, half going on directly into the nest, and the other half turning aside, skirting the board, ascending a bit of perpendicular canvas, and entering the nest from the rear. The entrance was well guarded by a veritable

moat and drawbridge of living ants. A foot away, a flat
mat of ants, mandibles outward, was spread, over which
every passing individual stepped. Six inches farther, and
the sides of the mat thickened, and in the last three inches
these sides met overhead, forming a short tunnel at the
end of which the nest began.

And here I noticed an interesting thing. Into this
organic moat or tunnel, this living mouth of an inferno,
passed all the booty-laden foragers, or those who for some
reason had returned empty-mouthed. But the outgoing
host seeped gradually from the outermost nest-layer—a
gradual but fundamental circulation, like that of ocean
currents. Scorpions, eggs, caterpillars, glass-like wasp
pupæ, roaches, spiders, crickets,—all were drawn into the
nest by a maelstrom of hunger, funneling into the narrow
tunnel; while from over all the surface of the swarm there
crept forth layer after layer of invigorated, implacable
seekers after food.

The mass of ants composing the nest appeared so
loosely connected that it seemed as if a touch would tear a
hole, a light wind rend the supports. It was suspended in
the upper corner of the doorway, rounded on the free
sides, and measured roughly two feet in diameter—an unnumbered host of ants. Those on the surface were in very
slow but constant motion, with legs shifting and antennæ
waving continually. This quivering on the surface of the
swarm gave it the appearance of the fur of some terrible
animal—fur blowing in the wind from some unknown,
deadly desert. Yet so cohesive was the entire mass, that I
sat close beneath it for the best part of two days and not
more than a dozen ants fell upon me. There was, however, a constant rain of egg-cases and pupa-skins and the
remains of scorpions and grasshoppers, the residue of the
booty which was being poured in. These wrappings and
inedible casing were all brought to the surface and
dropped. This was reasonable, but what I could not com-
prehend was a constant falling of small living larvæ. How
anything except army ants could emerge alive from such
a sinister swarm was inconceivable. It took some resolu-

tion to stand up under the nest, with my face only a foot away from this slowly seething mass of widespread jaws. But I had to discover where the falling larvæ came from, and after a time I found that they were immature army ants. Here and there a small worker would appear, carrying in its mandibles a young larva; and while most made their way through the maze of mural legs and bodies and ultimately disappeared again, once in a while the burden was dropped and fell to the floor of the outhouse. I can account for this only by presuming that a certain percentage of the nurses were very young and inexperienced workers and dropped their burdens inadvertently. There was certainly no intentional casting out of these offspring, as was so obviously the case with the débris from the food of the colony. The eleven or twelve ants which fell upon me during my watch were all smaller workers, no larger ones losing their grip.

While recording some of these facts, I dropped my pencil, and it was fully ten minutes before the black mass of enraged insects cleared away, and I could pick it up. Leaning far over to secure it, I was surprised by the cleanliness of the floor around my chair. My clothes and notepaper had been covered with loose wings, dry skeletons of insects and the other débris, while hundreds of other fragments had sifted down past me. Yet now that I looked seeingly, the whole area was perfectly clean. I had to assume a perfect jack-knife pose to get my face near enough to the floor; but, achieving it, I found about five hundred ants serving as a street-cleaning squad. They roamed aimlessly about over the whole floor, ready at once to attack anything of mine, or any part of my anatomy which might come close enough, but otherwise stimulated to activity only when they came across a bit of rubbish from the nest high overhead. This was at once seized and carried off to one of two neat piles in far corners. Before night these kitchen middens were an inch or two deep and nearly a foot in length, composed, literally, of thousands of skins, wings, and insect armor. There was not a scrap of dirt of any kind which had not been gathered into one of the two piles. The nest was nine feet above the floor, a distance (magnifying ant height to our own) of nearly a mile, and yet the care lavished on the cleanliness of the earth so far below was as thorough and well done as the actual provisioning of the colony.

As I watched the columns and the swarm-nest hour after hour, several things impressed me;—the absolute silence in which the ants worked;—such ceaseless activity without sound one associates only with a cinema film; all around me was tremendous energy, marvelous feats of achievement, super-human instincts, the ceaseless movement of tens of thousands of legionaries; yet no tramp of feet, no shouts, no curses, no welcomes, no chanties. It was uncanny to think of a race of creatures such as these, dreaded by every living being, wholly dominant in their continent-wide sphere of action, yet born, living out their lives, and dying, dumb and blind, with no possibility of comment on life and its fullness, of censure or of applause.

The sweeping squad on the floor was interesting because of its limited field of work at such a distance from the nest; but close to my chair were a number of other specialized zones of activity, any one of which would have afforded a fertile field for concentrated study. Beneath the swarm on the white canvas, I noticed two large spots of dirt and moisture, where very small flies were collected. An examination showed that this was a second, nearer dumping-ground for all the garbage and refuse of the swarm which could not be thrown down on the kitchen middens far below. And here were tiny flies and other insects acting as scavengers, just as the hosts of vultures gather about the slaughter-house of Georgetown.

The most interesting of all the phases of life of the ants' home town, were those on the horizontal board which projected from the beam and stretched for several feet to one side of the swarm. This platform was almost on a level with my eyes, and by leaning slightly forward on the chair, I was as close as I dared go. Here many ants came from the incoming columns, and others were constantly arriving from the nest itself. It was here that I realized my good fortune and the achievement of my desires, when I first saw an army ant at rest. One of the first arrivals after I had squatted to my post, was a big soldier with a heavy load of roach meat. Instead of keeping on straight up the post, he turned abruptly and dropped his load. It was instantly picked up by two smaller workers and carried on and upward toward the nest. Two other big fellows arrived in quick succession, one with a load which he relinquished to a drogher-in-waiting. Then the three weary warriors stretched their legs one after another and commenced to clean their antennæ. This lasted only for a moment, for three or four tiny ants rushed at each of the larger ones and began as thorough a cleaning as masseurs or Turkish-bath attendants. The three arrivals were at once hustled away to a distant part of the board and there cleaned from end to end. I found that the focal length of my 8-diameter lens was just out of reach of the ants, so I focused carefully on one of the soldiers and watched the entire process. The small ants scrubbed and scraped him with their jaws, licking him and removing every particle of dirt. One even crawled under him and worked away at his upper leg-joints, for all the world as a mechanic will creep under a car. Finally, I was delighted to see him do what no car ever does, turn completely over and lie quietly on his back with his legs in air, while his diminutive helpers overran him and gradually got him into shape for future battles and foraging expeditions.

On this resting-stage, within well-defined limits, were dozens of groups of two cleaning one another, and less numerous parties of the tiny professionals working their hearts out on battle-worn soldiers. It became more and more apparent that in the creed of the army ants, cleanliness comes next to military effectiveness.

Here and there I saw independent individuals cleaning themselves and going through the most un-ant-like movements. They scraped their jaws along the board, pushing forward like a dog trying to get rid of his muzzle; then they turned on one side and passed the opposite legs again and again through the mandibles; while the last performance was to turn over on their backs and roll from side to side, exactly as a horse or donkey loves to do.

One ant, I remember, seemed to have something seriously wrong. It sat up on its bent-under abdomen in a most comical fashion, and was the object of solicitude of every passing ant. Sometimes there were thirty in a dense group, pushing and jostling; and, like most of our city crowds, many seemed to stop only long enough to have a moment's morbid sight, or to ask some silly question as to the trouble, then to hurry on. Others remained, and licked and twiddled him with their antennæ for a long time. He was in this position for at least twenty minutes. My curiosity was so aroused that I gathered him up in a vial, whereat he became wildly excited and promptly regained full use of his legs and faculties. Later, when I examined him under the lens, I could find nothing whatever wrong.

Off at one side of the general cleaning and reconstruction areas was a pitiful assemblage of cripples which had had enough energy to crawl back, but which did not attempt, or were not allowed, to enter the nest proper. Some had one or two legs gone, others had lost an antenna or had an injured body. They seemed not to know what to do—wandering around, now and then giving one another a half-hearted lick. In the midst was one which had died, and two others, each badly injured, were trying to tug the body along to the edge of the board. This they succeeded in doing after a long series of efforts, and down and down fell the dead ant. It was promptly picked up by several kitchen-middenites and unceremoniously thrown on the pile of nest-débris. A load of booty had been dumped among the cripples, and as each wandered close to it, he seemed to regain strength for a moment, picked up the load, and then dropped it. The sight of that which symbolized almost all their life-activity aroused them to a momentary forgetfulness of their disabilities. There was no longer any place for them in the home or in the columns of the legionaries. They had been court-martialed under the most implacable, the most impartial law in the world —the survival of the fit, the elimination of the unfit.

The time came when we had to get at our stored supplies, over which the army ants were such an effective guard. I experimented on a running column with a spray of ammonia and found that it created merely temporary inconvenience, the ants running back and forming a new trail. Formaline was more effective, so I sprayed the nest-swarm with a fifty-per-cent solution, strong enough, one would think, to harden the very boards. It certainly created a terrible commotion, and strings of the ants, two feet long, hung dangling from the nest. The heart of the colony came into view, with thousands of eggs and larvæ, looking like heaps of white rice-grains. Every ant seized one or the other and sought escape by the nearest way, while the soldiers still defied the world. The gradual disintegration revealed an interior meshed like a wasp's nest, chambered and honeycombed with living tubes and walls. Little by little the taut guy-ropes, lathes, braces, joists, all sagged and melted together, each cell-wall becoming dynamic, now expanding, now contracting; the ceilings vibrant with waving legs, the floors a seething mass of jaws and antennæ. By the time it was dark, the swarm was dropping in sections to the floor.

On the following morning new surprises awaited me. The great mass of the ants had moved in the night, vanishing with every egg and immature larva; but there was left in the corner of the flat board a swarm of about one-quarter of the entire number, enshrouding a host of older larvæ. The cleaning zones, the cripples' gathering-room, all had given way to new activities, on the flat board, down near the kitchen middens, and in every horizontal crack.

The cause of all this strange excitement, this braving of the terrible dangers of fumes which had threatened to destroy the entire colony the night before, suddenly was made plain as I watched. A critical time was at hand in the lives of the all-precious larvæ, when they could not be moved—the period of spinning, of beginning the transformation from larvæ to pupæ. This evidently was an operation which had to take place outside the nest and demanded some sort of light covering. On the flat board were several thousand ants and a dozen or more groups of full-grown larvæ. Workers of all sizes were searching everywhere for some covering for the tender immature creatures. They had chewed up all available loose splinters of wood, and near the rotten, termite-eaten ends, the sound of dozens of jaws gnawing all at once was plainly audible. This unaccustomed, unmilitary labor produced a quantity of fine sawdust, which was sprinkled over the larvæ. I had made a partition of a bit of a British officer's tent which I had used in India and China, made of several layers of colored canvas and cloth. The ants found a loose end of this, teased it out and unraveled it, so that all the larvæ near by were blanketed with a gay, parti-colored covering of fuzz.

All this strange work was hurried and carried on under great excitement. The scores of big soldiers on guard appeared rather ill at ease, as if they had wandered by mistake into the wrong department. They sauntered about, bumped into larvæ, turned and fled. A constant stream of workers from the nest brought hundreds more larvæ; and no sooner had they been planted and débris of sorts sifted over them, than they began spinning. A few had already swathed themselves in cocoons—exceedingly thin coverings of pinkish silk. As this took place out of the nest,—in the jungle they must be covered with wood and leaves. The vital necessity for this was not apparent, for none of this débris was incorporated into the silk of the cocoons, which were clean and homogeneous. Yet the hundreds of ants gnawed and tore and labored to gather this little dust, as if their very lives depended upon it.

With my hand-lens focused just beyond mandible reach of the biggest soldier, I leaned forward from my insulated chair, hovering like a great astral eye looking down at this marvelously important business of little lives. Here were thousands of army ants, not killing, not carrying booty, nor even suspended quiescent as organic molecules in the structure of the home, yet in feverish activity equaled only by battle, making ready for the great change of their foster offspring. I watched the very first thread of silk drawn between the larva and the outside world, and in an incredibly short time the cocoon was outlined in a tissue-thin, transparent aura, within which the tenant could be seen skilfully weaving its own shroud.

When first brought from the nest, the larvæ lay quite straight and still; but almost at once they bent far over in the spinning position. Then some officious worker would come along, and the unfortunate larva would be snatched up, carried off, and jammed down in some neighboring empty space, like a bolt of cloth rearranged upon a shelf. Then another ant would approach, antennæ the larva, disapprove, and again shift its position. It was a real survival of the lucky, as to who should avoid being exhausted by kindness and over-solicitude. I uttered many a chuckle at the half-ensilked unfortunates being toted about like mummies, and occasionally giving a sturdy, impatient kick which upset their tormentors and for a moment created a little swirl of mild excitement.

There was no order of packing. The larvæ were fitted together anyway, and meagerly covered with dust of wood and shreds of cloth. One big tissue of wood nearly an inch square was too great a temptation to be let alone, and during the course of my observation it covered in turn almost every group of larvæ in sight, ending by being accidentally shunted over the edge and killing a worker near the kitchen middens. There was only a single layer of larvæ; in no case were they piled up, and when the platform became crowded, a new column was formed and hundreds taken outside. To the casual eye there was no difference between these legionaries and a column bringing in booty of insects, eggs, and pupæ; yet here all was solicitude, never a bite too severe, or a blunder of undue force.

The sights I saw in this second day's accessible nest-swarm would warrant a season's meditation and study, but one thing impressed me above all others. Sometimes, when I carefully pried open one section and looked deep within, I could see large chambers with the larvæ in piles, besides being held in the mandibles of the components of the walls and ceilings. Now and then a curious little ghost-like form would flit across the chamber, coming to rest, gnome-like, on larva or ant. Again and again I saw these little springtails skip through the very scimitar mandibles of a soldier, while the workers paid no attention to them. I wondered if they were not quite odorless, intangible to the ants, invisible guests which lived close to them, going where, doing what they willed, yet never perceived by the thousands of inhabitants. They seemed to live in a kind of fourth dimensional state, a realm comparable to that which we people with ghosts and spirits. It was a most uncanny, altogether absorbing, intensely interesting relationship; and sometimes, when I ponder on some general aspect of the great jungle,—a forest of greenheart, a mighty rushing river, a crashing, blasting thunderstorm,—my mind suddenly reverts by way of contrast to the tiny ghosts of springtails flitting silently among the terrible living chambers of the army ants.

On the following morning I expected to achieve still greater intimacy in the lives of the mummy soldier embryos; but at dawn every trace of nesting swarm, larvæ, pupæ and soldiers was gone. A few dead workers were being already carried off by small ants which never would have dared approach them in life. A big blue morpho butterfly flapped slowly past out of the jungle, and in its wake came the distant notes—high and sharp—of the white-fronted antbirds; and I knew that the legionaries were again abroad, radiating on their silent, dynamic paths of life from some new temporary nest deep in the jungle.

Logan Pearsall Smith

THE VICAR OF LYNCH

WHEN I heard through country gossip of the strange
happening at Lynch which had caused so great a scandal,
and led to the disappearance of the deaf old Vicar of that
remote village, I collected all the reports I could about
it, for I felt that at the centre of this uncomprehending
talk and wild anecdote there was something with more
meaning than a mere sudden outbreak of blasphemy and
madness.

It appeared that the old Vicar, after some years spent
in the quiet discharge of his parochial duties, had been
noticed to become more and more odd in his appearance
and behaviour; and it was also said that he had gradually
introduced certain alterations into the Church services.
These had been vaguely supposed at the time to be of a
High Church character, but afterwards they were put
down to a growing mental derangement, which had finally
culminated at that notorious Harvest Festival, when his
career as a clergyman of the Church of England had
ended. On this painful occasion the old man had come
into church outlandishly dressed, and had gone through
a service with chanted gibberish and unaccustomed gestures, and prayers which were unfamiliar to his congregation. There was also talk of a woman's figure on the altar,
which the Vicar had unveiled at a solemn moment in this
performance; and I also heard echo of other gossip—
gossip that was, however, authoritatively contradicted
and suppressed as much as possible—about the use of
certain other symbols of a most unsuitable kind. Then
a few days after the old man had disappeared—some of
the neighbours believed that he was dead; some, that he
was now shut up in an asylum for the insane.

Such was the fantastic and almost incredible talk I
listened to, but in which, as I say, I found much more

meaning than my neighbours. For one thing, although
they knew that the Vicar had come from Oxford to this
remote College living, they knew nothing of his work and
scholarly reputation in that University, and none of them
had probably ever heard of—much less read—an important book which he had written, and which was the
standard work on his special subject. To them he was
simply a deaf, eccentric, and solitary clergyman; and I
think I was the only person in the neighbourhood who had
conversed with him on the subject concerning which he
was the greatest living authority in England.

For I had seen the old man once—curiously enough at
the time of a Harvest Festival, though it was some years
before the one which had led to his disappearance.
Bicycling one day over the hills, I had ridden down into
a valley of cornfields, and then, passing along an un-
fenced road that ran across a wide expanse of stubble, I
came, after getting off to open three or four gates, upon
a group of thatched cottages, with a little, unrestored
Norman church standing among great elms. I left my
bicycle and walked through the churchyard, and as I went
into the church, through its deeply-recessed Norman doorway, a surprisingly pretty sight met my eyes. The dim,
cool, little interior was set out and richly adorned with an
abundance of fruit and vegetables, yellow gourds, apples
and plums and golden wheat-sheaves, great loaves of
bread, and garlands of September flowers. A shabby-
looking old clergyman was standing on the top of a step-
ladder, finishing the decorations, when I entered. As soon
as he saw me he came down, and I spoke to him, praising
the decorations, and raising my voice a little, for I noticed
that he was somewhat deaf. We talked of the Harvest
Festival, and as I soon perceived that I was talking with
a man of books and University education, I ventured to
hint at what had vividly impressed me in that old, gaudily-
decorated church—its pagan character, as if it were a
rude archaic temple in some corner of the antique world,
which had been adorned, two thousand years ago, by pious
country folk for some local festival. The old clergyman

was not in the least shocked by my remark; it seemed indeed rather to please him; there was, he agreed, something of a pagan character in the modern Harvest Festival—it was no doubt a bit of the old primitive Vegetation Ritual, the old Religion of the soil; a Festival, which, like so many others, had not been destroyed by Christianity, but absorbed into it, and given a new meaning. "Indeed," he added, talking on as if the subject interested him, and expressing himself with a certain donnish carefulness of speech that I found pleasant to listen to, "the Harvest Festival is undoubtedly a survival of the prehistoric worship of that Corn Goddess who, in classical times, was called Demeter and Ioulo and Ceres, but whose cult as an Earth-Mother and Corn-Spirit is of much greater antiquity. For there is no doubt that this Vegetation Spirit has been worshipped from the earliest times by agricultural peoples; the wheat fields and ripe harvests being naturally suggestive of the presence amid the corn of a kindly Being, who, in return for due rites and offerings, will vouchsafe nourishing rains and golden harvests." He mentioned the references in Virgil, and the description in Theocritus of a Sicilian Harvest Festival—these were no doubt familiar to me; but if I was interested in the subject, I should find, he said, much more information collected in a book which he had written, but of which I had probably never heard, about the Vegetation Deities in Greek Religion. As it happened I knew the book, and felt now much interested in my chance meeting with the distinguished author; and after expressing this as best I could, I rode off, promising to visit him again. This promise I was never able to fulfil; but when afterwards, on my return to the neighbourhood, I heard of that unhappy scandal, my memory of this meeting and our talk enabled me to form a theory as to what had really happened.

It seemed plain to me that the change had been too violent for this elderly scholar, taken from his books and college rooms and set down in the solitude of this remote valley, amid the richness and living sap of Nature. The

gay spectacle, right under his old eyes, of growing shoots
and budding foliage, of blossoming and flowering, and the
ripening of fruits and crops, had little by little (such was
my theory) unhinged his brains. More and more his
thoughts had come to dwell, not on the doctrines of the
Church in which he had long ago taken orders, but on the
pagan rites which had formed his life-long study, and
which had been the expression of a life not unlike the
agricultural life amid which he now found himself living.
So as his derangement grew upon him in his solitude, he
had gradually transformed, with a maniac's cunning, the
Christian services, and led his little congregation, all unknown to themselves, back toward their ancestral worship of the Corn-Goddess. At last he had thrown away all
disguise, and had appeared as a hierophant of Demeter,
dressed in a fawn skin, with a crown of poplar leaves,
and pedantically carrying the mystic basket and the
winnowing fan appropriate to these mysteries. The
wheaten posset he offered the shocked communicants belonged to these also, and the figure of a woman on the
altar was of course the holy Wheatsheaf, whose unveiling
was the culminating point in that famous ritual.

It is much to be regretted that I could not recover full
and more exact details of that celebration in which this
great scholar had probably embodied his mature knowledge concerning a subject which has puzzled generations
of students. But what powers of careful observation could
one expect from a group of labourers and small farmers?
Some of the things that reached my ears I refused to believe—the mention of pig's blood for instance, and especially the talk of certain grosser symbols, which the choir
boys, it was whispered, had carried about the church in
ceremonious procession. Village people have strange im-
aginations; and to this event, growing more and more
monstrous as they talked it over, they must themselves
have added this grotesque detail. However, I have written
to consult an Oxford authority on this interesting point,
and he has been kind enough to explain at length that
although at the *Haloa*, or winter festival of the Corn-

Goddess, and also at the *Chloeia*, or festival in early spring, some symbolization of the reproductive powers of Nature would be proper and appropriate, it would have been quite out of place at the *Thalysia*, or autumn festival of thanksgiving. I feel certain that a solecism of this nature—the introduction into a particular rite of features not sanctioned by the texts—would have seemed a shocking thing, even to the unhinged mind of one who had always been so careful a scholar.

E. B. White

INTERVIEW WITH DAISY

"WELL, he's gone," said Daisy cheerfully, after Mr. Caldwell had departed. "We got rid of him nice."

"*We?*" I snapped. "What do you mean *we* got rid of him? *You* got rid of him. And why? Because he dropped his cigarette case. All that fuss because a friend of mine drops his cigarette case."

Daisy pushed her two front paws straight out in front of her. "How did I know it was a cigarette case?" she said. "It might have been a rod."

"Ridiculous. Caldwell is an old friend."

"He never was at the apartment before. I should sit around on my tail while a total stranger pulls a rod on us!"

"It was a cigarette case," I said, wearily.

"Well, I couldn't see. I was sitting way the hell and gone across the . . ."

"Quiet!" I commanded. "Either you talk decently or you go back in the bathroom on your cushion."

"Oke," said Daisy. "As far as Caldwell goes, I didn't act so bad. You take a total stranger who drops his rod, and . . ."

"Cigarette case," I corrected.

". . . and I would ordinarily give him the ankle number. I didn't give Caldwell the ankle number, I just gave him the low growl and the steady look. Anybody who makes an unusual noise gets the low growl and the steady look. That's final. It's the way I am."

"Well, I wish you'd concentrate on my objectionable guests. I happen to like Caldwell."

"He's all right," said Daisy. "A little on the dull side, maybe."

"You mean he doesn't smell like the iceman. Well, neither do I, for that matter, and you don't think I'm dull."

"Some people do," said Daisy, yawning. "And speaking of the iceman, life is what you make it. If I had a chipmunk in the apartment I might adopt a different attitude toward tradespeople. I give the iceman my ankle number not because it does anything to him, but because it does something to me."

"It does something to all of us," I sneered. "It bores us all to tears. There'll be no chipmunks, either. This apartment is confusing enough without chipmunks. Besides, what's the matter with the little rubber dog that Mrs. Newberry brought you from Paris—*it* makes a squeaking noise like a chipmunk. You can shake that all you darn please."

"Can't I, though. If you knew what it costs me to throw myself into the spirit of rubber toys! It takes a lot out of a dog. I had a grandmother in the old country who bit the pants off an earl, the elegant bitch, and now it's come to rubber toys. You must admit, though, that the Scottish terrier approaches rubber toys with his eyes open—you have to hand the breed that."

"On the other hand, I sometimes think you approach a lot of things with your mind shut. I've never understood, for example, why you discriminate between our iceman, whom you meet informally here in the apartment, and the doorman of One Fifth Avenue, whom you meet ceremoniously on the street. Where do you draw the line? Both are honest working people, both are grotesquely dressed—why do you resent the one and cultivate the other?"

"You wouldn't understand," replied Daisy. "The doorman is the symbol of majesty—possibly that's it. I have to have that, even though I see through it, just as some men have to have a pretty girl even though they see through her. Don't throw One Fifth Avenue in my face —I go in with my eyes open. Besides, it seems to me I'm getting to be something of a symbol myself. I know what's going on. The Scottish terrier has been exploited in an unbridled manner: Scotty pins, Scotty buckles, Scotty hat ornaments, Scotty Kiddy Pants, Scotties on the bathmat, Scotties in the Texaco ads, wooden Scotties on suburban lawns. It's a crime the way we've been taken up. When I meet another Scotch dog on the street now we both feel like a couple of Elks (and I've met some I wouldn't be found dead with, too)."

"Yes, I've noticed that," I replied bitterly.

"It's a cock-eyed country," Daisy continued, "and it's the same all along the line. I know what's going on. Everything gets taken over by big business, I don't care what line you're in. Look at President Hoover: he makes some crazy scrawls with his pencil while he's answering the telephone and a concern gets hold of the design and brings out the Hoover Scribble Rompers for little folks. Hell, the President and I are in the same boat."

"You're talking awful big," I said.

"I'm feeling awful big," said Daisy. "Where's that rubber dog?"

P. G. Wodehouse

THE SMILE THAT WINS

THE conversation in the bar parlour of the Anglers' Rest had turned to the subject of the regrettably low standard of morality prevalent among the nobility and landed gentry of Great Britain.

Miss Postlethwaite, our erudite barmaid, had brought the matter up by mentioning that in the novelette which she was reading a viscount had just thrown a family solicitor over a cliff.

"Because he had found out his guilty secret," explained Miss Postlethwaite, polishing a glass a little severely, for she was a good woman. "It was his guilty secret this solicitor had found out, so the viscount threw him over a cliff. I suppose, if one did but know, that sort of thing is going on all the time."

Mr. Mulliner nodded gravely.

"So much so," he agreed, "that I believe that whenever a family solicitor is found in two or more pieces at the bottom of a cliff, the first thing the Big Four at Scotland Yard do is make a round-up of all the viscounts in the neighbourhood."

"Baronets are worse than viscounts," said a Pint of Stout vehemently. "I was done down by one only last month over the sale of a cow."

"Earls are worse than baronets," insisted a Whisky Sour. "I could tell you something about earls."

"How about O.B.E.'s?" demanded a Mild and Bitter. "If you ask me, O.B.E.'s want watching, too."

Mr. Mulliner sighed.

"The fact is," he said, "reluctant though one may be to admit it, the entire British aristocracy is seamed and honeycombed with immorality. I venture to assert that, if you took a pin and jabbed it down anywhere in the pages of *Debrett's Peerage* you would find it piercing the name of someone who was going about the place with a conscience as tender as a sunburned neck. If anything were needed to prove my assertion, the story of my nephew, Adrian Mulliner, the detective, would do it."

"I didn't know you had a nephew who was a detective," said the Whisky Sour.

* * *

Oh, yes. He has retired now, but at one time he was as keen an operator as anyone in the profession. After leaving Oxford and trying his hand at one or two uncongenial tasks, he had found his niche as a member of the firm of Widgery & Boon, Investigators, of Albemarle Street. And it was during his second year with this old-established house that he met and loved Lady Millicent Shipton-Bellinger, younger daughter of the fifth Earl of Brangbolton.

It was the Adventure of the Missing Sealyham that brought the young couple together. From the purely professional standpoint, my nephew has never ranked this among his greatest triumphs of ratiocination; but, considering what it led to, he might well, I think, be justified in regarding it as the most important case of his career. What happened was that he met the animal straying in the park, deduced from the name and address on its collar that it belonged to Lady Millicent Shipton-Bellinger, of 18A, Upper Brook Street, and took it thither at the conclusion of his stroll and restored it.

"Child's play" is the phrase with which, if you happen to allude to it, Adrian Mulliner will always airily dismiss this particular investigation; but Lady Millicent could not have displayed more admiration and enthusiasm had it been the supremest masterpiece of detective work. She fawned on my nephew. She invited him in to tea, consisting of buttered toast, anchovy sandwiches, and two kinds of cake; and at the conclusion of the meal they parted on terms which, even at that early stage in their acquaintance, were something warmer than those of mere friendship.

Indeed, it is my belief that the girl fell in love with Adrian as instantaneously as he with her. On him, it was her radiant blonde beauty that exercised the spell. She, on her side, was fascinated, I fancy, not only by the regularity of his features, which, as is the case with all the Mulliners, was considerable, but also by the fact that he was dark and thin and wore an air of inscrutable melancholy.

This, as a matter of fact, was due to the troublesome attacks of dyspepsia from which he had suffered since boyhood; but to the girl it naturally seemed evidence of a great and romantic soul. Nobody, she felt, could look so grave and sad, had he not hidden deeps in him.

One can see the thing from her point of view. All her life she had been accustomed to brainless juveniles who eked out their meagre eyesight with monocles and, as far as conversation was concerned, were a spent force after they had asked her if she had seen the academy or did she think she would prefer a glass of lemonade. The effect on her of a dark, keen-eyed man like Adrian Mulliner, who spoke well and easily of footprints, psychology, and the underworld, must have been stupendous.

At any rate, their love ripened rapidly. It could not have been two weeks after their first meeting when Adrian, as he was giving her lunch one day at the Senior Bloodstain, the detectives' club in Rupert Street, proposed and was accepted. And for the next twenty-four hours, one is safe in saying, there was in the whole of London, including the outlying suburban districts, no happier private investigator than he.

Next day, however, when he again met Millicent for lunch, he was disturbed to perceive on her beautiful face an emotion which his trained eye immediately recognized as anguish.

"Oh, Adrian," said the girl brokenly. "The worst has happened. My father refuses to hear of our marrying. When I told him we were engaged, he said 'Pooh!' quite a number of times, and added that he had never heard such dashed nonsense in his life. You see, ever since my

Uncle Joe's trouble in nineteen-twenty-eight, Father has had a horror of detectives."

"I don't think I have met your Uncle Joe."

"You will have the opportunity next year. With the usual allowance for good conduct he should be with us again about July. And there is another thing."

"Not another?"

"Yes. Do you know Sir Jasper Addleton, O.B.E.?"

"The financier?"

"Father wants me to marry him. Isn't it awful?"

"I have certainly heard more enjoyable bits of news," agreed Adrian. "This wants a good deal of careful thinking over."

The process of thinking over his unfortunate situation had the effect of rendering excessively acute the pangs of Adrian Mulliner's dyspepsia. During the past two weeks the ecstasy of being with Millicent and deducing that she loved him had caused a complete cessation of the attacks; but now they began again, worse than ever. At length, after a sleepless night during which he experienced all the emotions of one who has carelessly swallowed a family of scorpions, he sought a specialist.

The specialist was one of those keen, modern minds who disdain the outworn formulæ of the more conservative mass of the medical profession. He examined Adrian carefully, then sat back in his chair, with the tips of his fingers touching.

"Smile!" he said.

"Eh?" said Adrian.

"Smile, Mr. Mulliner."

"Did you say smile?"

"That's it. Smile."

"But," Adrian pointed out, "I've just lost the only girl I ever loved."

"Well, that's fine," said the specialist, who was a bachelor. "Come on, now, if you please. Start smiling."

Adrian was a little bewildered.

"Listen," he said. "What *is* all this about smiling? We started, if I recollect, talking about my gastric juices.

Now, in some mysterious way, we seem to have got onto the subject of smiles. How do you mean—smile? I never smile. I haven't smiled since the butler tripped over the spaniel and upset the melted butter on my Aunt Elizabeth, when I was a boy of twelve."

The specialist nodded.

"Precisely. And that is why your digestive organs trouble you. Dyspepsia," he proceeded, "is now recognized by the progressive element of the profession as purely mental. We do not treat it with drugs and medicines. Happiness is the only cure. Be gay, Mr. Mulliner. Be cheerful. And, if you can't do that, at any rate smile. The mere exercise of the risible muscles is in itself beneficial. Go out now and make a point, whenever you have a spare moment, of smiling."

"Like this?" said Adrian.

"Wider than that."

"How about this?"

"Better," said the specialist, "but still not quite so elastic as one could desire. Naturally, you need practice. We must expect the muscles to work rustily for a while at their unaccustomed task. No doubt things will brighten by and by."

He regarded Adrian thoughtfully.

"Odd," he said. "A curious smile, yours, Mr. Mulliner. It reminds me a little of the Mona Lisa's. It has the same underlying note of the sardonic and the sinister. It virtually amounts to a leer. Somehow it seems to convey the suggestion that you know all. Fortunately, my own life is an open book, for all to read, and so I was not discommoded. But I think it would be better if, for the present, you endeavoured not to smile at invalids or nervous persons. Good-morning, Mr. Mulliner. That will be five guineas, precisely."

On Adrian's face, as he went off that afternoon to perform the duties assigned to him by his firm, there was no smile of any description. He shrank from the ordeal before him. He had been told off to guard the wedding pres-

ents at a reception in Grosvenor Square, and naturally
anything to do with weddings was like a sword through
his heart. His face, as he patrolled the room where the
gifts were laid out, was drawn and forbidding. Hitherto,
at these functions, it had always been his pride that
nobody could tell that he was a detective. Today, a child
could have recognized his trade. He looked like Sherlock
Holmes.

To the gay throng that surged about him he paid little
attention. Usually tense and alert on occasions like this,
he now found his mind wandering. He mused sadly on
Millicent. And suddenly—the result, no doubt, of these
gloomy meditations, though a glass of wedding champagne may have contributed its mite—there shot through
him, starting at about the third button of his neat waistcoat, a pang of dyspepsia so keen that he felt the pressing necessity of doing something about it immediately.

With a violent effort he contorted his features into a
smile. And, as he did so, a stout, bluff man of middle
age, with a red face and a grey moustache, who had been
hovering near one of the tables, turned and saw him.

"Egad!" he muttered, paling.

Sir Sutton Hartley-Wesping, Bart.—for the red-
faced man was he—had had a pretty good afternoon.
Like all baronets who attended society wedding recep-
tions, he had been going round the various tables since
his arrival, pocketing here a fish slice, there a jewelled
egg boiler, until now he had taken on about all the cargo
his tonnage would warrant, and was thinking of strolling
off to the pawnbroker's in the Euston Road, with whom
he did most of his business. At the sight of Adrian's smile,
he froze where he stood, appalled.

We have seen what the specialist thought of Adrian's
smile. Even to him, a man of clear and limpid conscience,
it had seemed sardonic and sinister. We can picture, then,
the effect it must have had on Sir Sutton Hartley-
Wesping.

At all costs, he felt, he must conciliate this leering
man. Swiftly removing from his pockets a diamond neck-

lace, five fish slices, ten cigarette lighters, and a couple
of egg boilers, he placed them on the table and came over
to Adrian with a nervous little laugh.

"How *are* you, my dear fellow?" he said.

Adrian said that he was quite well. And so, indeed, he
was. The specialist's recipe had worked like magic. He
was mildly surprised at finding himself so cordially addressed by a man whom he did not remember ever having
seen before, but he attributed this to the magnetic charm
of his personality.

"That's fine," said the baronet heartily. "That's capital. That's splendid. Er—by the way—I fancied I saw
you smile just now."

"Yes," said Adrian. "I did smile. You see——"

"Of course I see. Of course, my dear fellow. You detected the joke I was playing on our good hostess, and
you were amused because you understood that there is
no animus, no *arrière-pensée*, behind these little practical
pleasantries—nothing but good, clean fun, at which nobody would have laughed more heartily than herself. And
now, what are you doing this week-end, my dear old
chap? Would you care to run down to my place in Sussex?"

"Very kind of you," began Adrian doubtfully. He was
not quite sure that he was in the mood for strange week-
ends.

"Here is my card, then. I shall expect you on Friday.
Quite a small party. Lord Brangbolton, Sir Jasper Addleton, and a few more. Just loafing about, you know, and
a spot of bridge at night. Splendid. Capital. See you,
then, on Friday."

And, carelessly dropping another egg boiler on the
table as he passed, Sir Sutton disappeared.

Any doubts which Adrian might have entertained as
to accepting the baronet's invitation had vanished as he
heard the names of his fellow guests. It always interests
a fiancé to meet his fiancée's father and his fiancée's pros-
pective fiancé. For the first time since Millicent had told

him the bad news, Adrian became almost cheerful. If, he felt, this baronet had taken such a tremendous fancy to him at first sight, why might it not happen that Lord Brangbolton would be equally drawn to him—to the extent, in fact, of overlooking his profession and welcoming him as a son-in-law?

He packed, on the Friday, with what was to all intents and purposes a light heart.

A fortunate chance at the very outset of his expedition increased Adrian's optimism. It made him feel that Fate was fighting on his side. As he walked down the platform of Victoria Station, looking for an empty compartment in the train which was to take him to his destination, he perceived a tall, aristocratic old gentleman being assisted into a first-class carriage by a man of butlerine aspect. And in the latter he recognized the servitor who had admitted him to 18A, Upper Brook Street, when he visited the house after solving the riddle of the missing sealyham. Obviously, then, the white-haired, dignified passenger could be none other than Lord Brangbolton. And Adrian felt that if on a long train journey he failed to ingratiate himself with the old buster, he had vastly mistaken his amiability and winning fascination of manner.

He leaped in, accordingly, as the train began to move, and the earl, glancing up from his paper, jerked a thumb at the door.

"Get out, blast you!" he said. "Full up."

As the compartment was empty but for themselves, Adrian made no move to comply with the request. Indeed, to alight now, to such an extent had the train gathered speed, would have been impossible. Instead, he spoke cordially.

"Lord Brangbolton, I believe?"

"Go to hell," said his lordship.

"I fancy we are to be fellow guests at Wesping Hall this week-end."

"What of it?"

"I just mentioned it."

"Oh?" said Lord Brangbolton. "Well, since you're here, how about a little flutter?"

As is customary with men of his social position, Millicent's father always travelled with a pack of cards. Being gifted by nature with considerable manual dexterity, he usually managed to do well with these on race trains.

"Ever played Persian Monarchs?" he asked, shuffling.

"I think not," said Adrian.

"Quite simple," said Lord Brangbolton. "You just bet a quid or whatever it may be that you can cut a higher card than the other fellow, and, if you do, you win, and, if you don't, you don't."

Adrian said it sounded a little like Blind Hooky.

"It is like Blind Hooky," said Lord Brangbolton. "Very like Blind Hooky. In fact, if you can play Blind Hooky, you can play Persian Monarchs."

By the time they alighted at Wesping Parva, Adrian was twenty pounds on the wrong side of the ledger. The fact, however, did not prey upon his mind. On the contrary, he was well satisfied with the progress of events. Elated with his winnings, the old earl had become positively cordial, and Adrian resolved to press his advantage home at the earliest opportunity.

Arrived at Wesping Hall, accordingly, he did not delay. Shortly after the sounding of the dressing gong he made his way to Lord Brangbolton's room and found him in his bath.

"Might I have a word with you, Lord Brangbolton?" he said.

"You can do more than that," replied the other, with marked amiability. "You can help me find the soap."

"Have you lost the soap?"

"Yes. Had it a minute ago, and now it's gone."

"Strange," said Adrian.

"Very strange," agreed Lord Brangbolton. "Makes a fellow think a bit, that sort of thing happening. My own soap, too. Brought it with me."

Adrian considered.

"Tell me exactly what occurred," he said. "In your

own words. And tell me everything, please, for one never knows when the smallest detail may not be important."

His companion marshalled his thoughts.

"My name," he began, "is Reginald Alexander Montacute James Bramfylde Tregennis Shipton-Bellinger, fifth Earl of Brangbolton. On the sixteenth of the present month—today, in fact—I journeyed to the house of my friend Sir Sutton Hartley-Wesping, Bart.—here, in short—with the purpose of spending the week-end there. Knowing that Sir Sutton likes to have his guests sweet and fresh about the place, I decided to take a bath before dinner. I unpacked my soap and in a short space of time had lathered myself thoroughly from the neck upwards. And then, just as I was about to get at my right leg, what should I find but that the soap had disappeared. Nasty shock it gave me, I can tell you."

Adrian had listened to this narrative with the closest attention. Certainly the problem appeared to present several points of interest.

"It looks like an inside job," he said thoughtfully. "It could scarcely be the work of a gang. You would have noticed a gang. Just give me the facts briefly once again, if you please."

"Well, I was here, in the bath, as it might be, and the soap was here—between my hands, as it were. Next moment it was gone."

"Are you sure you have omitted nothing?"

Lord Brangbolton reflected.

"Well, I was singing, of course."

A tense look came into Adrian's face.

"Singing what?"

" 'Sonny Boy.' "

Adrian's face cleared.

"As I suspected," he said, with satisfaction. "Precisely as I had supposed. I wonder if you are aware, Lord Brangbolton, that in the singing of that particular song the muscles unconsciously contract as you come to the final 'boy'? Thus—'I still have you, Sonny Boy.' You observe? It would be impossible for anyone, rendering the number with the proper gusto, not to force his hands together at this point, assuming that they were in anything like close juxtaposition. And if there were any slippery object between them, such as a piece of soap, it would inevitably shoot sharply upwards and fall"—he scanned the room keenly—"outside the bath on the mat. As, indeed," he concluded, picking up the missing object and restoring it to its proprietor, "it did."

Lord Brangbolton gaped.

"Well, dash my buttons," he cried, "if that isn't the smartest bit of work I've seen in a month of Sundays!"

"Elementary," said Adrian with a shrug.

"You ought to be a detective."

Adrian took the cue.

"I am a detective," he said. "My name is Mulliner."

For an instant the words did not appear to have made any impression. The aged peer continued to beam through the soapsuds. Then suddenly his geniality vanished with an ominous swiftness.

"Mulliner? Did you say Mulliner?"

"I did."

"You aren't by any chance the feller——"

"—who loves your daughter Millicent with a fervour he cannot begin to express? Yes, Lord Brangbolton, I am. And I am hoping that I may receive your consent to the match."

A hideous scowl had darkened the earl's brow. His fingers, which were grasping a loofah, tightened convulsively.

"Oh?" he said. "You are, are you? You imagine, do you, that I propose to welcome a blighted footprint-and-cigar-ash inspector into my family? It is your idea, is it, that I shall acquiesce in the union of my daughter to a dashed feller who goes about the place on his hands and knees with a magnifying glass, picking up small objects and putting them carefully away in his pocketbook? I seem to see myself! Why, rather than permit Millicent to marry a bally detective——"

"What is your objection to detectives?"

"Never you mind what's my objection to detectives. Marry my daughter, indeed! I like your infernal cheek. Why, you couldn't keep her in lipsticks."

Adrian preserved his dignity.

"I admit that my services are not so amply remunerated as I could wish, but the firm hint at a rise next Christmas——"

"Tchah!" said Lord Brangbolton. "Pshaw! If you are interested in my daughter's matrimonial arrangements, she is going, as soon as he gets through with this Bramah-Yamah Gold Mines flotation of his, to marry my old friend Jasper Addleton. As for you, Mr. Mulliner, I have only two words to say to you. One is POP, the other is OFF. And do it now."

Adrian sighed. He saw that it would be hopeless to endeavour to argue with the haughty old man in his present mood.

"So be it, Lord Brangbolton," he said quietly.

And, affecting not to notice the nailbrush which struck him smartly on the back of the head, he left the room.

The food and drink provided for his guests by Sir Sutton Hartley-Wesping at the dinner which began some half-hour later were all that the veriest gourmet could have desired; but Adrian gulped them down, scarcely tasting them. His whole attention was riveted on Sir Jasper Addleton, who sat immediately opposite him.

And the more he examined Sir Jasper, the more revolting seemed the idea of his marrying the girl he loved.

Of course, an ardent young fellow inspecting a man who is going to marry the girl he loves is always a stern critic. In the peculiar circumstances Adrian would, no doubt, have looked askance at a John Barrymore or a Ronald Colman. But, in the case of Sir Jasper, it must be admitted that he had quite reasonable grounds for his disapproval.

In the first place, there was enough of the financier to make two financiers. It was as if Nature, planning a financier, had said to itself: "We will do this thing well. We will not skimp," with the result that, becoming too enthusiastic, it had overdone it. And then, in addition to being fat, he was also bald and goggle-eyed. And, if you overlooked his baldness and the goggly protuberance of his eyes, you could not get away from the fact that he was well advanced in years. Such a man, felt Adrian, would have been better employed in pricing burial lots in Kensal Green Cemetery than in forcing his unwelcome attentions on a sweet young girl like Millicent; and as soon as the meal was concluded he approached him with cold abhorrence.

"A word with you," he said, and led him out on to the terrace.

The O.B.E., as he followed him into the cool night air, seemed surprised and a little uneasy. He had noticed Adrian scrutinizing him closely across the dinner table, and if there is one thing a financier who has just put out a prospectus of a gold mine dislikes, it is to be scrutinized closely.

"What do you want?" he asked nervously.

Adrian gave him a cold glance.

"Do you ever look in a mirror, Sir Jasper?" he asked curtly.

"Frequently," replied the financier, puzzled.

"Do you ever weigh yourself?"

"Often."

"Do you ever listen while your tailor is toiling round you with the tape measure and calling out the score to his assistant?"

"I do."

"Then," said Adrian, "and I speak in the kindest spirit of disinterested friendship, you must have realized that you are an overfed old bohunkus. And how you ever got the idea that you were a fit mate for Lady Millicent Shipton-Bellinger frankly beats me. Surely it must have occurred to you what a priceless ass you will look, walking up the aisle with that young and lovely girl at your side? People will mistake you for an elderly uncle taking his niece to the zoo."

The O.B.E. bridled.

"Ho!" he said.

"It is no use saying 'Ho!'" saild Adrian. "You can't get out of it with any 'Ho's.' When all the talk and argument have died away, the fact remains that, millionaire though you be, you are a nasty-looking, fat, senile millionaire. If I were you, I should give the whole thing a miss. What do you want to get married for, anyway? You are much happier as you are. Besides, think of the risks of a financier's life. Nice it would be for that sweet girl suddenly to get a wire from you telling her not to wait dinner for you as you had just started a seven-year stretch at Dartmoor!"

An angry retort had been trembling on Sir Jasper's lips during the early portion of this speech, but at these concluding words it died unspoken. He blenched visibly and stared at the speaker with undisguised apprehension.

"What do you mean?" he faltered.

"Never mind," said Adrian.

He had spoken, of course, purely at a venture, basing his remarks on the fact that nearly all O.B.E.'s who dabble in High Finance go to prison sooner or later. Of Sir Jasper's actual affairs he knew nothing.

"Hey, listen!" said the financier.

But Adrian did not hear him. I have mentioned that during dinner, preoccupied with his thoughts, he had bolted his food. Nature now took its toll. An acute spasm suddenly ran through him, and with a brief "Ouch!" of pain he doubled up and began to walk round in circles.

Sir Jasper clicked his tongue impatiently.

"This is no time for doing the Astaire pom-pom dance," he said sharply. "Tell me what you meant by that stuff you were talking about prison."

Adrian had straightened himself. In the light of the moon which flooded the terrace with its silver beams, his clean-cut face was plainly visible. And with a shiver of apprehension Sir Jasper saw that it wore a sardonic, sinister smile—a smile which, it struck him, was virtually tantamount to a leer.

I have spoken of the dislike financiers have for being scrutinized closely. Still more vehemently do they object to being leered at. Sir Jasper reeled, and was about to press his questions when Adrian, still smiling, tottered off into the shadows and was lost to sight.

The financier hurried into the smoking room, where he knew there would be the materials for a stiff drink. A stiff drink was what he felt an imperious need of at the moment. He tried to tell himself that that smile could not really have had the inner meaning which he had read into it; but he was still quivering nervously as he entered the smoking room.

As he opened the door, the sound of an angry voice smote his ears. He recognized it as Lord Brangbolton's.

"I call it dashed low," his lordship was saying in his high-pitched tenor.

Sir Jasper gazed in bewilderment. His host, Sir Sutton Hartley-Wesping, was standing backed against the wall, and Lord Brangbolton, tapping him on the shirtfront with a piston-like forefinger, was plainly in the process of giving him a thorough ticking off.

"What's the matter?" asked the financier.

"I'll tell you what's the matter," cried Lord Brangbolton. "This hound here has got down a detective to watch his guests. A dashed fellow named Mulliner. So much," he said bitterly, "for our boasted English hospitality. Egad!" he went on, still tapping the baronet round and about the diamond solitaire. "I call it thoroughly low. If I have a few of my society chums down to my little place for a visit, naturally I chain up the hairbrushes and tell the butler to count the spoons every night, but I'd never dream of going so far as to employ beastly detectives. One has one's code. *Noblesse*, I mean to say, *oblige*, what, what?"

"But, listen," pleaded the baronet. "I keep telling you. I had to invite the fellow here. I thought that if he had eaten my bread and salt, he would not expose me."

"How do you mean, expose you?"

Sir Sutton coughed.

"Oh, it was nothing. The merest trifle. Still, the man undoubtedly could have made things unpleasant for me, if he had wished. So, when I looked up and saw him smiling at me in that frightful sardonic, knowing way——"

Sir Jasper Addleton uttered a sharp cry.

"Smiling!" He gulped. "Did you say smiling?"

"Smiling," said the baronet, "is right. It was one of those smiles that seem to go right through you and light up all your inner being as if with a searchlight."

Sir Jasper gulped again.

"Is this fellow—this smiler fellow—is he a tall, dark, thin chap?"

"That's right. He sat opposite you at dinner."

"And he's a detective?"

"He is," said Lord Brangbolton. "As shrewd and smart a detective," he added grudgingly, "as I ever met in my life. The way he found that soap . . . Feller struck me as having some sort of a sixth sense, if you know what I mean, dash and curse him. I hate detectives," he said with a shiver. "They give me the creeps. This one wants to marry my daughter, Millicent, of all the dashed nerve!"

"See you later," said Sir Jasper. And with a single bound he was out of the room and on his way to the terrace. There was, he felt, no time to waste. His florid face, as he galloped along, was twisted and ashen. With one hand he drew from his inside pocket a check book, with the other from his trouser pocket a fountain pen.

Adrian, when the financier found him, was feeling a good deal better. He blessed the day when he had sought the specialist's advice. There was no doubt about it, he felt, the man knew his business. Smiling might make the cheek muscles ache, but it undoubtedly did the trick as regarded the pangs of dyspepsia.

For a brief while before Sir Jasper burst onto the terrace, waving fountain pen and check book, Adrian had been giving his face a rest. But now, the pain in his cheeks having abated, he deemed it prudent to resume the treatment. And so it came about that the financier, hurrying towards him, was met with a smile so meaning,

so suggestive, that he stopped in his tracks and for a
moment could not speak.

"Oh, there you are!" he said, recovering at length.
"Might I have a word with you in private, Mr. Mulliner?"

Adrian nodded, beaming. The financier took him by
the coat sleeve and led him across the terrace. He was
breathing a little stertorously.

"I've been thinking things over," he said, "and I've
come to the conclusion that you were right."

"Right?" said Adrian.

"About me marrying. It wouldn't do."

"No?"

"Positively not. Absurd. I can see it now. I'm too old
for the girl."

"Yes."

"Too bald."

"Exactly."

"And too fat."

"Much too fat," agreed Adrian. This sudden change of
heart puzzled him, but none the less the other's words
were as music to his ears. Every syllable the O.B.E. had
spoken had caused his heart to leap within him like a
young lamb in springtime, and his mouth curved in a
smile.

Sir Jasper, seeing it, shied like a frightened horse. He
patted Adrian's arm feverishly.

"So I have decided," he said, "to take your advice and
—if I recall your expression—give the thing a miss."

"You couldn't do better," said Adrian heartily.

"Now, if I were to remain in England in these circumstances," proceeded Sir Jasper, "there might be unpleas-
antness. So I propose to go quietly away at once to some
remote spot—say, South America. Don't you think I am
right?" he asked, giving the check book a twitch.

"Quite right," said Adrian.

"You won't mention this little plan of mine to anyone?
You will keep it as just a secret between ourselves? If, for
instance, any of your cronies at Scotland Yard should

express curiosity as to my whereabouts, you will plead ignorance?"

"Certainly."

"Capital!" said Sir Jasper, relieved. "And there is one other thing. I gather from Brangbolton that you are anxious to marry Lady Millicent yourself. And as by the time of the wedding I shall doubtless be in—well, Callao is a spot that suggests itself offhand, I would like to give you my little wedding present now."

He scribbled hastily in his check book, tore out a page and handed it to Adrian.

"Remember!" he said. "Not a word to anyone!"

"Quite," said Adrian.

He watched the financier disappear in the direction of the garage, regretting that he could have misjudged a man who so evidently had much good in him. Presently the sound of a motor engine announced that the other was on his way. Feeling that one obstacle, at least, between himself and his happiness had been removed, Adrian strolled indoors to see what the rest of the party were doing.

It was a quiet, peaceful scene that met his eyes as he wandered into the library. Overruling the request of some of the members of the company for a rubber of bridge, Lord Brangbolton had gathered them together at a small table and was initiating them into his favourite game of Persian Monarchs.

"It's perfectly simple, dash it," he was saying. "You just take the pack and cut. You bet—let us say ten pounds—that you will cut a higher card than the feller you're cutting against. And, if you do, you win, dash it. And, if you don't, the other dashed feller wins. Quite clear, what?"

Somebody said that it sounded a little like Blind Hooky.

"It is like Blind Hooky," said Lord Brangbolton. "Very like Blind Hooky. In fact, if you can play Blind Hooky, you can play Persian Monarchs."

They settled down to their game, and Adrian wandered about the room, endeavouring to still the riot of emotion which his recent interview with Sir Jasper Addleton had aroused in his bosom. All that remained for him to do now, he reflected, was by some means or other to remove the existing prejudice against him from Lord Brangbolton's mind.

It would not be easy, of course. To begin with, there was the matter of his straitened means.

He suddenly remembered that he had not yet looked at the check which the financier had handed him. He pulled it out of his pocket.

And, having glanced at it, Adrian Mulliner swayed like a poplar in a storm.

Just what he had expected, he could not have said. A fiver, possibly. At the most, a tenner. Just a trifling gift, he had imagined, with which to buy himself a cigarette lighter, a fish slice, or an egg boiler.

The check was for a hundred thousand pounds.

So great was the shock that, as Adrian caught sight of himself in the mirror opposite to which he was standing, he scarcely recognized the face in the glass. He seemed to be seeing it through a mist. Then the mist cleared, and he saw not only his own face clearly, but also that of Lord Brangbolton, who was in the act of cutting against his left-hand neighbour, Lord Knubble of Knopp.

And, as he thought of the effect this sudden accession of wealth must surely have on the father of the girl he loved, there came into Adrian's face a sudden, swift smile.

And simultaneously from behind him he heard a gasping exclamation, and, looking in the mirror, he met Lord Brangbolton's eyes. Always a little prominent, they were now almost prawn-like in their convexity.

Lord Knubble of Knopp had produced a banknote from his pocket and was pushing it along the table.

"Another ace!" he exclaimed. "Well, I'm dashed!"

Lord Brangbolton had risen from his chair.

"Excuse me," he said in a strange, croaking voice. "I just want to have a little chat with my friend, my dear old friend, Mulliner here. Might I have a word in private with you, Mr. Mulliner?"

There was a silence between the two men until they had reached a corner of the terrace out of earshot of the library window. Then Lord Brangbolton cleared his throat.

"Mulliner," he began, "or, rather—what is your Christian name?"

"Adrian."

"Adrian, my dear fellow," said Lord Brangbolton, "my memory is not what it should be, but I seem to have a distinct recollection that, when I was in my bath before dinner, you said something about wanting to marry my daughter Millicent."

"I did," replied Adrian. "And, if your objections to me as a suitor were mainly financial, let me assure you that, since we last spoke, I have become a wealthy man."

"I never had any objections to you, Adrian, financial or otherwise," said Lord Brangbolton, patting his arm affectionately. "I have always felt that the man my daughter married ought to be a fine, warm-hearted young fellow like you. For you, Adrian," he proceeded, "are essentially warm-hearted. You would never dream of distressing a father-in-law by mentioning any . . . any little . . . well, in short, I saw from your smile in there that you had noticed that I was introducing into that game of Blind Hooky—or, rather, Persian Monarchs—certain little—shall I say variations?—designed to give it additional interest and excitement, and I feel sure that you would scorn to embarrass a father-in-law by . . . Well, to cut a long story short, my boy, take Millicent and with her a father's blessing."

He extended his hand. Adrian clasped it warmly.

"I am the happiest man in the world," he said, smiling.

Lord Brangbolton winced.

"Do you mind not doing that?" he said.

"I only smiled," said Adrian.

"I know," said Lord Brangbolton.

Little remains to be told. Adrian and Millicent were married three months later at a fashionable West End church. All society was there. The presents were both numerous and costly, and the bride looked charming. The service was conducted by the Very Reverend the Dean of Bittlesham.

It was in the vestry afterwards, as Adrian looked at Millicent, and seemed to realize for the first time that all his troubles were over and that this lovely girl was indeed his, for better or worse, that a full sense of his happiness swept over the young man.

All through the ceremony he had been grave, as befitted a man at the most serious point of his career. But now, fizzing as if with some spiritual yeast, he clasped her in his arms, and over her shoulder his face broke into a quick smile.

He found himself looking into the eyes of the Dean of Bittlesham. A moment later he felt a tap on his arm.

"Might I have a word with you in private, Mr. Mulliner?" said the dean in a low voice.

Noel Coward

MILD OATS

1922

(*When the curtain rises the stage is in darkness. There is the sound of voices. Enter* YOUNG MAN *followed by* YOUNG WOMAN. *He turns up lights, disclosing a comfortable little study with a sofa, arm-chairs, books, etc., and the remains of a fire in the grate.*)

HE. Won't you sit down?

SHE. Yes—thank you. (*She comes slowly down and sits on the sofa. She takes off her coat.*)

HE (*after a slight pause*). Do you know—the weather really is quite chilly.

SHE (*with an effort*). Isn't it? One can feel the tang of autumn in the air.

HE. Yes, one can.

(*Another pause.*)

SHE (*defiantly*). I *like* London in the autumn!

HE (*with equal defiance*). So do I!

SHE. It's so—so—melancholy.

HE. Yes—yes, melancholy—that's what it is.

SHE. What's the time?

HE (*glaring at his watch*). Half-past twelve.

SHE. It's late, isn't it?

HE. Very late.

SHE. What a pretty room.

HE. Yes, isn't it?—I mean—do you think so?

SHE. Oh yes—it's so—so cosy and home-like.

HE. I'm so glad.

SHE (*rising*). Books, too. Do you read much?

HE. Now and then. I mean—you know—sometimes.

SHE (*at shelves*). Nice books—specially that one.

HE. Which one?

336

SHE. Here—Strindberg.

HE. Oh, Strindberg—rather depressing fellow, isn't he?

SHE. Yes, but life—real life all the time—no false sentiment and—and—hypocrisy.

HE. Oh no, rather not—as a matter of fact I haven't read him much. This flat isn't really mine, you know—only lent to me.

SHE. Oh, I see. (*She sits down again.*)

HE. I haven't been here long.

SHE. It's very central.

HE. Yes—isn't it? (*Another pause.*) Would you like something to drink?

SHE (*quickly*). Oh no, thank you. (*Correcting herself.*) That is—perhaps—— (*With determination*) Yes, I would.

HE. I'm afraid there's only whiskey and soda. (*Crosses to table.*)

SHE (*blankly*). Whiskey and soda!

HE. *Yes*—is that all right?

SHE. *Yes*—that's all right.

HE. Say when.

SHE (*hurriedly*). Not much, you know—just a little—now—there—that's enough.

HE (*handing her a colourless drink*). It's very weak.

SHE (*shutting her eyes and handing it back*). Put some more whiskey in, then.

HE (*startled by her sudden vehemence*). Oh, all right —here you are.

SHE (*taking it*). Thank you——(*She sniffs it.*) Oh dear!

HE. What is it?

SHE. Nothing——

    (*She sips it and shudders. He doesn't notice.*)

HE (*sitting next to her on sofa*). Funny my meeting you like that.

SHE (*with a nervous laugh*). Yes—wasn't it?

HE. I could have sworn I'd seen you before somewhere.

SHE. I don't think so.

He. Silly mistake to make. Look here, I——

She (*edging away*). What is it?

He. Oh, nothing.

She (*after a pause*). I should like you to understand that——

He. Yes?

She (*looking down*). Oh, nothing.

He (*suddenly*). It's no use; I can't——

She. Can't what?

He. Can't go on any longer. (*With vehemence*) Look here, I don't care what you think of me—you're probably laughing up your sleeve all the time—but it doesn't matter—I mean—look here, will you go now?

She (*with her hand to her head*). You mean—— Oh dear! (*She faints on to his shoulder.*)

He. Good God! (*He fans her.*) This is awful—awful! Wake up for heaven's sake—— Oh, this is terrible! (*He props her up with a cushion.*)

She (*opening her eyes*). Oh—what have I done?

He. You fainted.

She (*bursting into tears*). Oh, this is awful—horrible! (*She leans on the edge of sofa and buries her head in her arms.*)

He. I say, what's the matter? I didn't mean to be rude —honestly I didn't——

She (*sobbing*). I'm so ashamed—so dreadfully, dreadfully ashamed.

He. Here, drink a little of this. (*He offers her her untasted drink.*)

She (*pushing it away*). Take it away, it makes me sick.

He. All right. I say, I'm so sorry—do please stop crying.

She. Leave me alone—just for a minute, then I shall feel better. (*She sits up.*)

He. I am a beast!

She. No you're not—that's just it—you're not, thank God. (*She rises.*) I must go at once.

He. Where do you live?

She. Kensington.

HE. I'll see you home.

SHE. Oh no, please don't—it isn't necessary——

HE. I'll get you a taxi, then.

SHE. Very well—thank you.

HE. Wait here. (*He goes to door.*)

SHE. Stop.

HE (*startled*). What is it?

SHE. Please come and sit down—just for a moment. I want to tell you something——

HE. *But*——

SHE. Please—I really must—it may relieve this feeling of beastly degradation to tell you the truth——

HE. I wish you wouldn't look so unhappy.

SHE (*vehemently*). Unhappy! I'm desperately, bitterly ashamed—I've no words to express my utter contempt of myself——

HE. I don't understand.

SHE. I'm not what you thought I was at all.

HE (*embarrassed*). I didn't think you were after the first few minutes.

SHE. That's why you asked me to go?

HE. No, not exactly. I mean——

SHE. Oh, I am so grateful—you're a dear—I've been very, very fortunate—I—— (*She almost breaks down again.*)

HE. I say—please——

SHE (*pulling herself together*). All right—I won't cry any more—you must think I'm an abject fool—I am too —worse than that. Listen to me, I'm a perfectly ordinary girl—I live in Rutland Gate with my Aunt, I go to matinées and dances and walk in the Park and help get up Tableaux Vivants for charity——

HE. But—I——

SHE. Don't look so shocked—it makes it much harder to tell you everything—I read an awful lot—all the modern writers and the papers. I've over-educated myself in all the things I shouldn't have known about at all. I've been railing against the dullness of my life—a woman's life in general—I've read vehement feminist articles and pamphlets. I've worked myself up into a state of boiling indignation at the injustice of sex relationships—why shouldn't women have the same chances as men—lead the same lives as men—you know the sort of thing. I've been thinking myself a clever emancipated modernist—with a cool clear sense of values—and look at me—look at me ——— (*She giggles hysterically.*) My Aunt went away to Bournemouth the day before yesterday for a week and I decided to make my experiment—to see life, real life, at close quarters—young men are allowed to go out and enjoy themselves when they're of age—why shouldn't young women have the same opportunities? Last night I went out to the theatre by myself and I started to walk home—feeling frightfully dashing—then it began to pour with rain, so I squashed into a bus and went straight to bed. To-night I was quite determined. I had dinner—by myself—at a place in Oxford Street, then I walked down into Piccadilly Circus—and down Haymarket and along the Strand, then back again to Leicester Square. I sat on a seat in the little garden place in the middle until a filthy drunk man came and sat down next to me—then I began walking again and looking at all the people—hundreds and hundreds of them—all pouring out of the theatres and crowding the pavements—it really was rather an exciting feeling——— You wouldn't understand it, I know, because you're a man and you haven't always been looked after and coddled all your life—you've been encouraged to be independent—but to me it was thrilling. I was all alone—absolutely my own mistress—then I suddenly realised how tired I was, so I went into Appendrodt's and had a cup of chocolate. Two awful women were at the next table with a squirmy little man, and they started to have a row over his head—it was beastly—all the things they said—but very funny; in the end they were all turned out swearing like anything! Then I went out again and everything was different—all the crowds had disappeared and there was hardly any traffic except a few taxis going very fast. I walked all down Piccadilly—awfully quickly—because all the other women were sauntering so—I was

just passing the Berkeley when an arc lamp in the middle
of the road suddenly spluttered loudly—I nearly jumped
out of my skin. Then I laughed at myself and began to
walk more slowly—taking notice of things—the people's
faces—it was strange—then—then—— Oh dear! (*She
closes her eyes for a moment.*) Then a man smiled at me.
I thought just for a second that I knew him, so I looked
round and he was standing still. Then he began to stroll
after me—my heart beat horribly and I strained every
nerve to try to keep cool and think what to do—calmly
—but I couldn't. I lost my head and ran up a side street
like a rabbit—he must have laughed. Then I leant against
some railings in Curzon Street and pulled myself together—I was a coward—a weak, silly coward, so then,
more in order to punish myself for my lack of courage
than anything else—I made up my mind to let a man—
pick me up—— Oh, I know it's contemptible—don't look
at me like that—but remember all this is the outcome of
months—almost years—of modern literature—I wanted
experience of life. Nothing could happen to me really—
I'm quite capable of taking care of myself—I just wanted
to see—then with the full flush of my determination still
on me—I met you in Downs Street. Oh dear, hasn't it
been horrible! (*She sobs.*) Too utterly horrible for
words——

He. Look here, it hasn't really, you know—I won't
breathe a word——

She. I know you won't—but—I don't feel as if I could
ever shake off the shame of it——

He. There hasn't been any shame——

She. I should like to go into a convent—straight away
—this minute.

He. You're taking it all much too seriously—it's funny
rather—when you analyse it.

She. When I'm married and middle-aged I may look
back upon it as being funny, but until then I shall blush
down to my feet every time I think of it——

He. I've never been out in London alone until this week
—a friend of mine asked me up to stay here in this flat.

Then he had to go away suddenly on business and so I was left on my own.

SHE. Is that true—really?

HE. Yes—that's why I asked you to go at first—I felt rotten.

SHE. Did you?

HE. Yes—absolutely. I thought you were laughing at me.

SHE. Laughing—— Good heavens!

HE. Yes—isn't it silly the way one is always so terrified of being laughed at?—it matters so little really.

SHE. Less than anything.

HE. All my friends talk such a lot about the gay times they have in Town—you know——

SHE. Yes.

HE. I thought to myself this is a wonderful opportunity—being alone—and everything——

SHE. Just like me.

HE. Yes—exactly——

SHE. How old are you?

HE. Twenty-one.

SHE. So am I.

HE. I'm most awfully sorry if I upset you and made you feel horrid.

SHE. You've been very kind and considerate. I don't know what I should have done if it had been anyone else.

HE. Neither do I.

SHE. I wish you'd empty that whiskey away—I do hate the smell of it.

HE. I'm not crazy about it. I say—shall we make some tea?

SHE. No, I must go now—really——

HE. It would be nice—are you sure?

SHE. Yes, quite—I must.

HE. All right. (*He goes to window.*) There's probably a cab in the rank. Why, it's pouring——

SHE. Oh! Is there a cab there?

HE (*looking out sideways against the glass*). No——
Damn. I'm so sorry.

SHE. I'll soon find one.

HE. No—look here—do stay a little longer until the rain stops. We could have some tea after all——

SHE. But—but——

HE. We *are* friends—aren't we? (*He holds out his hand.*)

SHE. Yes—very well—just a little longer.

(*They shake hands.*)

HE. You'd better take off your coat again.

SHE. All right.

(*He helps her off with it and puts it on the chair.*)

HE. Now for some tea.

SHE. Where's the kettle?

HE. In the kitchen. I'll go and fill it and we can boil it in here—there's just enough fire. Will you get two cups out—they're in that cupboard, also some biscuits.

SHE. All right.

(*He goes off.*)

(*She takes cups from cupboard and puts them on table, also a biscuit tin.*)

HE (*off*). How many spoonfuls in the pot?

SHE (*going to door*). Two, I should think—and a half a one.

HE. Righto.

(*She goes over and pokes up the fire a little. He comes in with a small tray, upon which is a tea-pot and the kettle.*)

I haven't put much water in so it ought to boil quickly. (*He places it on the fire.*)

SHE. Now we must possess our souls in patience. (*She sits down on sofa.*)

HE. We won't take any notice of it at all—we won't look round even if it sings.

SHE. Yes, I'm sure that's the only way.

HE. What's your name?

SHE (*hesitatingly*). Oh——

HE (*quickly*). I'm so sorry—I forgot—if you'd rather not tell me I shall quite understand—mine is Hugh Lombard.

SHE. Mine is Mary Jevon.

HE. That's a pretty name.

SHE. I used to think it was much too phlegmatic and English—but still, if you think it's pretty——

HE. Oh, rather—I like it all the better for being English.

SHE. So do I—in my heart—I've been hankering after something a little more exotic lately——

HE. Further effects of modern literature on the young.

SHE. Now don't laugh at me——

HE. Sorry.

SHE. You know what we are, don't you?

HE. No, what?

SHE. We're the victims of civilisation.

HE. Are we?

SHE. Yes we are—because we're really quite simple-minded and ordinary—deep down inside—but we've both been trying awfully hard to keep pace with the modern rate of living. If we went on much longer we'd kill all our real niceness——

HE. I say, you know you are clever.

SHE (*suddenly*). Oh, don't—don't——

HE. Don't what?

SHE. Don't pander to me—you'll undo all the good you've done!

HE. The *good* I've done—what *are* you talking about?

SHE. You've done me all the good in the world—you're thoroughly honest—and nice—and you're not really shocked at me and you like my name.

HE. I don't see where the good comes in?

SHE. You've saved me from myself—I know that sounds melodramatic—but it's true—absolutely.

HE. You've done the same for me—you made me feel awfully ashamed of myself—specially when you cried.

SHE. I am glad.

HE. So am I—why did you ask me not to pander to you?

SHE. Because I was being clever—and modern thought-ish——

He. No you weren't—you were being sweet.

She. Don't be silly.

He. But you were—awfully——

She (*vehemently*). Never again—never, never, never again.

He. Never again what?

She. From this moment on I'm going to be myself—my real self—not my Chelsea edition——

He. So am I—not my "young man about town" edition——

She. Splendid!

He. I say—I've got an idea——

She. What——

He. Look here—why shouldn't we——

She. The kettle's boiling.

He. Oh—— (*He gets up.*) No it isn't.

She. I saw some steam coming out.

He. Only very little—it fairly spouts when it's really ready——

She. What were you going to say?

He. I won't say it yet—after all——

She. Why not?

He. I'm afraid of spoiling things.

She. Oh!

(*They sit silent for a moment.*)

I wonder if it's stopped raining. (*She gets up and goes to window.*)

He. Has it?

She. It's not so bad as it was—it's rather difficult to see here—one can only tell by the puddles.

He (*joining her at window*). Aren't the pavements shining—like glass.

She. Yes, exactly—if you screw round the corner a bit you can just catch a glimpse of the Park. (*She flattens her face against the pane.*)

He. Yes, it's jolly being so near——

She. What part of the country do you come from?

He. Kent—the marshes.

She. No!

He. Yes, why?

She. I know that well—between Rye and Folkestone——

He. Yes—Ivychurch—my home's just near Ivychurch.

She. How lovely—it's beautiful on the marsh with all the dykes and space and the smell of the sea——

He. I am glad you know it—and like it——

She. Look, the kettle really is boiling now.

He. Come and hold the tea-pot.

(*They crouch together by the fireplace—and make the tea, then they put the pot on the tray.*)

Let's have it on the sofa—we can rest the tray on our knees.

She. All right. I'll sit down just—here—give it to me——

He. All right—biscuits first.

(*He places tin on the floor at their feet—then he hands her tray and sits down gingerly beside her.*)

She. Be careful.

He. Isn't that cosy!

She. It isn't really drawn yet but it doesn't matter. (*She pours out.*)

He. I don't think I've ever liked anybody so much—so quickly—before.

She. What nonsense!—— Sugar?

He. Yes, please—two.

She. I've been pretending I like lemon in my tea for months—instead of milk.

He. I know—so Russian!

She (*laughing*). Exactly——

He. I really do want to say something—important—and you keep stopping me.

She. I know.

He. Why——

She. For the same reason you said just now—it might spoil things——

He. It wouldn't—I don't think——

She. Don't let's risk it—yet.

He (*gloomily*). All right——

(They drink in silence for a moment.)

SHE. What do you do?

HE. How do you mean?

SHE. Work.

HE. I'm going to be a soldier.

SHE. Oh——

HE. The worst of it is—it will probably mean India——

SHE. Oh, that kind of soldier.

HE. Yes—life on verandahs with punkahs waving and clinking ices in tumblers and beautiful catty women in sequin dresses——

SHE. And spotless white breeches and polo ponies and sudden native risings and thrilling escapes—lovely!

HE. Do you think you'd like it?

SHE. Yes—anyhow at first—it sounds so—so different.

HE. I'm glad you don't hate the idea——

SHE. What's the time?

HE *(putting down his cup.)* Early—look. *(He shows her his watch.)*

SHE *(putting down her cup with a bang).* I must go now—at once—really I must.

HE. Oh——

SHE. Even if it's coming down in torrents—— *(She goes to window.)*

HE. I wish you'd stay—a little longer.

SHE. No—it would be silly to linger on—I feel frightfully tired and I'm sure you are too—we should only get sleepy and bored. The rain's quite stopped—and there's actually a cab there——

HE. Damn it!

SHE. Now then!

HE. I wanted to walk with you until we found one.

SHE. You can walk with me all the way downstairs.

HE. All right.

SHE. Help me with my coat.

HE. Here.

> *(He helps her on with her coat—then he takes her hand.)*

Thank you ever so much—it's been lovely.

SHE. Yes, it has——

HE. Let me say it—now.

SHE. What?

HE. Will you marry me?

SHE. Don't be silly.

HE. I'm not silly. I mean it.

SHE. We don't know one another.

HE. Yes, we do—frightfully well.

SHE. No—it's too soon.

HE. I'm beginning to love you terribly——

SHE. No you don't—not really—you can't——

HE. Why not?

SHE. I don't know.

HE. Time doesn't make the least difference—you *know* it doesn't.

SHE. Perhaps—perhaps it doesn't——

HE. Could you ever care for me—do you think?

SHE. I don't know.

HE. Will you try?

SHE (*nods*). Don't—else I shall cry again.

HE. You are a dear!

(*He takes her in his arms and kisses her.*)

SHE (*tremulously*). Now my hat's crooked——

(*They go out together, his arm protectively round her.*)

CURTAIN

Henry Beston

NIGHT ON THE GREAT BEACH

Our fantastic civilization has fallen out of touch with many aspects of nature, and with none more completely than with night. Primitive folk, gathered at a cave mouth round a fire, do not fear night; they fear, rather, the energies and creatures to whom night gives power; we of the age of the machines, having delivered ourselves of nocturnal enemies, now have a dislike of night itself. With lights and ever more lights, we drive the holiness and beauty of night back to the forests and the sea; the little villages, the crossroads even, will have none of it. Are modern folk, perhaps, afraid of night? Do they fear that vast serenity, the mystery of infinite space, the austerity of stars? Having made thmselves at home in a civilization obsessed with power, which explains its whole world in terms of energy, do they fear at night for their dull acquiescence and the pattern of their beliefs? Be the answer what it will, to-day's civilization is full of people who have not the slightest notion of the character or the poetry of night, who have never even seen night. Yet to live thus, to know only artificial night, is as absurd and evil as to know only artificial day.

Night is very beautiful on this great beach. It is the true other half of the day's tremendous wheel; no lights without meaning stab or trouble it; it is beauty, it is fulfilment, it is rest. Thin clouds float in these heavens, islands of obscurity in a splendour of space and stars: the Milky Way bridges earth and ocean; the beach resolves itself into a unity of form, its summer lagoons, its slopes and uplands merging; against the western sky and the falling bow of sun rise the silent and superb undulations of the dunes.

My nights are at their darkest when a dense fog streams

in from the sea under a black, unbroken floor of cloud.
Such nights are rare, but are most to be expected when
fog gathers off the coast in early summer; this last
Wednesday night was the darkest I have known. Between
ten o'clock and two in the morning three vessels stranded
on the outer beach—a fisherman, a four-masted schooner,
and a beam trawler. The fisherman and the schooner have
been towed off, but the trawler, they say, is still ashore.

I went down to the beach that night just after ten
o'clock. So utterly black, pitch dark it was, and so thick
with moisture and trailing showers, that there was no sign
whatever of the beam of Nauset; the sea was only a sound,
and when I reached the edge of the surf the dunes themselves had disappeared behind. I stood as isolate in that
immensity of rain and night as I might have stood in
interplanetary space. The sea was troubled and noisy,
and when I opened the darkness with an outlined cone of
light from my electric torch I saw that the waves were
washing up green coils of sea grass, all coldly wet and
bright in the motionless and unnatural radiance. Far off
a single ship was groaning its way along the shoals. The
fog was compact of the finest moisture; passing by, it
spun itself into my lens of light like a kind of strange,
aërial, and liquid silk. Effin Chalke, the new coast guard,
passed me going north, and told me that he had had news
at the halfway house of the schooner at Cahoon's.

It was dark, pitch dark to my eye, yet complete darkness, I imagine, is exceedingly rare, perhaps unknown in
outer nature. The nearest natural approximation to it is
probably the gloom of forest country buried in night and
cloud. Dark as the night was here, there was still light
on the surface of the planet. Standing on the shelving
beach, with the surf breaking at my feet, I could see the
endless wild uprush, slide, and withdrawal of the sea's
white rim of foam. The men at Nauset tell me that on such
nights they follow along this vague crawl of whiteness,
trusting to habit and a sixth sense to warn them of their
approach to the halfway house.

Animals descend by starlight to the beach. North, be-

yond the dunes, muskrats forsake the cliff and nose about
in the driftwood and weed, leaving intricate trails and
figure eights to be obliterated by the day; the lesser folk
—the mice, the occasional small sand-coloured toads, the
burrowing moles—keep to the upper beach and leave their
tiny footprints under the overhanging wall. In autumn
skunks, beset by a shrinking larder, go beach combing
early in the night. The animal is by preference a clean
feeder and turns up his nose at rankness. I almost stepped
on a big fellow one night as I was walking north to meet
the first man south from Nauset. There was a scamper,
and the creature ran up the beach from under my feet;
alarmed he certainly was, yet was he contained and continent. Deer are frequently seen, especially north of the
light. I find their tracks upon the summer dunes.

Years ago, while camping on this beach north of
Nauset, I went for a stroll along the top of the cliff at
break of dawn. Though the path followed close enough
along the edge, the beach below was often hidden, and I
looked directly from the height to the flush of sunrise at
sea. Presently the path, turning, approached the brink of
the earth precipice, and on the beach below, in the cool,
wet rosiness of dawn, I saw three deer playing. They
frolicked, rose on their hind legs, scampered off, and returned again, and were merry. Just before sunrise they
trotted off north together down the beach toward a hollow
in the cliff and the path that climbs it.

Occasionally a sea creature visits the shore at night.
Lone coast guardsmen, trudging the sand at some deserted hour, have been startled by seals. One man fell flat
on a creature's back, and it drew away from under him,
flippering toward the sea, with a sound "halfway between
a squeal and a bark." I myself once had rather a start. It
was long after sundown, the light dying and uncertain,
and I was walking home on the top level of the beach and
close along the slope descending to the ebbing tide. A
little more than halfway to the Fo'castle a huge unexpected something suddenly writhed horribly in the darkness under my bare foot. I had stepped on a skate left

stranded by some recent crest of surf, and my weight had momentarily annoyed it back to life.

Facing north, the beam of Nauset becomes part of the dune night. As I walk toward it, I see the lantern, now as a star of light which waxes and wanes three mathematic times, now as a lovely pale flare of light behind the rounded summits of the dunes. The changes in the atmosphere change the colour of the beam; it is now whitish, now flame golden, now golden red; it changes its form as well, from a star to a blare of light, from a blare of light to a cone of radiance sweeping a circumference of fog. To the west of Nauset I often see the apocalyptic flash of the great light at the Highland reflected on the clouds or even on the moisture in the starlit air, and, seeing it, I often think of the pleasant hours I have spent there when George and Mary Smith were at the light and I had the good fortune to visit as their guest. Instead of going to sleep in the room under the eaves, I would lie awake, looking out of a window to the great spokes of light revolving as solemnly as a part of the universe.

All night long the lights of coastwise vessels pass at sea, green lights going south, red lights moving north. Fishing schooners and flounder draggers anchor two or three miles out, and keep a bright riding light burning on the mast. I see them come to anchor at sundown, but I rarely see them go, for they are off at dawn. When busy at night, these fishermen illumine their decks with a scatter of oil flares. From shore, the ships might be thought afire. I have watched the scene through a night glass. I could see no smoke, only the waving flares, the reddish radiance on sail and rigging, an edge of reflection overside, and the enormous night and sea beyond.

One July night, as I returned at three o'clock from an expedition north, the whole night, in one strange, burning instant, turned into a phantom day. I stopped and, questioning, stared about. An enormous meteor, the largest I have ever seen, was consuming itself in an effulgence of light west of the zenith. Beach and dune and ocean appeared out of nothing, shadowless and motionless, a landscape whose every tremor and vibration were stilled, a landscape in a dream.

The beach at night has a voice all its own, a sound in fullest harmony with its spirit and mood—with its little, dry noise of sand forever moving, with its solemn, over-spilling, rhythmic seas, with its eternity of stars that sometimes seem to hang down like lamps from the high heavens—and that sound the piping of a bird. As I walk the beach in early summer my solitary coming disturbs it on its nest, and it flies away, troubled, invisible, piping its sweet, plaintive cry. The bird I write of is the piping plover, *Charadrius melodus*, sometimes called the beach plover or the mourning bird. Its note is a whistled syllable, the loveliest musical note, I think, sounded by any North Atlantic bird.

Now that summer is here I often cook myself a camp supper on the beach. Beyond the crackling, salt-yellow driftwood flame, over the pyramid of barrel staves, broken boards, and old sticks all atwist with climbing fire, the un-seen ocean thunders and booms, the breaker sounding hollow as it falls. The wall of the sand cliff behind, with its rim of grass and withering roots, its sandy crumblings and erosions, stands gilded with flame; wind cries over it; a covey of sandpipers pass between the ocean and the fire. There are stars, and to the south Scorpio hangs curving down the sky with ringed Saturn shining in his claw.

Learn to reverence night and to put away the vulgar fear of it, for, with the banishment of night from the experience of man, there vanishes as well a religious emo-tion, a poetic mood, which gives depth to the adventure of humanity. By day, space is one with the earth and with man—it is his sun that is shining, his clouds that are float-ing past; at night, space is his no more. When the great earth, abandoning day, rolls up the deeps of the heavens and the universe, a new door opens for the human spirit, and there are few so clownish that some awareness of the mystery of being does not touch them as they gaze. For a moment of night we have a glimpse of ourselves and of our world islanded in its stream of stars—pilgrims of mortality, voyaging between horizons across eternal seas of space and time. Fugitive though the instant be, the spirit of man is, during it, ennobled by a genuine moment of emotional dignity, and poetry makes its own both the human spirit and experience.

II

At intervals during the summer, often enough when the tides are high and the moon is near the full, the surf along the beach turns from a churn of empty moonlit water to a mass of panic life. Driven in by schools of larger fish, swarms of little fish enter the tumble of the surf, the eaters follow them, the surf catches them both up and throws them, mauled and confused, ashore.

Under a sailing moon, the whole churn of sea close off the beach vibrates with a primeval ferocity and intensity of life; yet is this war of rushing mouth and living food without a sound save for the breaking of the seas. But let me tell of such a night.

I had spent an afternoon ashore with friends, and they had driven me to Nauset Station just after nine o'clock. The moon, two days from the full, was very lovely on the moors and on the channels and flat, moon-green isles of the lagoon; the wind was southerly and light. Moved by its own enormous rhythms, the surf that night was a stately incoming of high, serried waves, the last wave alone breaking. This inmost wave broke heavily in a smother and rebound of sandy foam, and thin sheets of seethe, racing before it up the beach, vanished endlessly into the endless thirst of the sands. As I neared the surf rim to begin my walk to the southward, I saw that the beach close along the breakers, as far as the eye would reach, was curiously atwinkle in the moonlight with the convulsive dance of myriads of tiny fish. The breakers were spilling them on the sands; the surf was aswarm with the creatures; it was indeed, for the time being, a surf of life. And this surf of life was breaking for miles along the Cape.

Little herring or mackerel? Sand eels? I picked a dancer out of the slide and held him up to the moon. It was the familiar sand eel or sand launce, *Ammodytes americanus*, of the waters between Hatteras and Labrador. This is no kin of the true eels, though he rather resembles one in general appearance, for his body is slender, eel-like, and round. Instead of ending bluntly, however, this "eel" has a large, well-forked tail. The fish in the surf were two and three inches long.

Homeward that night I walked barefooted in the surf, watching the convulsive, twinkling dance, now and then feeling the squirm of a fish across my toes. Presently something occurred which made me keep to the thinnest edge of the foam. Some ten feet ahead, an enormous dogfish was suddenly borne up the beach on the rim of a slide of foam; he moved with it unresisting while it carried him; the slide withdrawing and drying up, it rolled him twice over seaward; he then twisted heavily, and another minor slide carried him back again to shore. The fish was about three feet long, a real junior shark, purplish black in the increasing light—for the moon was moving west across the long axis of the breakers—and his dark, important bulk seemed strange in the bright dance of the smaller fish about him.

It was then that I began to look carefully at the width of gathering seas. Here were the greater fish, the mouths, the eaters who had driven the "eels" ashore to the edge of their world and into ours. The surf was alive with dogfish, aswarm with them, with the rush, the cold bellies, the twist and tear of their wolfish violence of life. Yet there was but little sign of it in the waters—a rare fin slicing past, and once the odd and instant glimpse of a fish embedded like a fly in amber in the bright, overturning volute of a wave.

Too far in, the dogfish were now in the grip of the surf, and presently began to come ashore. As I walked the next half mile every other breaker seemed to leave behind its ebb a mauled and stranded sharklet feebly sculling with his tail. I kicked many back into the seas, risking a toe, perhaps; some I caught by the tails and flung, for I did not want them corrupting on the beach. The next morning, in the mile and three quarters between the Fo'castle and the station, I counted seventy-one dogfish lying dead on the upper beach. There were also a dozen or two skates—the skate is really a kind of shark—which had stranded the same night. Skates follow in many things, and are forever being flung upon these sands.

I sat up late that night at the Fo'castle, often putting down the book I read to return to the beach.

A little after eleven came Bill Eldredge to the door, with a grin on his face and one hand held behind his back. "Have you ordered to-morrow's dinner yet?" said he. "No." "Well, here it is," and Bill produced a fine cod from behind his back. "Just found him right in front of your door, alive and flopping. Yes, yes, haddock and cod often chase those sand eels in with the bigger fish; often find them on the beach about this time of the year. Got any place to keep him? Let me have a piece of string and I'll hang him on your clothesline. He'll keep all right." With a deft unforking of two fingers, Bill drew the line through the gills, and as he did so the heavy fish flopped noisily. No fear about him being dead. Make a nice chowder. Bill stepped outside; I heard him at the clothesline. Afterward we talked till it was time for him to shoulder his clock and Coston case again, pick up his watch cap, whistle in his little black dog, and go down over the dune to the beach and Nauset Station.

There were nights in June when there was phosphorescence in the surf and on the beach, and one such night I think I shall remember as the most strange and beautiful of all the year.

Early this summer the middle beach moulded itself into a bar, and between it and the dunes are long, shallow runnels into which the ocean spills over at high tide. On the night I write of, the first quarter of the moon hung in the west, and its light on the sheets of incoming tide coursing thin across the bar was very beautiful to see. Just after sundown I walked to Nauset with friends who had been with me during the afternoon; the tide was still rising, and a current running in the pools. I lingered at the station with my friends till the last of sunset had died, and the light upon the planet, which had been moonlight mingled with sunset pink, had cleared to pure cold moon.

Southward, then, I turned, and because the flooded runnels were deep close by the station, I could not cross them and had to walk their inner shores. The tide had fallen half a foot, perhaps, but the breakers were still leaping up against the bar as against a wall, the greater ones still spilling over sheets of vanishing foam.

It grew darker with the westing of the moon. There was light on the western tops of the dunes, a fainter light on the lower beach and the breakers; the face of the dunes was a unity of dusk.

The tide had ebbed in the pools, and their edges were wet and dark. There was a strange contrast between the still levels of the pool and the seethe of the sea. I kept close to the land edge of the lagoons, and as I advanced my boots kicked wet spatters of sand ahead as they might have kicked particles of snow. Every spatter was a crumb of phosphorescence; I walked in a dust of stars. Behind me, in my footprints, luminous patches burned. With the double-ebb moonlight and tide, the deepening brims of the pools took shape in smouldering, wet fire. So strangely did the luminous speckles smoulder and die and glow that it seemed as if some wind were passing, by whose breath they were kindled and extinguished. Occasional whole breakers of phosphorescence rolled in out of the vague sea —the whole wave one ghostly motion, one creamy light— and, breaking against the bar, flung up pale sprays of fire.

A strange thing happens here during these luminous tides. The phosphorescence is itself a mass of life, sometimes protozoan its origin, sometimes bacterial, the phosphorescence I write of being probably the latter. Once this living light has seeped into the beach, colonies of it speed-

ily invade the tissues of the ten thousand thousand sand
fleas which are forever hopping on this edge of ocean.
Within an hour the grey bodies of these swarming amphi-
pods, these useful, ever hungry sea scavengers (*Orchestia
agilis; Talorchestia megalophthalma*), show phosphorescent pin points, and these points grow and unite till the
whole creature is luminous. The attack is really a disease,
an infection of light. The process had already begun
when I arrived on the beach on the night of which I am
writing, and the luminous fleas hopping off before my
boots were an extraordinary sight. It was curious to see
them hop from the pool rims to the upper beach, paling
as they reached the width of peaceful moonlight lying
landward of the strange, crawling beauty of the pools.
This infection kills them, I think; at least, I have often
found the larger creature lying dead on the fringe of the
beach, his huge porcelain eyes and water-grey body one
core of living fire. Round and about him, disregarding,
ten thousand kinsmen, carrying on life and the plan of
life, ate of the bounty of the tide.

III

All winter long I slept on a couch in my larger room,
but with the coming of warm weather I have put my bedroom in order—I used it as a kind of storage space during the cold season—and returned to my old and rather
rusty iron cot. Every once in a while, however, moved by
some obscure mood, I lift off the bedclothing and make
up the couch again for a few nights. I like the seven windows of the larger room, and the sense one may have
there of being almost out-of-doors. My couch stands
alongside the two front windows, and from my pillow I
can look out to sea and watch the passing lights, the stars
rising over ocean, the swaying lanterns of the anchored
fishermen, and the white spill of the surf whose long sound
fills the quiet of the dunes.

Ever since my coming I have wanted to see a thunderstorm bear down upon this elemental coast. A thunder-storm is a "tempest" on the Cape. The quoted word, as Shakespeare used it, means lightning and thunder, and it is in this old and beautiful Elizabethan sense that the word is used in Eastham. When a schoolboy in the Orleans or the Wellfleet High reads the Shakespearean play, its title means to him exactly what it meant to the man from Stratford; elsewhere in America, the terms seems to mean anything from a tornado to a blizzard. I imagine that this old significance of the word is now to be found only in certain parts of England and Cape Cod.

On the night of the June tempest, I was sleeping in my larger room, the windows were open, and the first low roll of thunder opened my eyes. It had been very still when I went to bed, but now a wind from the west-nor'west was blowing through the windows in a strong and steady current, and as I closed them there was lightning to the west and far away. I looked at my watch; it was just after one o'clock. Then came a time of waiting in the darkness, long minutes broken by more thunder, and intervals of quiet in which I heard a faintest sound of light surf upon the beach. Suddenly the heavens cracked open in an immense instant of pinkish-violet lightning. My seven windows filled with the violent, inhuman light, and I had a glimpse of the great, solitary dunes staringly empty of familiar shadows; a tremendous crash then mingled with the with-drawal of the light, and echoes of thunder rumbled away and grew faint in a returning rush of darkness. A moment after, rain began to fall gently as if someone had just re-leased its flow, a blessed sound on a roof of wooden shingles, and one I have loved ever since I was a child. From a gentle patter the sound of the rain grew swiftly to a drumming roar, and with the rain came the chuckling of water from the eaves. The tempest was crossing the Cape, striking at the ancient land on its way to the heavens above the sea.

Now came flash after stabbing flash amid a roaring of rain, and heavy thunder that rolled on till its last echoes were swallowed up in vast detonations which jarred the walls. Houses were struck that night in Eastham village. My lonely world, full of lightning and rain, was strange to look upon. I do not share the usual fear of lightning, but that night there came over me, for the first and last time of all my solitary year, a sense of isolation and remoteness from my kind. I remember that I stood up, watching, in the middle of the room. On the great marshes the lightning surfaced the winding channels with a metallic splendour and arrest of motion, all very strange through windows blurred by rain. Under the violences of light the great dunes took on a kind of elemental passivity, the quiet of earth enchanted into stone, and as I watched them appear and plunge back into a darkness that had an intensity of its own I felt, as never before, a sense of the vast time, of the thousands of cyclic and uncounted years which had passed since these giants had risen from the dark ocean at their feet and given themselves to the wind and the bright day.

Fantastic things were visible at sea. Beaten down by the rain, and sheltered by the Cape itself from the river of west wind, the offshore brim of ocean remained unusually calm. The tide was about halfway up the beach, and rising, and long parallels of low waves, forming close inshore, were curling over and breaking placidly along the lonely, rain-drenched miles. The intense crackling flares and quiverings of the storm, moving out to sea, illumined every inch of the beach and the plain of the Atlantic, all save the hollow bellies of the little breakers, which were shielded from the light by their overcurling crests. The effect was dramatic and strangely beautiful, for what one saw was a bright ocean rimmed with parallel bands of blackest advancing darkness, each one melting back to light as the wave toppled down upon the beach in foam.

Stars came out after the storm, and when I woke again before sunrise I found the heavens and the earth rainwashed, cool, and clear. Saturn and the Scorpion were setting, but Jupiter was riding the zenith and paling on his throne. The tide was low in the marsh channels; the gulls had scarcely stirred upon their gravel banks and bars. Suddenly, thus wandering about, I disturbed a song sparrow on her nest. She flew to the roof of my house, grasped the ridgepole, and turned about, apprehensive, inquiring . . . *'tsiped* her monosyllable of alarm. Then back toward her nest she flew, alighted in a plum bush, and, reassured at last, trilled out a morning song.

James Thurber

THE GREATEST MAN IN THE WORLD

LOOKING back on it now, from the vantage point of 1940, one can only marvel that it hadn't happened long before it did. The United States of America had been, ever since Kitty Hawk, blindly constructing the elaborate petard by which, sooner or later, it must be hoist. It was inevitable that some day there would come roaring out of the skies a national hero of insufficient intelligence, background, and character successfully to endure the mounting orgies of glory prepared for aviators who stayed up a long time or flew a great distance. Both Lindbergh and Byrd, fortunately for national decorum and international amity, had been gentlemen; so had our other famous aviators. They wore their laurels gracefully, withstood the awful weather of publicity, married excellent women, usually of fine family, and quietly retired to private life and the enjoyment of their varying fortunes. No untoward incidents, on a worldwide scale, marred the perfection of their conduct on the perilous heights of fame. The exception to the rule was, however, bound to occur and it did, in July, 1935, when Jack ("Pal") Smurch, erstwhile mechanic's helper in a small garage in Westfield, Iowa, flew a second-hand, single-motored Bresthaven Dragon-Fly III monoplane all the way around the world, without stopping.

Never before in the history of aviation had such a flight as Smurch's ever been dreamed of. No one had even taken seriously the weird floating auxiliary gas tanks, invention of the mad New Hampshire professor of astronomy, Dr. Charles Lewis Gresham, upon which Smurch placed full reliance. When the garage worker, a slightly built, surly, unprepossessing young man of twenty-two, appeared at Roosevelt Field early in July, 1935, slowly chewing a great quid of scrap tobacco, and announced "Nobody ain't seen no flyin' yet," the newspapers touched briefly and satirically upon his projected twenty-five-thousand-mile flight. Aëronautical and automotive experts dismissed the idea curtly, implying that it was a hoax, a publicity stunt. The rusty, battered, second-hand plane wouldn't go. The Gresham auxiliary tanks wouldn't work. It was simply a cheap joke.

Smurch, however, after calling on a girl in Brooklyn who worked in the flap-folding department of a large paper-box factory, a girl whom he later described as his "sweet patootie," climbed nonchalantly into his ridiculous plane at dawn of the memorable seventh of July, 1935, spit a curve of tobacco juice into the still air, and took off, carrying with him only a gallon of bootleg gin and six pounds of salami.

When the garage boy thundered out over the ocean the papers were forced to record, in all seriousness, that a mad, unknown young man—his name was variously misspelled—had actually set out upon a preposterous attempt to span the world in a rickety, one-engined contraption, trusting to the long-distance refuelling device of a crazy schoolmaster. When, nine days later, without having stopped once, the tiny plane appeared above San Francisco Bay, headed for New York, spluttering and choking, to be sure, but still magnificently and miraculously aloft, the headlines, which long since had crowded everything else off the front page—even the shooting of the Governor of Illinois by the Capone gang—swelled to unprecedented size, and the news stories began to run to twenty-five and thirty columns. It was noticeable, however, that the accounts of the epoch-making flight touched rather lightly upon the aviator himself. This was not because facts about the hero as a man were too meagre, but because they were too complete.

Reporters, who had been rushed out to Iowa when Smurch's plane was first sighted over the little French coast town of Serly-le-Mer, to dig up the story of the great man's life, had promptly discovered that the story of his life could not be printed. His mother, a sullen short-order cook in a shack restaurant on the edge of a tourists' camping ground near Westfield, met all inquiries as to her son with an angry "Ah, the hell with him; I hope he drowns." His father appeared to be in jail somewhere for stealing spotlights and laprobes from tourists' automobiles; his young brother, a weak-minded lad, had but recently escaped from the Preston, Iowa, Reformatory and was already wanted in several Western towns for the theft of money-order blanks from post offices. These alarming discoveries were still piling up at the very time that Pal Smurch, the greatest hero of the twentieth century, bleareyed, dead for sleep, half-starved, was piloting his crazy junk-heap high above the region in which the lamentable story of his private life was being unearthed, headed for New York and a greater glory than any man of his time had ever known.

The necessity for printing some account in the papers of the young man's career and personality had led to a remarkable predicament. It was of course impossible to reveal the facts, for a tremendous popular feeling in favor of the young hero had sprung up, like a grass fire, when he was halfway across Europe on his flight around the globe. He was, therefore, described as a modest chap, taciturn, blond, popular with his friends, popular with girls. The only available snapshot of Smurch, taken at the wheel of a phony automobile in a cheap photo studio at an amusement park, was touched up so that the little vulgarian looked quite handsome. His twisted leer was smoothed into a pleasant smile. The truth was, in this way, kept from the youth's ecstatic compatriots; they did not dream that the Smurch family was despised and feared by its neighbors in the obscure Iowa town, nor that the hero himself, because of numerous unsavory exploits, had come to be regarded in Westfield as a nuisance and a menace. He had, the reporters discovered, once knifed the principal of his high school—not mortally, to be sure, but he had knifed him; and on another occasion, surprised in the act of stealing an altarcloth from a church, he had bashed the sacristan over the head with a pot of Easter lilies; for each of these offences he had served a sentence in the reformatory.

Inwardly, the authorities, both in New York and in Washington, prayed that an understanding Providence might, however awful such a thing seemed, bring disaster to the rusty, battered plane and its illustrious pilot, whose unheard-of flight had aroused the civilized world to hosannas of hysterical praise. The authorities were convinced that the character of the renowned aviator was such that the limelight of adulation was bound to reveal him, to all the world, as a congenital hooligan mentally and morally unequipped to cope with his own prodigious fame. "I trust," said the Secretary of State, at one of many secret Cabinet meetings called to consider the national dilemma, "I trust that his mother's prayer will be answered," by which he referred to Mrs. Emma Smurch's wish that her son might be drowned. It was, however, too late for that—Smurch had leaped the Atlantic and then the Pacific as if they were millponds. At three minutes after two o'clock on the afternoon of July 17, 1935, the garage boy brought his idiotic plane into Roosevelt Field for a perfect three-point landing.

It had, of course, been out of the question to arrange a modest little reception for the greatest flier in the history of the world. He was received at Roosevelt Field with such elaborate and pretentious ceremonies as rocked the world. Fortunately, however, the worn and spent hero promptly swooned, had to be removed bodily from his plane, and was spirited from the field without having opened his mouth once. Thus he did not jeopardize the dignity of this first reception, a reception illumined by the presence of the Secretaries of War and the Navy, Mayor Michael J. Moriarity of New York, the Premier of Canada, Governors Fanniman, Groves, McFeely, and Critchfield, and a brilliant array of European diplomats. Smurch did not, in fact, come to in time to take part in the gigantic hullabaloo arranged at City Hall for the next day. He was rushed to a secluded nursing home and confined in bed. It was nine days before he was able to get up, or to be more exact, before he was permitted to get up. Meanwhile the greatest minds in the country, in solemn assembly, had arranged a secret conference of city, state, and government officials, which Smurch was to attend for the purpose of being instructed in the ethics and behavior of heroism.

On the day that the little mechanic was finally allowed to get up and dress and, for the first time in two weeks, took a great chew of tobacco, he was permitted to receive the newspapermen—this by way of testing him out. Smurch did not wait for questions. "Youse guys," he said —and the *Times* man winced—"youse guys can tell the cock-eyed world dat I put it over on Lindbergh, see? Yeh —an' made an ass o' them two frogs." The "two frogs" was a reference to a pair of gallant French fliers who, in attempting a flight only halfway round the world, had, two weeks before, unhappily been lost at sea. The *Times* man was bold enough, at this point, to sketch out for Smurch the accepted formula for interviews in cases of this kind; he explained that there should be no arrogant statements belittling the achievements of other heroes, particularly heroes of foreign nations. "Ah, the hell with that," said Smurch. "I did it, see? I did it, an' I'm talkin' about it." And he did talk about it.

None of this extraordinary interview was, of course, printed. On the contrary, the newspapers, already under the disciplined direction of a secret directorate created for the occasion and composed of statesmen and editors, gave out to a panting and restless world that "Jacky," as he had been arbitrarily nicknamed, would consent to say only that he was very happy and that anyone could have done what he did. "My achievement has been, I fear, slightly exaggerated," the *Times* man's article had him protest, with a modest smile. These newspaper stories were kept from the hero, a restriction which did not serve to abate the rising malevolence of his temper. The situation was indeed, extremely grave, for Pal Smurch was, as he kept insisting, "rarin' to go." He could not much longer be kept from a nation clamorous to lionize him. It was the most desperate crisis the United States of America had faced since the sinking of the *Lusitania.*

On the afternoon of the twenty-seventh of July, Smurch was spirited away to a conference-room in which were gathered mayors, governors, government officials, behaviorist psychologists, and editors. He gave them each a limp, moist paw and a brief unlovely grin. "Hah ya?" he said. When Smurch was seated, the Mayor of New York arose and, with obvious pessimism, attempted to explain what he must say and how he must act when presented to the world, ending his talk with a high tribute to the hero's courage and integrity. The Mayor was followed by Governor Fanniman of New York, who, after a touching declaration of faith, introduced Cameron Spottiswood, Second Secretary of the American Embassy in Paris, the gentleman selected to coach Smurch in the amenities of public ceremonies. Sitting in a chair, with a soiled yellow tie in his hand and his shirt open at the throat, unshaved, smoking a rolled cigarette, Jack Smurch listened with a leer on his lips. "I get ya, I get ya," he cut in, nastily. "Ya want me to ack like a softy, huh? Ya want me to ack like that —— —— baby-face Lindbergh, huh? Well, nuts to that, see?" Everyone took in his breath sharply; it was a sigh and a hiss. "Mr. Lindbergh," began a United States Senator, purple with rage, "and Mr. Byrd——" Smurch, who was paring his nails with a jackknife, cut in again. "Byrd!" he exclaimed. "Aw fa God's sake, *dat* big——" Somebody shut off his blasphemies with a sharp word. A newcomer had entered the room. Everyone stood up except Smurch, who, still busy with his nails, did not even glance up. "Mr. Smurch," said someone, sternly "the President of the United States!" It had been thought that the presence of the Chief Executive might have a chastening effect upon the young hero, and the former had been, thanks to the remarkable coöperation of the press, secretly brought to the obscure conference-room.

A great, painful silence fell. Smurch looked up, waved a hand at the President. "How ya comin'?" he asked, and began rolling a fresh cigarette. The silence deepened.

Someone coughed in a strained way. "Geez, it's hot, ain't it?" said Smurch. He loosened two more shirt buttons, revealing a hairy chest and the tattooed word "Sadie" enclosed in a stencilled heart. The great and important men in the room, faced by the most serious crisis in recent American history, exchanged worried frowns. Nobody seemed to know how to proceed. "Come awn, come awn," said Smurch. "Let's get the hell out of here! When do I start cuttin' in on de parties, huh? And what's they goin' to be *in* it?" He rubbed a thumb and forefinger together meaningly. "Money!" exclaimed a state senator, shocked, pale. "Yeh, money," said Pal, flipping his cigarette out of a window. "An' big money." He began rolling a fresh cigarette. "Big money," he repeated, frowning over the rice paper. He tilted back in his chair, and leered at each gentleman, separately, the leer of an animal that knows its power, the leer of a leopard loose in a bird-and-dog shop. "Aw fa God's sake, let's get some place where it's cooler," he said. "I been cooped up plenty for three weeks!"

Smurch stood up and walked over to an open window, where he stood staring down into the street, nine floors below. The faint shouting of newsboys floated up to him. He made out his name. "Hot dog!" he cried, grinning, ecstatic. He leaned out over the sill. "You tell 'em babies!" he shouted down. "Hot diggity dog!" In the tense little knot of men standing behind him, a quick, mad impulse flared up. An unspoken word of appeal, of command, seemed to ring through the room. Yet it was deadly silent. Charles K. L. Brand, secretary to the Mayor of New York City, happened to be standing nearest Smurch; he looked inquiringly at the President of the United States. The President, pale, grim, nodded shortly. Brand, a tall, powerfully built man, once a tackle at Rutgers, stepped forward, seized the greatest man in the world by his left shoulder and the seat of his pants, and pushed him out the window.

"My God, he's fallen out the window!" cried a quick-witted editor.

"Get me out of here!" cried the President. Several men

sprang to his side and he was hurriedly escorted out of a door toward a side-entrance of the building. The editor of the Associated Press took charge, being used to such things. Crisply he ordered certain men to leave, others to stay; quickly he outlined a story which all the papers were to agree on, sent two men to the street to handle that end of the tragedy, commanded a Senator to sob and two Congressmen to go to pieces nervously. In a word, he skillfully set the stage for the gigantic task that was to follow, the task of breaking to a griefstricken world the sad story of the untimely, accidental death of its most illustrious and spectacular figure.

The funeral was, as you know, the most elaborate, the finest, the solemnest, and the saddest ever held in the United States of America. The monument in Arlington Cemetery, with its clean white shaft of marble and the simple device of a tiny plane carved on its base, is a place for pilgrims, in deep reverence, to visit. The nations of the world paid lofty tributes to little Jacky Smurch, America's greatest hero. At a given hour there were two minutes of silence throughout the nation. Even the inhabitants of the small, bewildered town of Westfield, Iowa, observed this touching ceremony; agents of the Department of Justice saw to that. One of them was especially assigned to stand grimly in the doorway of a little shack restaurant on the edge of the tourists' camping ground just outside the town. There, under his stern scrutiny, Mrs. Emma Smurch bowed her head above two hamburger steaks sizzling on her grill—bowed her head and turned away, so that the Secret Service man could not see the twisted, strangely familiar, leer on her lips.

Edgar Wallace

THE MAN WITH THE RED BEARD

To the average reader the name of Miska Guild is associated with slight and possibly amusing eccentricities. For example, he once went down Regent Street at eleven o'clock at night at sixty miles an hour, crippled two unfortunate pedestrians, and smashed a lamp standard and his car. The charge that he was drunk failed, because indisputably he was sober when he was dragged out of the wreckage, himself unhurt.

Nevertheless, an unsympathetic magistrate convicted, despite the conflict of medical evidence. Miska Guild went to the Sessions with the best advocates that money could buy and had the conviction quashed.

The inner theatrical set knew him as a giver of freakish dinner parties; had an idea that he gave other parties even more freakish but less descriptive. Once he went to Paris, and the French police most obligingly hushed up a lurid incident as best they could.

They could not quite hush up the death of the pretty chorus-girl who was found on the pavement outside the hotel, having fallen from a fifth-floor window, but they were very helpful in explaining that she had mistaken the French windows for the door of her sitting-room. Nobody at the inquiry asked how she managed to climb the balcony.

The only person who evinced a passionate interest in the proceedings was one Henry Arthur Milton, a fugitive from justice, who was staying at the hotel—not as Henry Arthur Milton, certainly not as "The Ringer," by which title he was known; indeed, he bore no name by which the English police could identify him as the best-wanted man in Europe.

Mr. Guild paid heavily for all the trouble he had caused divers police officials and came back to London and to his magnificent flat in Carlton House Terrace quite unabashed, even though some of the theatrical celebrities with whom he was acquainted cut him dead whenever they met him; even though the most unpleasant rumours surrounded his Paris trip.

He was a man of thirty, reputedly a millionaire three times over. It is certain that he was very rich, and had the queerest ideas about what was and what was not the most amusing method of passing time. Had the Paris incident occurred in London neither his two nor his three millions would have availed him, nor all the advocacy of the greatest lawyers averted the most unpleasant consequences.

One bright November morning, when the sun rose in a clear blue sky and the leafless trees of Green Park had a peculiar splendour of their own, the second footman brought his breakfast to his bedside, and on the tray there was a registered letter. The postmark was Paris, the envelope was marked "Urgent and confidential; not to be opened by the secretary."

Miska Guild sat up in bed, pushed back his long, yellowish hair from his eyes, bleared for a moment at the envelope and tore it open with a groan. There was a single sheet of paper, closely typewritten. It bore no address and began without a conventional preamble:

On October 18 you went to Paris, accompanied by a small party. In that party was a girl called Ethel Seddings, who was quite unaware of your character. She committed suicide in order to escape from you. I am called The Ringer; my name is Henry Arthur Milton, and Scotland Yard will furnish you with particulars of my past. As you are a man of considerable property and may wish to have time to make arrangements as to its disposal, I will give you a little grace. At the end of a reasonable period I shall come to London and kill you.

That was all the letter contained. Miska read it through; looked at the back of the sheet for further inspiration; read it through again.

"Who the devil is The Ringer?" he asked.

The footman, who was an authority upon such matters, gave him a little inaccurate information. Miska examined the envelope without being enlightened any further, and then with a chuckle he was about to tear the letter into pieces but thought better of it.

"Send it up to Scotland Yard," he commanded his secretary later in the morning, and would have forgotten the unpleasant communication if he had not returned from lunch to find a rather sinister-looking man with a short black beard who introduced himself as Chief Inspector Bliss from Scotland Yard.

"About that letter? Oh, rot! You're not taking that seriously, are you?"

Bliss nodded slowly.

"So seriously that I'm putting on two of my best men to guard you for a month or two."

Miska looked at him incredulously.

"Do you really mean that? But surely . . . my footman tells me he's a criminal: he wouldn't dare come to London?"

Inspector Bliss smiled grimly.

"He dared go into Scotland Yard when it suited him. This is the kind of case that would interest him."

He recounted a few of The Ringer's earlier cases, and Miska Guild became of a sudden a very agitated young man.

"Monstrous . . . a murderer at large, and you can't catch him? I've never heard anything like it! Besides, that business in Paris—it was an accident. The poor, silly dear mistook the window for her sitting-room door——"

"I know all about that, Mr. Guild," said Bliss quietly. "I'd rather we didn't discuss that aspect of the matter. The only thing I can tell you is that, if I know The Ringer —and nobody has better reason for knowing him and his methods—he will try to keep his word. It's up to us to protect you. You're to employ no new servants without consulting me. I want a daily notification telling me where you're going and how you're spending your time. The

Ringer is the only criminal in the world, so far as I know, who depends entirely upon his power of disguise. We haven't a photograph of him as himself at Scotland Yard, and I'm one of the few people who have seen him as himself."

Miska jibbed at the prospect of accounting for his movements in advance. He was, he said, a creature of impulse, and was never quite sure where he would be next. Besides which, he was going to Berlin——

"If you leave the country I will not be responsible for your life," said Bliss shortly, and the young man turned pale.

At first he treated the matter as a joke, but as the weeks became a month the sight of the detective sitting by the side of his chauffeur, the unexpected appearance of a Scotland Yard man at his elbow wherever he moved, began to get on his nerves.

And then one night Bliss came to him with the devastating news.

"The Ringer is in England," he said.

Miska's face was ghastly.

"How—how do you know?" he stammered.

But Bliss was not prepared to explain the peculiar qualities of Wally the Nose, or the peculiar behaviour of the man with the red beard.

When Wally the Nose passed through certain streets in Notting Dale he chose daylight for the adventure, and he preferred that a policeman should be in sight. Not that any of the less law-abiding folk of Notting Dale had any personal reason for desiring Wally the least harm, for, as he protested in his pathetic, lisping way, "he never did no harm" to anybody in Notting Dale.

He lived in a back room in Clewson Street, a tiny house rented by a deaf old woman who had had lodgers even more unsavoury than Wally, with his greasy, threadbare clothes, his big, protruding teeth, and his silly, moist face.

He came one night furtively to Inspector Stourbridge at the local police station, having been sent for.

"There's goin' to be a 'bust' at Lowes, the jewellers, in Islington, to-morrer, Mr. Stourbridge; some lads from Nottin' Dale are in it, and Elfus is fencin' the stuff. Is that what you wanted me about?"

He stood, turning his hat in his hands, his ragged coat almost touching the floor, his red eyelids blinking, Stourbridge had known many police informers, but none like Wally.

He hesitated, and then, with a "Wait here," he went into a room that led from the charge room and closed the door behind him.

Chief Inspector Bliss sat at a table, his head on his hand, turning over a thick dossier of documents that lay on the table before him.

"That man I spoke to you about is here, sir——the Nose. He's the best we've ever had, and so long as he hasn't got to take any extraordinary risk——or doesn't know he's taking it——he'll be invaluable."

Bliss pulled at his little beard and scowled.

"Does he know why you have brought him here now?" he asked.

Stourbridge grinned.

"No——I put him on to inquire about a jewel burglary ——but we knew all about it beforehand."

"Bring him in."

Wally came shuffling into the private room, blinking from one to the other with an ingratiating grin.

"Yes, sir?" His voice was shrill and nervous.

"This is Mr. Bliss, of Scotland Yard," said Stourbridge, and Wally bobbed his head.

"Heard about you, sir," he said, in his high, piping voice. "You're the bloke that got The Ringer——"

"To be exact, I didn't," said Bliss gruffly, "but you may."

"Me, sir?" Wally's mouth was open wide, his protruding rabbit's teeth suggested to Stourbridge the favourite figure of a popular comic artist. "I don't touch no Ringer, sir, with kind regards to you. If there's any kind of work you want me to do, sir, I'll do it. It's a regular 'obby of mine—I ought to have been in the p'lice. Up in Manchester they'll tell you all about me. I'm the feller that found Spicy Brown when all the Manchester busies was lookin' for him."

"That's why Manchester got a bit too hot for you, eh, Wally?" said Stourbridge.

The man shifted uncomfortably.

"Yes, they was a bit hard on me—the lads, I mean. That's why I come back to London. But I can't help nosing, sir, and that's a fact."

"You can do a little nosing for me," interrupted Bliss.

And thereafter a new and a more brilliant spy watched the movements of the man with the red beard.

He had arrived in London by a ship which came from India but touched at Marseilles. He had on his passport the name of Tennett. He had travelled third-class. He was by profession an electrical engineer. Yet, despite his seeming poverty, he had taken a small and rather luxurious flat in Kensington.

It was his presence in Carlton House Terrace one evening that had first attracted the attention of Mr. Bliss. He came to see Guild, he said, on the matter of a project connected with Indian water power. The next day he was seen prospecting the house from the park side.

Ordinarily, it would have been a very simple matter to have pulled him in and investigated his credentials; but quite recently there had been what the Press had called a succession of police scandals. Two perfectly innocent men had been arrested in mistake for somebody else, and Scotland Yard was chary of taking any further risks.

Tennett was traced to his flat, and he was apparently a most elusive man, with a habit of taking taxicabs in crowded thoroughfares. What Scotland Yard might not do officially, it could do, and did do, unofficially. Wally the Nose listened with apparent growing discomfort.

"If it's him, he's mustard," he said huskily. "I don't like messing about with no Ringers. Besides, *he* hasn't got a red beard."

"Oh, shut up!" snarled Bliss. "He could grow one, couldn't he? See what you can find out about him. If you happen to get into his flat and see any papers lying about, they might help you. I'm not suggesting you should do so, but if you did . . ."

Wally nodded wisely.

In three days he furnished a curious report to the detective who was detailed to meet him. The man with the red beard had paid a visit to Croydon aerodrome and had made inquiries about a single-seater taxi to carry him to the Continent. He had spent a lot of his time at an electrical supply company in the East End of London, and had made a number of mysterious purchases which he had carried home with him in a taxicab.

Bliss consulted his superior.

"Pull him in," he suggested. "You can get a warrant to search his flat."

"His flat's been searched. There's nothing there of the slightest importance," reported Bliss.

He called that night at Carlton House Terrace and found Mr. Miska Guild a very changed man. These three months had reduced him to a nervous wreck.

"No news?" he asked apprehensively when the detective came in. "Has that wretched little creature discovered anything? By gad! he's as clever as any of you fellows. I was talking with him last night. He was outside on the Terrace with one of your men. Now, Bliss, I'd better tell you the truth about this girl in Paris——"

"I'd rather you didn't," said Bliss, almost sternly.

He wanted to preserve, at any rate, a simulation of interest in Mr. Guild's fate.

He had hardly left Carlton House Terrace when a taxicab drove in and Wally the Nose almost fell into the arms of the detective.

"Where's Bliss?" he squeaked. "That red-whiskered feller's disappeared . . . left his house, and he's shaved off his beard, Mr. Connor. I didn't recognise him when he come out. When I made inquiries I found he'd gorn for good."

"The chief's just gone," said Connor, worried.

He went into the vestibule and was taken up to the floor on which Mr. Guild had his suite. The butler led him to the dining-room, where there was a 'phone connection, and left Wally the Nose in the hall. He was standing there disconsolately when Mr. Guild came out.

"Hullo! What's the news?" he asked quickly.

Wally the Nose looked left and right.

"He's telephonin' to the boss," he whispered hoarsely, "but I ain't told him about the letter."

He followed Miska into the library and gave that young man a piece of news that Mr. Guild never repeated.

He was waiting in the hall below when Connor came down.

"It's all right—they arrested old red whiskers at Liverpool Street Station. We had a man watching him as well."

Wally the Nose was pardonably annoyed.

"What's the use of having me and then puttin' a busy on to trail him?" he demanded truculently. "That's what I call double-crossing."

"You hop off to Scotland Yard and see the chief," said Connor, and Wally, grumbling audibly, vanished in the darkness.

The once red-bearded man sat in Inspector Bliss's private room, and he was both indignant and frightened.

"I don't know that there's any law preventing me taking off my beard, is there?" he demanded. "I was just going off to Holland, where I'm seeing a man who's putting money into my power scheme."

Bliss interrupted with a gesture.

"When you came to England you were broke, Mr. Tennett, and yet immediately you reached London you took a very expensive flat, bought yourself a lot of new clothes, and seemingly have plenty of money to travel on the Continent. Will you explain that?"

The man hesitated.

"Well, I'll tell you the truth. When I got to London

I was broke, but I got into conversation with a fellow at the station who told me he was interested in engineering. I explained my power scheme to him, and he was interested. He was not the kind of man I should have thought would have had any money, yet he weighed in with two hundred pounds, and told me just what I had to do. It was his idea that I should take the flat. He told me where to go every day and what to do. I didn't want to part with the old beard, but he made me do that in the end, and then gave me three hundred pounds to go to Holland."

Bliss looked at him incredulously.

"Did he also suggest you should call at Carlton House Terrace and interview Mr. Guild?"

Tennett nodded.

"Yes, he did. I tell you, it made me feel that things weren't right. I wasn't quite sure of him, mind you, Mr. Bliss; he was such a miserable-looking devil—a fellow with rabbit's teeth and red eyelids. . . ."

Bliss came to his feet with a bound, stared across at Stourbridge, who was in the room.

"Wally!" he said.

A taxicab took him to Carlton House Terrace. Connor told him briefly what had happened.

"Did Wally see Mr. Guild?"

"Not that I know," said Connor, shaking his head.

Bliss did not wait for the lift; he flew up the stairs, met the footman in the hall.

"Where's Mr. Guild?"

"In his room, sir."

"Have you seen him lately?"

The man shook his head.

"No, sir; I never go unless he rings for me. He hasn't rung for half an hour."

Bliss turned the handle of the door and walked in. Miska Guild was lying on the hearthrug in the attitude of a man asleep, and when he turned him over on his back and saw his face Bliss knew that the true story of the chorus-girl and her "suicide" would never be told.

William McFee

ON A BALCONY

There are some men whom a staggering emotional shock, so far from making them mental invalids for life, seems, on the other hand, to awaken, to galvanize, to arouse into an almost incredible activity of soul. They are somewhat in the same cast as the elderly expressman who emerged from a subway smash untouched, save that he began to write free verse. Those who do not read free verse may consider the comparison too flippant. But the point must be insisted on, that there is far too much talk of love and grief benumbing the faculties, turning the hair gray, and destroying a man's interest in his work. Grief has made many a man look younger.

Or, one may compare the emotions with wine. The faculties of some men become quiescent with wine. Others are like Sheridan writing "The School for Scandal" right on through the night, with a decanter of port at his elbow getting emptier as the pages (and Sheridan) got full; or like Mozart drinking wine to stimulate his brain to work, and employing his wife to keep him awake at the same time.

There was a singular disparity between the above trivial reflections and the scene upon which they were staged. I was seated on the balcony outside my room on the third floor of the Grand Hôtel Splendide Palace at Smyrna. I was to leave that afternoon for Constantinople, having been relieved, and I had been watching with some attention the arrival of the destroyer upon whose deck, as a passenger, I was to travel.

I was distracted from this pastime by the growing excitement in the street below. Greek troops, headed by extremely warlike bands, were marching along the quay, gradually extending themselves into a thin yellowish-green line with sparkling bayonets, and congesting the

populace into the fronts of the cafés. A fantastic notion
assailed me that my departure was to be carried out with
military honours. There is an obscure memorandum ex-
tant in some dusty office-file, in which I am referred to as
"embarrassing His Majesty's Government"—the nearest
I have ever got to what is known as public life. The intoxication engendered proved conclusively that public life
was not my *métier*.

But I was not to be deceived for long on this occasion.
Motor-cars drove up, bearing little flags on sticks. A
Greek general, a French admiral, an Italian captain, and
a British lieutenant of the Royal Naval Volunteer Reserve jumped out of their respective chariots and, after
saluting with the utmost decorum, shook hands with the
utmost cordiality. Looked at from above, the scene was
singularly like the disturbance caused by stirring up a
lot of ants with a stick.

By this time it was perfectly obvious that something
more than the departure of a mere lieutenant of reserve
was in the air. I knew that Royal Naval Volunteer lieutenant, and the hope, the incipient prospect, of another
taste of public life died within me. After all, I reflected
(and this is how I led up to the other reflections already
recorded), after all, one must choose between Obscurity
with Efficiency, and Fame with its inevitable collateral of
Bluff. There is a period, well on toward middle life, when
a man can say such things to himself and feel comforted.

I knew that Royal Naval Volunteer lieutenant, and I
began to recall some remarks he had made the previous
evening at dinner. He had said something about some big
man coming. This was at the British Naval Residency,
which was to be found, by the intrepid, in the Austrian
Consulate. The British Naval Residency filled the Austrian Consulate very much as a penny fills the pocket of a
fur overcoat. You could spend a pleasant morning wandering through the immense chambers of the Austrian
Consulate and come away without having discovered any
one save a fat Greek baby whose mother washed in some
secret subterranean chamber.

I was supposed to be messing at the British Naval
Residency. I had even been offered by my country's naval
representative (this same Royal Naval Volunteer lieutenant) the use of any room I liked, to sleep in, if I had
a bed, and bed-clothes to put on it. He even offered me
the throne-room—a gigantic affair about the size of the
Pennsylvania Terminal and containing three hassocks
and a catafalque like a half-finished sky-scraper. At night,
when we dined, an intrepid explorer who, we may suppose,
had reached the great doors after perils which had turned
him gray, would see, afar off across the acres of dried and
splitting parquetry flooring, a table with one tiny electric
light, round which several humans were feasting. If his
travels had not bereft him of his senses, he might have
gathered that these extraordinary beings were continually
roaring with laughter at their own wit. Out of the gloom
at intervals would materialize a sinister oriental figure
bearing bottles whose contents he poured out in libations
before his humorous masters.

This frightful scene (near on midnight) was the
British Naval Residency at dinner. I ought to have paid
attention—only I was distracted by an imaginary bow-
string murder going on in the throne-room beyond the
vast folding doors—and then I would have heard the
details of the function taking place below my hotel windows. But it is impossible to pay attention to the details
of a ceremonial while a beautiful Circassian, on her knees
between two husky Ottoman slaves who are hauling at the
cord which has been passed in a clove-hitch about her
neck, is casting a last glance of despair upon the ragged
and cobwebbed scarlet silk portière. It may be objected
that, as the tragedy was an imaginary one, I was not
compelled to dwell upon it. The reader and I will not
quarrel over the point. I will even make him a present of
the fact that there are no beautiful Circassians in that
part of the world. They have all been kidnapped and carried away to the seraglios of our popular novelists, who
marry them, in the last chapter, to dashing young college
men of the "clean-cut" breed. But the British Naval

Resident's cook is an artist, and the British Naval Resident's kümmel, while it closes the front doors of the mind
to the trivial tattle of conversation, draws up the dark
curtain that hangs at the back and reveals a vast and
shadowy stage, whereon are enacted the preposterous per-
formances of the souls of men.

II

But however hazy I might be myself about this event,
all Smyrna seemed cognizant. As I sat on my balcony, I
was joined by the children of the family in the next room.
Who the family in the next room may be I am somewhat
at a loss to explain. At first I imagined they were a
family of Russian refugees named Buttinsky; but Katia,
the eldest, who is ten and speaks French, says her father
is a major of artillery and is named Priam Callipoliton.
From occasional glances through the open door while
passing, one imagines that a married major in the army
of the Hellenes has a fierce time when he is at home.
There are three beds in the room, besides a gas-stove and
a perambulator. Leaning over my balcony railing one
early morning, and poking with a walking-stick at an
enigmatic crimson patch on the Callipoliton window-sill,
I discovered, to my horror, that it was a raw liver, left
out to keep cool.

Priam seems to be fairly hard at it at the front.
Madame, a shapeless and indomitable creature, regards
me with that look of mysterious yet comfortable *cama-
raderie* which women with large families seem to reserve
for strange bachelors. I like her. She uses my balcony
(having none of her own) with a frank disregard of the
small change of etiquette which is beyond praise. I come
up from the street in the middle of the morning and find
Madame and the *femme de chambre* leaning comfortably
on my balcony-rail, a sisterly pair, each couple of high
French heels worn sideways, each broad-hipped skirt gap-

ing at the back, each with a stray hank of hair waving wildly in the strong breeze blowing across the glittering gulf. If I cough, they turn and nod genially. If I explain apologetically that I wish to change, they nod again and shut the big *jalousies* upon me and my astounding modesty.

And if they are not there, the children are. Katia is the possessor of three small sisters and a small brother. They are Evanthe, Theodosia, and Sophia with Praxiteles sifted in somewhere between them. They were rather amazing at first. "*Êtes-vous marié?*" they squeaked in their infantile Hellenic trebles. "*Pas encore*" only made them point melodramatic fingers at a photograph, with their ridiculous black pigtails hanging over their shoulders. "*C'est elle, peut-être. Oui? Très jolie!*" And the pigtails vibrated with vehement nods.

They use my balcony. Praxiteles has a horrifying habit of sitting astride the rail. Katia takes the most comfortable chair and asks me genially why I do not go and make a promenade. "*Avec votre fiancée*," she adds, with enervating audacity. And I am supposed to have the exclusive use of this room, with balcony, for three pounds (Turkish) *per diem!*

The point, however, is that, if this be the state of affairs on ordinary days, on this particular morning my balcony, like all the other balconies, is full. Madame and the *femme de chambre* are there. Katia, Evanthe, Theodosia, Sophia, and Praxiteles are to be heard of all men. Praxiteles endeavours to drag an expensive pair of field-glasses from their case, and is restraind only by main force. George, the floor-porter, a sagacious but unsatisfactory creature, who plays a sort of Jekyll-and-Hyde game with the *femme de chambre*, comes in, on the pretence of cleaning the electric light fittings, and drifts casually to the balcony. George, descended no doubt from the famous George family of Cappadocia, if rung for, goes away to find Marthe, the *femme de chambre*. Marthe appears, merely to go away again to find George. It is a relief to see the two of them at once, if only to dispel the dreadful notion that George is Marthe and Marthe a sinister manifestation of George.

It is a gratifying thing to record, too, that all these people are perfectly willing that I should see the show as well. Katia, commanded by Madame, resigns the best chair, sulks a moment on one leg, and then forgets her annoyance in the thunder of the guns booming from the Greek warships in the roadstead. I forge my way through and find a stranger in the corner of my balcony.

For a moment I am in the grip of that elusive yet impenetrable spirit of benevolent antipathy which is the main cause of the Englishman's reputation for icy coldness toward those to whom he has not been introduced. Now you can either break ice or melt it; but the best way is to let the real human being, whom you can see through the cold blue transparencies, thaw himself out, as he will in time. Very few foreigners give us time. They jump on the ice with both feet. They attempt to be breezy and English, and leave us aghast at their inconceivable fatuity. While we are struggling within our deliquescent armour, and on the very point of escaping into the warm sunlight of genial conversation, they freeze us solid again with some frightful banality or racial solecism. The reader will perceive from this that the Englishman is not having such a pleasant time in the world as some people imagine.

However, the stranger on my balcony turns out to be, not a foreigner, but another Englishman, which is an even worse trial to some of us. He is, of course, smoking a cigarette. He wears an old straw hat, an old linen suit, and his boots are slightly burst at the sides. His moustache and scanty hair are iron gray. His eyes are pale blue. While he talks they remain fixed upon Cordelio, which is on the other side of the gulf. No doubt, if he were talking in Cordelio, they would be fixed upon Smyrna. He wears a plain gold wedding-ring. His clothes are stylish, which is not to say they are new. They might have been worn by a wealthy Englishman abroad, say nine or ten years ago. No Greek tailor, for example, would hole all those buttons on the cuffs, nor would he make the coat-collar "lay" with such glovelike contiguity to the shoulders. Also, the trousers hang as Greek trousers never hang, in spite of their bagginess at the knees.

Keeping a watchful eye upon Cordelio, he bends toward me as I sit in my chair, and apologizes for the intrusion. Somehow the phrase seems homelike. Greeks, for example, never "intrude": they come in, generally bringing a powerful whiff of garlic with them, and go out again, unregretted. They do not admit an intrusion. Even my friend Kaspar Dring, *Stab-Ober-Leutnant* attached to the defunct Imperial German Consulate, would scarcely appreciate the fine subtlety implied in apologizing for an intrusion. It may be that so gay a personality cannot conceive a psychological condition which his undefeated optimism would fail to illuminate. And so, when the stranger, who is, I imagine, on the verge of forty, murmurs his apology for his intrusion, I postulate for him a past emerging from the muzzy-minded ideals of the English middle class. He adds that, in fact, he had made a mistake in the number of the room. Quite thought this was number seventy-seven, which was, I might know, the official residence of the Bolivian vice-consul, a great friend of his. Had arranged to see the affair from the Bolivian vice-consul's balcony. However, it didn't matter now, so long as I didn't mind—What? Of course, I knew what was going on. There! There he is, just stepping out of the launch. That's Skaramapopulos shaking hands with him now. English, eh? Just look at him! By Jove! who can beat us, eh? And just look at that upholstered old pork-butcher, with his eighteen medals and crosses, and never saw active service in his life. Too busy making his percentage on—What? No, not him—he's been asleep all his life. Oh, it was a game! However, now *he's* come, we may get something like order into the country. Did I mind if he took a few notes?

I did not mind. I tipped a member of the Callipoliton family off one of the other chairs, and begged my new friend to sit down. I fetched my binoculars and exam-

ined the scene below, where a famous British general
stood, with his tan-gloved hand at the salute beside his
formidable monocle, and was introduced to the Greek general, the French admiral, the Italian captain, and the
British lieutenant. "A cavalryman," I muttered, as he
started off down the line of Greek troops, hand at the
salute, the sun gleaming on his brown harness and shining
spurs. The Greek band was playing "See the Conquering
Hero Comes," very much off the key, and it almost seemed
as if the tune was too much for the conquering hero himself, for he dived suddenly into a motor-car and moved
rapidly away. Whereupon the band took breath and began to form fours, the yellowish green lines of troops
coagulated into oblong clots, the motor cars, with their
little flags, whooped and snarled at the crowds swarming,
from the cafés and side streets, and the quay began to
assume its wonted appearance (from above) of a dis-
organized ant-heap.

And my balcony began also to thin out. The Callipoliton faction dwindled to Madame, who was established
on a chair at the other end, elbow on the rail, contemplating Mount Sipylus like a disillusioned sybil. Katia
bounced back for a moment to inquire, in a piercing
treble, whether my baggage was ready, and if so, should
George descend with it to the entrance hall?

I informed her that, if George was really bursting to
do somthing useful, he could go ahead and do as she said.

She bounced away, and later the baggage was found
down below; but I am inclined to believe that George
sublet the contract to the Armenian boots and merely took
a rake-off. George is built on those lines.

"So you are a reporter," I remarked to my friend, eyeing the mangy-looking note book he was returning to his
pocket.

"Oh, yes," he assured me, adding hastily, though I
had made no comment, "I'm getting on very well, too."

He didn't look it, but I let that pass. You can never
tell these millionaires nowadays. I thought I was safe in
asking what paper he worked for.

"I've an article in to-day's *Mercure de Smyrne*. You've seen it, I suppose?"

I hadn't. I'd never even heard of it. I had read the *Levant*, the *Independent*, the *Matin*, the *Orient*, and so forth; but the *Mercure* was a new one. It came out of his pocket like a shot—a single sheet with three columns on each side, three fourths of the back occupied by an insurance company's ad.

"This is mine," he informed me, laying a finger on a couple of paragraphs signed "Bijou."

The article was entitled, *"Les Bas de Soie,"* and was in the boulevardese style dear to the Parisian journalist.

"You write French easily?" I said, quite unable to keep down my envy.

He waved his cigarette.

"Just the same as English," he assured me. "Italian and Spanish also."

"Then for the love of Michael Angelo why do you stop here in this part of the world? You might make your thousands a year on a big paper as a special commission. Why don't you go home?"

III

Well, he told me why he didn't go home, though not in so many words. If the reader will turn back to the beginning, he will see some reflections upon the behaviour of men under emotional shock and stress. It is possible he may have already turned back, wondering what those remarks portended, what it was all about anyway. Well——

It seems that Mr. Satterley Thwaiteson (I quote his card, which he pressed upon me) had been in the Levant some time. He had had a very pleasant probation as articled pupil to an architect in Norwich—did I know it? —and had made quite a hobby of studying French architecture, in his own time, of course. Used to take his autumn vacation in northern France, visiting the abbeys

and ruins and so forth. Got quite a facility, for an Englishman, in the language. Perhaps it was because of this
that, when he had been in a Bloomsbury architect's office
for a year or so, and a clerk of works was needed for a
Protestant church which some society was erecting in
Anatolia, he, Satterley Thwaiteson, got the job. "Secured
the appointment," were his exact words, but I imagine
he meant, really, that he got the job. He came out, on
one of the Pappayanni boats—did I know them?—and
as far as I could gather, got his church up without any
part of it falling down before the consecration service.
Which, considering the Levantine contractor's concep-
tions of probity, was a wonder.

So far Mr. Satterley Thwaiteson's history seemed
simple enough. Like many others of his imperial race, he
had gone abroad and had added to the prestige of the
English name by erecting a Protestant church in a country where Protestants are as plentiful as pineapples in
Labrador. But—and here seems to be the joint in the stick
—he didn't go home. All the time regarding Cordelio
across the gulf with his pale-blue eyes, an expression of
extraordinary pride and pleasure comes over his features,
and banishes for a few moments the more permanent indication of a man who had lost the art of life. Extraordinary pride and pleasure! He didn't go home. Never did
go home. It is obvious that the memory of this emotional
treachery to the call of home is something to be treasured
as one of the great things in life. No, on the contrary,
he got married out here. Yes, a foreigner, too—a Rou-
manian. And they didn't get married in his wonderful
Protestant church either, for she was a Roman Catholic.
"Here's a photo of her as she was then."

He takes from his pocket an old wallet stuffed with
folded letters, and fishes out a small flat oval frame that
opens on a hinge. There are two portraits, photos coloured
like miniatures. One is the Mr. Satterley Thwaiteson of
that day fifteen or sixteen years ago, not so different
save as to the hair, of which there is not much at present.
But the woman is beautiful. In these days of high-tension

fiction, when novelists, like the Greek in one of Aristophanes's plays, walk about, each with his string of lovely female slaves, it is tame enough to say a woman is beautiful. And perhaps it would be better to say that this woman in the little coloured photo was startling. The bronze hair piled high, the broad fair brow, the square indomitable chin, the pallor contrasting with the heavily lashed brown eyes, the exquisite lips, all formed a combination which must have had a rather curious effect upon the studious young man from Norwich *via* Bloomsbury. Filled him with pride for one thing, or he wouldn't be showing this picture to a stranger.

But what struck me about that girl's picture, even before he fished out a picture postcard photo of his family taken a month or two ago, was something in her face which can be expressed only by the word rapacity. Not, be it noted, a vampire. If the truth were known, there are very few vampires about, outside of high-tension fiction. But I saw rapacity, and it seemed a curious thing to find in a woman who, it transpired, had married him and borne him children, eight in all, and had made him so happy that he had never gone home.

For that was what had aged him and paralyzed him and kept him there until he was a shabby failure—happiness. That was what brought to his face that expression of extraordinary pride and pleasure. As I listened to his tale I wondered, and at the back of my mind, on the big shadowy stage of which I spoke, there seemed to be something going on which he forgot to mention. And when he showed me, with tender pride, the picture-postcard photo of his wife and her eight children, I could not get rid of the notion that there was something rapacious about her. Even now she was handsome, in a stout and domineering kind of way. It was absurd to accuse such a woman of rapacity. Was she not a pearl? Everything a woman should do, she had done. She had been fruitful, she had been a good mother, a virtuous wife, and her husband assumed an expression of extraordinary pride and pleasure when he showed a stranger her portrait. His happiness in her was so rounded and complete that he would never have another thought away from her. He would never go to England again. Was not this marvellous?

As I pondered upon the marvel of it, I heard him telling me how he had found some difficulty in making a living out of the few architectural commissions which happened along, and gradually fell into the habit of giving lessons in English to Greeks and Armenians who were anxious to achieve social distinction. And when the war came, and he was shut up with everybody else in the city, he had to depend entirely upon the language lessons. And then, of course, he "wrote for the press" as well, as he had shown me. He was very successful, he thought, taking everything into consideration. Why, he would get three pounds Turkish (about four dollars) for that little thing. Always signed himself "Bijou." His wife liked it. It was her name for him when they were lovers. And though, of course, the teaching was hard work, for Armenian girls were inconceivably thick-headed, and sometimes it occupied him twelve or fourteen hours a day, yet it paid and he was happy.

And in the very middle of my irritation at him for harping on what he called happiness, I saw that I was right, after all: that girl had been rapacious. She had devoured his personality, fed on it, destroyed it, and had grown stout and virtuous upon it. His hair was thin and gray, he had a hunted and dilapidated look, and his boots were slightly burst at the sides. And he was happy. He had abandoned his profession, and he toiled like a pack-horse for the bare necessities; yet he was happy. He was proud. It was plain he believed his position among men was to be gauged by his having won his peerless woman. He rambled on about local animosities and politics, and it was forced upon me that he would not do for a great newspaper. He would have to go away and find out how the people of the world thought and felt about things, and I was sure he would never consent to do that. His wife would not like it. And he might not be happy.

※　　　　※　　　　※

It is evening, and the sun, setting behind Cordelio shines straight through my room and along the great dusty corridor beyond. In the distance can be seen those antiphonal personalities, Marthe and George, in harmony at last, waiting to waylay me for a tip. On the balcony is the mother of all the Callipolitons, elbow on the rail, contemplating Mount Sipylus like some shrewd sybil who has found out the worthlessness of most of the secrets of the gods.

When I have packed an attaché case, I am ready. The destroyer on which I am to travel to Constantinople is signalling the flagship. In an hour she will depart. I go out once more on the balcony, to contemplate for the last time the familiar scene. The roadstead sparkles in the sun and the distant waters are aflame. The immense heave of the mountain-ranges is purple and ruddy gold, and in the distance I can see white houses in quiet valleys above the gray-green of the olive grounds. There is one in particular, among great cypresses, and I turn the binoculars upon it for a brief sentimental moment. As I return the glasses to the case, Madame regards me with attention.

"Vous partez ce soir, monsieur?" she murmurs.

And I nod, wondering why one can detect nothing of rapacity in her rather tired face. *"Oui, madame, je pars pour Constantinople ce soir,"* I assure her, thinking to engage her in conversation.

So far, in spite of our propinquity and the vociferous curiosity of Katia, we have not spoken together to any extent.

"Et après?"

"Après, madame, je vais à Malte, Marseille, Paris, et Londres. Peut-être, à l'Amérique aussi—je ne sais pas."

"Mon Dieu!" She seems quietly shocked at the levity of a man who prances about the world like this. Then comes the inevitable query: *"Vous êtes marié, monsieur?"* and the inevitable reply, *"Pas encore."*

She abandons Mount Sipylus for a while and turns on the chair, one high-heeled and rather slatternly shoe tapping on the marble flags. "*Mais dîtes moi, monsieur; vous avez une amante de cœur, sans doute?*"

"*Vous croyez ça? Pourquoi?*"

She shrugs her shoulders.

"*N'importe. C'est vrai. Vous êtes triste.*"

"*Oui. Mais c'est la guerre.*"

She was silent a moment, observing later that I was a philosopher, which was flattering but irrelevant. And then she said something that I carried away with me, as the destroyer fled over the dark waters of the Ægean.

"*Oui, c'est la guerre, mais il faut que vous n'oubliez, monsieur, que chaque voyage est un petit mort.*"

I left her there, looking out across the hard blue glitter of the gulf, when I went down to go aboard.

Arnold Bennett

THE NIGHT VISITOR

MARRIAGE, said someone, is one long patience. It usually is not. But it ought to be. Although Anthony Reels was held to be a remarkable inventor, and by reason of his gifts held a fine and a rather free position in an immense new, efficient manufacturing combine which was trying to destroy the British reputation for muddle, he was little, if anything, above the average, considered as a husband. And Luce Reels was little, if anything, above the average of wives.

The twain had their difficulties from time to time. They had also a child, which was continuous. Rosie had reached the age of three. Some of the marital difficulties originated in Rosie. Luce contended that Rosie was no ordinary child. Anthony, partly in order to tease his wife, contended that Rosie was just an ordinary child. This divergence of view—whether genuine or assumed—about the most important subject on earth was apt to produce a general domestic atmosphere not entirely favourable to peace and tranquillity, an atmosphere in which discord and conflict flourished.

The season was winter, the weather bleak. Influenza raged. Theatres were full of coughs. Sixty per cent of invitations were refused on account of illness. The Reelses had decided to go south. Anthony had done a great work, likely to lead to vast profits for his firm, and he needed a change. Excellent! But Luce had said that the child, complete with nurse and all impedimenta, must accompany them.

Anthony had protested with customary violence against the preposterous notion of taking an infant on a thirty-hour journey by sea and land into an alien clime. What Anthony wanted was a *change*. There could be no change for him if he was to be charged with the

responsibilities of a family. A wife, yes! A family—no!
Moreover, the infant would be better and safer at home,
in its fixed daily routine, with a nurse faithful and competent. Change was bad for infants, who were all Tories
and objected to any disturbance of routine.

Luce won. All arrangements were accomplished for
shutting up the flat; tickets taken; rooms engaged. But
Anthony, a wonderful comedian, carried his dark grievance beneath a lightsome exterior. Anthony was secretly
resentful, not because he felt himself to be in the right,
but because he felt himself to be in the wrong. (Luce
had handsomely defeated him in argument.) We others
of course are only rendered gloomy and resentful when,
being beaten, we know ourselves to be in the right. Anthony was different. We are Anthony's moral superiors.

Anthony said to himself: "If she thinks I'm going for
a very necessary holiday with this child, this nurse, this
perambulator, this special bed, these special foods, these
kettles and contraptions, she is mistaken. I will be ill. I
will be too ill to travel." So on the morning before the
planned departure he began to be ill. His acting was
brilliant and diplomatically contrived. He stayed in bed,
but he said: "It's nothing. I'm only tired. I'll get up for
lunch."

He managed to give to his optimistic assurance a tone
of unreality, the tone of a brave man resisting adversity
for the sake of beloved creatures. He did not get up for
lunch. He would get up for dinner. But he did not get
up for dinner. He laughed nobly at the suggestion of a
doctor.

It was an odious spectacle, this spectacle of a clever
and successful man of thirty-six, a genius perhaps, fully
grown, entirely adult, naughtily feigning to be ill when
he was not ill.

Left alone for a few minutes by his attendant loving
wife, he smiled devilishly to himself:

"I'll teach her!" he thought.

Then he was startled by the unexpected arrival of the
doctor whom he had refused to see.

"There will be trouble now," thought he. "This fiend of a medico will see through my sham."

But no! There was not the least trouble. Dr. Bain accepted seriously Anthony's ingenious account of his symptoms. He took the false patient's temperature and, shaking the thermometer, pronounced it to be a fraction under a hundred. He would not say whether or not the patient could safely travel on the morrow; but he promised to call very early the next morning and decide then.

Luce was exceedingly worried. However, she too was brave and optimistic on the surface, and continued her elaborate preparations for departure on the assumption that everything would turn out for the best.

Having awakened in the middle of the night, Anthony, for some reason which he could not explain, began to read the Bible. He was not by habit an ardent reader, and particularly not an ardent reader of the Bible; but he always kept a Bible on the table by his bedside, in case he might feel a desire to read it, and he never felt the desire. Now, almost before being aware of the fact, lo! he was reading the Bible,—the love story of Amnon and Tamar.

"After all," said he to himself, "it's great stuff, the Bible is," implying that he was appreciating the greatness of the book for the first time.

All very odd! His right hand, exposed to the air of the room, grew cold. Then he realized that the door communicating with Luce's chamber was being cautiously opened.

"A stroke of luck!" thought he wickedly, "that I should be awake. A bit of convincing detail, that! What's she after?"

Out of the tail of his eye he saw her—her auburn hair (disarranged), her flushed girlish face, her sapphire-coloured dressing gown (his favourite).

"Hello!" he murmured, with an affected weakness of voice. "Anything wrong?"

"No," answered Luce, in one of her affectionate, anxious tones. "But I saw the light under the door and I wondered whether you were worse or whether you'd gone to sleep and left the light on."

"I'm perfectly all right, thanks," said he, with an accent to show that in his opinion he was far, far from perfectly all right. "I couldn't sleep, so I thought I'd try to read a bit."

Luce was bending over him. Yes, she looked surprisingly young for thirty-two.

"What are you reading?"

"Oh! The Bible. Now you get back to bed, and sleep, my girl."

She put her hand on his forehead.

"You are a bit hot," said she.

"My hand isn't," said he.

She was about to kiss him fondly.

"Don't kiss me," he warned her. "I'm infectious—or contagious. You might give it to Rosie." She withdrew her lips.

"I'll kiss the back of your neck," said she, with a celestial smile.

She inclined her long body, and she did kiss him on the back of his neck.

"Sure you aren't worse?" she asked, apprehensive.

"Oh, no!" Again with artful unconvincingness.

Luce sighed courageously, and departed. A delicious experience for Anthony. It proved that their hostility had vanished, that she was still passionately attached to him. He felt ashamed of his duplicity. Imagine deceiving so loyal and tender a creature! Still, he had begun the fraud, and he must carry it through. Besides, she had defied and vanquished him about the child, and she deserved some punishment.

He extinguished the light (so that it should not disturb her loving watchfulness), but for a long period he could not sleep. Indeed, he felt quite unwell. Curious, how the soul reacts on the body!

The next morning Dr. Bain arrived very early, saying brightly that he had to start his day's work at dawn because of the epidemic of influenza, which was running him off his feet. He was a middle-aged man, but apparently incapable of being fatigued. His examination of Anthony was absurdly rapid.

"Out of the question," he remarked.

"What's out of the question?" Anthony demanded.

The doctor glanced aside at Anthony's trunk, which lay in a corner all packed save for a few trifles.

"Your leaving to-day—*or* to-morrow or the next day," said he; and, having said it, Dr. Bain went away. Luce followed him out of the room.

"The fellow's mad!" thought Anthony. "I've a good mind to get up."

Still, the prestige of a doctor is such that, though he may be mad, he must be obeyed. Anthony had successfully deceived the world; but he was conscious of a regret.

"Well," said Luce, returning, "it's all off then. So that's that." She gave her husband a smile, as if to inspire him with hope in his illness.

"What's supposed to be the matter with me?" Anthony questioned.

"Flu, naturally!" said Luce. "The doctor thinks you ought to have a nurse."

"Rot!" Anthony ejaculated.

Luce calmly continued:

"He says they're difficult to get just now; but he'll get one. He'll have her here this afternoon."

Anthony was dumbfounded. The whole world was mad.

"But how shall you manage?" he asked at length, in amaze. The sensation of being a criminal crushed him.

"Oh!" Luce answered with spurious calm. "Mary will stay. Quite simple."

Mary was the sole private servant in the home, which was a service flat.

"We can use the railway tickets later on," said Anthony. "But the train seats to Dover and in the Blue Train will be wasted."

"Don't *worry*," Luce enjoined him masterfully. "I shall telephone about them."

A capable little thing, she was!

Anthony slept. Upon waking he noticed that the trunk had gone from the room.

The nurse arrived in the afternoon, according to prophecy. She struck Anthony as hard and domineering. Within a very brief time she was mistress of the room, and the bedside table was laden with such things as a jug of lemonade, a box of cough lozenges, some oranges, a bottle of medicine, a glass, a tablespoon, and aspirin. Also, the nurse announced that she would sit up, at least during the first part of the night, and that she could sleep or doze quite comfortably in Anthony's easy-chair.

All of which was highly disconcerting. And an even more disconcerting event occurred at about ten o'clock. Dr. Bain paid a second visit.

"I happened to be in the neighbourhood," said he, playing the casual, "so I thought I might as well look in."

Anthony, hardly a man to be deceived by any clumsy imitation of casualness, reflected:

"This looks fishy. Doctor twice in one day! *Am* I ill? The fellow's a fool. Or is he cadging visits at a guinea a go?"

Just as the fool or cadger was finishing, Luce appeared in the doorway.

"Before you go, Doctor, I'd like a word."

Luce left. The doctor left.

After a quarter of an hour or so Luce reappeared.

"Nurse," she said, "can you spare a minute?" And to Anthony: "Rosie's not well."

Luce left. The nurse left, and as she passed out she switched off the electric light.

About an hour and a half elapsed before the burglar sneaked into the room.

But in the meantime much had happened—in Anthony's soul. He had begun to feel lonely, neglected, and once more the influence of the soul on the body became evident. For, feeling lonely and neglected, he felt ill again. He was hot. The red glow of the electric radiator seemed like some dim glare from Hades. It produced in him a very uncomfortable sensation, and he slipped out of bed and extinguished the radiator. Which unconsidered action left him in complete darkness far from the bed.

He reached the bed, by a roundabout route of groping, hurt his toe against the foot of the night table, jarred the table and heard something drop from it onto the floor. By the sound of its fall on the carpet he knew that the misplaced object must be the metal box of cough lozenges which among other things the doctor had prescribed for him. Yes, he had had a very slight cough.

The cough now suddenly grew worse—for no reason except that that box was lost on the floor. But, from mere contrariness, he would not search for the box. He insinuated himself into the bed, pulled the clothes round his neck, and coughed loudly in the hope that he would be heard over the whole flat. He was not heard. He determined to be a martyr. His body ached as though it had been whipped. He was conscious of a pain behind his eyes. His lips were dry.

Then the soles of his feet discovered that the hot-water bag was practically a cold-water bag. Monstrous! His grievance as a dying man forsaken waxed colossal. Strange, if he was too hot, that he should manufacture a grievance out of the coldness of the hot-water bag! Surely illogical? Not at all! The women responsible for the temperature of the bag did not know that he was too hot. For anything they knew he might be shivering with cold. He was indeed being criminally neglected. . . . There could be no excuse.

Ages passed. He looked at the little radium timepiece on the table. To his astonishment and disgust the silver-green signs on the dial indicated that the hour was eleven-thirty. He had been utterly abandoned for some ninety minutes! Infamous! He might have died.

And why had he been abandoned? Simply because the infant was a little unwell, or deemed to be a little unwell. The infant, then, was everything; and he was nothing! Naught! Yet who was the more important: the babe, who might develop into a brainless and insipid female creature, or himself, a genius of an inventor, a man who had done marvels in the application of science to industry, a celebrity whose name was not infrequently in the papers and whom the mightiest chairmen and directors of enormous commercial enterprises saluted with marked respect? . . . No sense of proportion in the minds of women! No justice on earth! His resentment was righteous and acute, and he held it at a white heat.

Now Mr. Michael Fassbrooke, who was about to be in the same room as this resentment, had none of the characteristics of the ordinary burglar—except the desire to possess other people's property by stealth and without paying for it. Some Irish blood pulsated in his veins. He "worked" alone, eschewing all gangs or cliques. He knew a very great deal about the police, having been a sergeant inspector of constabulary in an important provincial city.

He had been drawn, much against his will, into a blackmail conspiracy in the force of that city. The conspiracy having been exposed, Mr. Fassbrooke, partly by reason of his pleasant manners and partly of a certain difficulty in establishing his guilt, had been allowed to resign.

The episode had filled him with a grievance against society. After some starvation he had come to London, and, by the dodge of forged credentials and answering letters of inquiry addressed to himself under a false name, had obtained a clerical post in the West End Travel Agency.

A small but growing agency. A small but not growing salary. However, the smallness of the salary did not trouble him; what he wanted was the post. The post enabled him to know when people of means were shutting up their homes. Only a week earlier Mrs. Luce Reels, across a counter of the agency, while receiving from him various tickets and vouchers, had herself told him all relevant details of the Reels family movements.

He had asked her if she had an "All-in" insurance policy on the Reels flat. No, she had not. In her opinion to insure the contents—especially jewelry—of a flat on the eighth floor of a vast block was to throw money away.

True, she possessed a ruby necklace, far too valuable to
expose to the risks of trains-de-luxe. But Mrs. Reels, as
she quietly and confidentially explained to the urbane and
confidential Mr. Fassbrooke, had discovered the ideal
method of keeping jewelry from harm. Saying no word
to anybody, not even to her husband, she had just deposited it, as it was, without cases, on the top of a wardrobe, where no burglar would ever dream of looking. Mr.
Fassbrooke had openly expressed his admiration of her
ingenuity.

Thus, on the night of Anthony's resentment, Mr. Fassbrooke knew positively that the Reels flat would be empty.
He knew almost everything as to the flat and its tenants.
The one trifling item which he did not know was that
Mrs. Reels had telephoned to the agency in the morning
to ask whether the train reservations could be disposed of,
and had been regretfully told that they could not be,
time being too short for so complex an operation.

Mr. Fassbrooke, in evening dress, had reached the
eighth floor of the vast block by the simple device of going up in the lift—to the ninth floor, and walking down
the stairs to the eighth. The night liftman, incurious and
utterly unsuspicious, had saluted him with respect, taking
him for a friend of some tenant of the ninth floor—a
friend who knew his way about the place. The principal
bedrooms of the Reels flat gave on the north quadrangle.
The squalid service room (for waiters) next to the Reels
flat was, as generally at that hour, empty. Mr. Fassbrooke entered it by the door and left it by the window.

In a minute he was on one of the Reels balconies. In
another minute he had by means of an instrument easily
opened a French window. The blind was drawn; the curtains were drawn; but neither blind nor curtains can present any serious obstacle to a determined malefactor.
. . . Mr. Fassbrooke stood within the room, which was
as dark as a polar night when snow is about to fall. He
used his electric torch. Then it was that his ear caught a
sound—indeed a cough.

Thoughts ran through Mr. Fassbrooke's head in a

galloping procession. Burglary was a mug's game, the last resource of idiots. As a member of the force he had been well aware of this fact; but he had forgotten it. Now he was aware of it again. You ran fantastic risks. And the profits, even when you could realize them with safety, were entirely insufficient to atone for the risks.

He had never been caught, though at least once he had escaped arrest only by the clemency of heaven. (In any case he was caught now.) He had in store at home a quantity of precious things which he dared not yet attempt to dispose of. Once he had laid hands on a couple of hundred pounds in old and crumpled bank notes. He had been sure that the owner, a lady, was unacquainted with the numbers of the notes. Nevertheless he could never change one without horrid, nauseating pangs of apprehension. He was an ass. And so on.

In the tenth part of a second all these reflections crowded into his brain. He must act instantly, wisely, perfectly.

He shut off the torch as preliminary precaution. Futile. Anthony Reels switched on the bed light. The pair were face to face. Anthony had the formidable appearance of a tousled madman, capable of inordinate homicidal furies. And Mr. Fassbrooke, though admittedly an idiot, was not idiot enough to carry arms in the pursuit of his nocturnal profession.

"Are you a specialist they've sent?" Anthony asked at a loss.

"Yes," Mr. Fassbrooke replied.

"I'm supposed to be very ill," said Anthony. "Do specialists carry torches?"

"I do," said Mr. Fassbrooke.

A pause.

"I see what it is," Anthony went on with a lunatic smile, suddenly enlightened. "You're a cat-burglar, that's what you are. Evening dress and all!"

"No," said Mr. Fassbrooke, feebly and unconvincingly.

"Then what the devil are you doing here? What *are* you?"

"I'm an ass," said Mr. Fassbrooke.

"I daresay," Anthony agreed, glancing at the time-piece. "But you can't come along being an ass in people's bedrooms at twelve o'clock at night. It isn't done." Anthony sprang up threateningly. "You get out. No, not by the door. The way you got in. By the window—must have been. And look quick!"

"I can't," said Mr. Fassbrooke.

Anthony's tone suddenly changed to the mildly inquiring:

"Now tell me why not? I've often wanted to know all about cat-burglars. Tell me, and I'll let you go. I promise."

"It's like this," said Mr. Fassbrooke. "I took off my overcoat——"

"Oh! So you had an overcoat?"

"Yes. I was in the service room, and I took off my overcoat and threw it from the window there onto your balcony here, and then I just sort of sprang from the window sill onto the edge of the balcony, and hung onto the rail and climbed over, and here I was. But I couldn't jump back *from* the balcony *to* the window sill. I hope I make myself clear."

"You do! You do!" said Anthony. "And where's your overcoat now?"

"Hanging on the balcony rail."

"That'll do," said Anthony. "Remove yourself. I've had enough of you. If you meet anybody in the passage or the hall, don't argue. Just go straight on. There are two latches on the front door. It's the top one that you need. Hey! One moment. I've dropped my cough lozenges under the bed. You might pick them up for me, there's a good fellow."

It was while Mr. Fassbrooke was obediently ferreting under the bed that Luce Reels added herself to the scene.

Mr. Fassbrooke recognized the vivacious voice of his late customer Luce Reels, and he feigned death—an example of what is called nature's protective mimicry. Luce inspected his moveless hinterland. Her mind had been full of another matter; but the strange spectacle of a man on his knees, and his head beneath the bed, dislodged the other matter with a jerk.

"Who is this gentleman?" she demanded.

The imitation corpse did not stir.

"He just looked in to pick up my cough lozenges. They've dropped somewhere," Anthony explained, with a half-maniacal laugh.

"But who *is* he?"

"I know everything about him except his name, my dear," Anthony continued.

"But who let him in?"

"He let himself in—by the window. He's a burglar, and the finest kind of burglar—a cat-burglar. As he's been so kind about my cough lozenges, I've promised him to let him go." And to Mr. Fassbrooke, sternly: "Now then! Those cough lozenges! Get *up!*"

Mr. Fassbrooke got up, with what dignity he could summon, and, seizing his hat, deposited the box of cough lozenges on its stand on the table.

Luce Reels gazed at him. He was rather a handsome fellow, and possessed a good, slim figure. Further, he was stylishly dressed, though at the moment his clothes happened to be a bit rumpled.

"Anthony," said Luce at length, mildly reproving, and yet humouring—as was proper to a sick man, "how absurd of you! This is one of the gentlemen from the travel agency. I expect he's called about those train reservations. It was very kind of you, Mr.—er—I don't quite remember your name. Please excuse my husband—he's far from well."

"Of course, madam," said Mr. Fassbrooke.

Luce added, to nobody in particular:

"Though why Mary should have shown him in here I don't understand!"

Whereupon Anthony said crossly:

"*Do* people call at midnight about train reservations? And Mary didn't show him in. Haven't I told you he came in by the window too modestly, too unassumingly?

Why can't you believe me? If you will take the trouble
to look you will see his overcoat hanging on the balcony
—unless it's fallen into the quadrangle. And I wish you'd
shut either the door or the window. Why do you always
leave doors open? The draught in this room is enough to
blow the carpet off the floor."

A slight, chill current of air was indeed noticeable.

Luce went to the window and shut it, and in doing
so she descried the overcoat: which vision had the effect
of changing the direction of her ideas.

At the same instant, that is to say, simultaneously with
the turning of Luce's back, Mr. Fassbrooke shot toward
the door. But with an even greater velocity Anthony, all
radiant in bright pajamas and outraged fury, shot from
the bed, and grasped Mr. Fassbrooke's retreating arm as
in a steely vise; the grip of the homicidal insane.

"No, you don't!" cried he. "No, you don't! I promised
I'd let you go, and I will; but you're making mischief
between me and my wife and I won't stand it. My wife
thinks I'm off my head, and you're letting her think so.
Why did you say 'Of course, madam'? Are you a burglar
or aren't you? Yes or no?"

"Yes," responded Mr. Fassbrooke.

"You go and stand in that corner," commanded Anthony, indicating a corner by the window and far from
the door.

Mr. Fassbrooke obeyed.

"I see it all!" Luce burst out.

And she did see it all.

"You better get back into bed," she said to her husband.

"I *am* getting back into bed," said Anthony bitterly.

And he did get back into bed—coughed, and took a
cough lozenge.

"To think," said Luce, "that a so-called travel agency
should deliberately employ a man like you—worming
things out of their customers, and——"

"Don't be silly!" Anthony stopped her. " 'Deliberately'? You surely don't suppose they had the slightest

idea what kind of a man the man was. The travel agency is perfectly innocent!"

Ignoring this reproof, Luce Reels said, with a new excitement:

"Has he been into my bedroom? My rubies———"

"He hasn't." Anthony stopped her again.

"Are you sure?"

"Of course I'm sure!" Anthony shouted, nearly beside himself with rage at her doubts. "Why can't you believe me? You wouldn't believe me when I told you the fellow was a cat-burglar and now for the second time you aren't believing me. Why is it that women will believe anybody sooner than their husbands?"

Ignoring this reproof also, Luce said: "I shall go round to the agency first thing to-morrow morning and tell them. You'll see———"

"Unnecessary, madam. I shall not be there any more," Mr. Fassbrooke put in.

"No," said Luce with liveliness. "You won't be there. You'll be in the lockup."

"Come here, my girl!" Come here, I say!" Anthony ordered his wife, in such a savage tone as no decent husband would use to his wife—unless of course he were alone with her.

Luce, an independent enough wife of the latest modern pattern, obeyed him, to her own astonishment. Perhaps only her legs were frightened, not herself. She stood defiantly by the sick bed.

"Didn't I tell you," said Anthony, "that I've given the man my word that he may go free?"

"If you did, you were very silly," said Luce, suddenly enheartened by the sound of her own voice.

"That's neither here nor there," said Anthony. "The point is that I gave him my word. And permit me to say that it's very bad manners for you to call me silly in front of a complete stranger—especially a burglar. What will the criminal classes think of the intellectual classes?"

"If you don't want to be called silly," Luce retorted, "you shouldn't *be* silly. I say it was very silly of you,

and I stick to it. And anyhow I've not given *my* word,
and I won't. I mean to telephone to the police and neither
you nor anyone else can stop me."

Her accents had been quietly firm. Her self-control,
however, seemed to be powerless to induce self-control
in her husband.

He seized her innocent wrist in a grip even crueler
than that which he had employed on the guilty shoulder
of Mr. Fassbrooke. Then he seized her other wrist in a
similar grip. Then he shook her. The victimized wife was
being subjected to physical violence. She had an impulse
to cry out; but she nobly restrained it. As for Anthony,
he felt happy; he felt masculine; he felt that he was
revenging upon the person of Luce the innumerable grievances of the whole splendid, too-patient tribe of husbands
against all wives. He exulted in the infliction of pain on
the defenseless, weak woman. It was the greatest moment
of his life.

"Don't forget you're ill," said Luce, grimly setting
her teeth. "You'll only make yourself worse by these goings on."

"Oh!" cried Anthony. "So at last you've remembered
that I'm ill, have you? Here am I, ill, and I have a nurse
and a doctor, and you take them both away from me—
together. I'm left alone, for hours and hours. Nobody
cares. I might have died. I might be a perfect nobody in
this flat that you made me take, though I didn't want it.

"Who's the most important person in this flat? Possibly you think it's yourself. Well, it isn't. Who are you,
after all? What do you do? Nothing but spend, spend,
spend. Did you ever earn a penny in your life? Not you!
And you never will. You couldn't! You haven't got the
brains to earn anything, nor the application, nor the
concentration. You're nobody, nobody! And you think
you're everybody. Every woman thinks she's everybody.
That's what's the matter with women, and the matter
with men is that they stand it, because they're so cursedly
good-natured. The harem ought to be introduced into
this country. It's needed. And the worst sign of civiliza-

tion is that the Turks are doing away with the harem.
The Turks had some sense—once. Now they've lost it.
Everything's going to the dogs. And I suppose this is
what I fought for in the war.

"Am I one of the hopes of applied science or am I
not? Am I a first-rate inventor or am I not?" His voice
rose higher. "Am I superior to Edison or am I not? Has
there ever been any inventor equal to me or has there
not? Am I the youngest member of the Royal Society, or
am I not? Everyone knows the answer. And here I'm
lying dangerously ill, shamefully neglected, left, you may
say, to die like a dog in a ditch. And my wife has the
cheek to tell me I'm very silly. That's all she can think
of—naturally—being a woman!"

At this point in his enormous and shocking tirade Anthony paused, not for want of breath, but apparently because he could not think of anything more effective to say
and wished to avoid an anticlimax.

Luce thought, horror-struck:

"This is the end of the world for me! This is what
he really thinks about me in his heart. At last I know the
truth and my life is ruined. All is over with our marriage.
We shall have to separate. Will he take the child from
me?"

But Luce, like every woman, was an astounding person, capable in a supreme crisis of feats of self-mastery
and heroic duplicity which no male could hope to rival.
Aloud, she merely remarked, with breath-taking calm-
ness:

"Mr. Burglar, will you please fetch the doctor? He's
in the room opposite, across the passage."

There was no answer. She looked round. The burglar
had vanished. The door was open.

Luce's first thought was not: "He has escaped me after
all," but "How much did he hear?"

She then addressed Anthony:

"I should like you to know that poor Rosie has got
influenza. A rather high temperature. That's why I
fetched both the nurse and the doctor."

Any reasonable husband would have subsided at these tidings. But not Anthony, who was thereby roused to an even more formidable fury.

"Ah!" he yelled. "I knew it. I knew it was that horrible spoilt child of yours!" ("Yours," not "ours"!) "And so I'm nobody! If you have to choose between me and the child, you choose the child, who'll grow up into a woman as selfish and futile as you are. Didn't I always say that that brat was born to make some good man unhappy? A nice thing! I tell you once for all——"

The doctor entered, and at sight of the excellent, middle-aged, conscientious Dr. Bain, Anthony did subside, relinquishing Luce's reddened wrist and falling back on the pillows.

"Did you hear him?" Luce murmured.

"Yes," replied the doctor. "He's delirious, that's all." He pushed a thermometer into Anthony's lax and unresisting mouth, and there was silence. "Yes. H'm! Excited. It's nothing. I'll give him a dose. Rosie'll be all right. The nurse is really A-1."

"I never thought of delirium," Luce muttered.

"What do you say?" said the doctor.

"Nothing."

She began to cry. She bent down, and kissed and kissed the unofficial representative of the great trade union of husbands, and stroked his damp hair.

"Poor neglected darling!" she whispered.

"You know you're simply *asking* for flu, kissing the patient like that!" remarked the doctor.

"I don't care," said Luce.

And she didn't care. More, she utterly forgot about Mr. Fassbrooke.

Don Marquis

THE OLD TROUPER

i ran onto mehitabel again
last evening
she is inhabiting
a decayed trunk
which lies in an alley
in greenwich village
in company with the
most villainous tom cat
i have ever seen
but there is nothing
wrong about the association
archy she told me
it is merely a plutonic
attachment
and the thing can be
believed for the tom
looks like one of pluto s demons
it is a theatre trunk
archy mehitabel told me
and tom is an old theatre cat
he has given his life
to the theatre
he claims that richard
mansfield once
kicked him out of the way
and then cried because
he had done it and
petted him
and at another time
he says in a case
of emergency
he played a bloodhound
in a production of

uncle tom s cabin
the stage is not what it
used to be tom says
he puts his front paw
on his breast and says
they don t have it any more
they don t have it here
the old troupers are gone
there s nobody can troupe
any more
they are all amateurs nowadays
they haven t got it
here
there are only
five or six of us oldtime
troupers left
this generation does not know
what stage presence is
personality is what they lack
personality
where would they get
the training my old friends
got in the stock companies
i knew mr booth very well
says tom
and a law should be passed
preventing anybody else
from ever playing
in any play he ever
played in
there was a trouper for you
i used to sit on his knee
and purr when i was
a kitten he used to tell me
how much he valued my opinion
finish is what they lack
finish
and they haven t got it
here

and again he laid his paw
on his breast
i remember mr daly very
well too
i was with mr daly s company
for several years
there was art for you
there was team work
there was direction
they knew the theatre
and they all had it
here
for two years mr daly
would not ring up the curtain
unless i was in the
prompter s box
they are amateurs nowadays
rank amateurs all of them
for two seasons i played
the dog in joseph
jefferson s rip van winkle
it is true i never came
on the stage
but he knew i was just off
and it helped him
i would like to see
one of your modern
theatre cats
act a dog so well
that it would convince
a trouper like jo jefferson
but they haven t got it
nowadays
they haven t got it
here
jo jefferson had it he had it
here
i come of a long line
of theatre cats

my grandfather
was with forrest
he had it he was a real trouper
my grandfather said
he had a voice
that used to shake
the ferryboats
on the north river
once he lost his beard
and my grandfather
dropped from the
fly gallery and landed
under his chin
and played his beard
for the rest of the act
you don t see any theatre
cats that could do that
nowadays
they haven t got it they
haven t got it
here
once i played the owl
in modjeska s production
of macbeth
i sat above the castle gate
in the murder scene
and made my yellow
eyes shine through the dusk
like an owl s eyes
modjeska was a real
trouper she knew how to pick
her support i would like
to see any of these modern
theatre cats play the owl s eyes
to modjeska s lady macbeth
but they haven t got it nowadays
they haven t got it
here

mehitabel he says
both our professions
are being ruined
by amateurs

archy

Ellen Glasgow

THE SHADOWY THIRD

When the call came I remember that I turned from the telephone in a romantic flutter. Though I had spoken only once to the great surgeon, Roland Maradick, I felt on that December afternoon that to speak to him only once —to watch him in the operating-room for a single hour— was an adventure which drained the colour and the excitement from the rest of life. After all these years of work on typhoid and pneumonia cases, I can still feel the delicious tremor of my young pulses; I can still see the winter sunshine slanting through the hospital windows over the white uniforms of the nurses.

"He didn't mention me by name. Can there be a mistake?" I stood, incredulous yet ecstatic, before the superintendent of the hospital.

"No, there isn't a mistake. I was talking to him before you came down." Miss Hemphill's strong face softened while she looked at me. She was a big, resolute woman, a distant Canadian relative of my mother's, and the kind of nurse I had discovered in the month since I had come up from Richmond, that Northern hospital boards, if not Northern patients, appear instinctively to select. From the first, in spite of her hardness, she had taken a liking —I hesitate to use the word "fancy" for a preference so impersonal—to her Virginia cousin. After all, it isn't every Southern nurse, just out of training, who can boast a kinswoman in the superintendent of a New York hospital.

"And he made you understand positively that he meant me?" The thing was so wonderful that I simply couldn't believe it.

"He asked particularly for the nurse who was with Miss Hudson last week when he operated. I think he didn't even remember that you had a name. When I asked if he

415

meant Miss Randolph, he repeated that he wanted the nurse who had been with Miss Hudson. She was small, he said, and cheerful-looking. This, of course, might apply to one or two of the others, but none of these was with Miss Hudson."

"Then I suppose it is really true?" My pulses were tingling. "And I am to be there at six o'clock?"

"Not a minute later. The day nurse goes off duty at that hour, and Mrs. Maradick is never left by herself for an instant."

"It is her mind, isn't it? And that makes it all the stranger that he should select me, for I have had so few mental cases."

"So few cases of any kind," Miss Hemphill was smiling, and when she smiled I wondered if the other nurses would know her. "By the time you have gone through the treadmill in New York, Margaret, you will have lost a good many things besides your inexperience. I wonder how long you will keep your sympathy and your imagination? After all, wouldn't you have made a better novelist than a nurse?"

"I can't help putting myself into my cases. I suppose one ought not to?"

"It isn't a question of what one ought to do, but of what one must. When you are drained of every bit of sympathy and enthusiasm, and have got nothing in return for it, not even thanks, you will understand why I try to keep you from wasting yourself."

"But surely in a case like this—for Doctor Maradick?"

"Oh, well, of course—for Doctor Maradick." She must have seen that I implored her confidence, for, after a minute, she let fall carelessly a gleam of light on the situation: "It is a very sad case when you think what a charming man and a great surgeon Doctor Maradick is."

Above the starched collar of my uniform I felt the blood leap in bounds to my cheeks. "I have spoken to him only once," I murmured, "but he is charming, and so kind and handsome, isn't he?"

"His patients adore him."

"Oh, yes, I've seen that. Everyone hangs on his visits." Like the patients and the other nurses, I also had come by delightful, if imperceptible, degrees to hang on the daily visits of Doctor Maradick. He was, I suppose, born to be a hero to women. From my first day in his hospital, from the moment when I watched, through closed shutters, while he stepped out of his car, I have never doubted that he was assigned to the great part in the play. If I had been ignorant of his spell—of the charm he exercised over his hospital—I should have felt it in the waiting hush, like a drawn breath, which followed his ring at the door and preceded his imperious footstep on the stairs. My first impression of him, even after the terrible events of the next year, records a memory that is both careless and splendid. At that moment, when, gazing through the chinks in the shutters, I watched him, in his coat of dark fur, cross the pavement over the pale streaks of sunshine, I knew beyond any doubt—I knew with a sort of infallible prescience—that my fate was irretrievably bound up with his in the future. I knew this, I repeat, though Miss Hemphill would still insist that my foreknowledge was merely a sentimental gleaning from indiscriminate novels. But it wasn't only first love, impressionable as my kinswoman believed me to be. It wasn't only the way he looked. Even more than his appearance—more than the shining dark of his eyes, the silvery brown of his hair, the dusky glow in his face—even more than his charm and his magnificence, I think, the beauty and sympathy in his voice won my heart. It was a voice, I heard someone say afterwards, that ought always to speak poetry.

So you will see why—if you do not understand at the beginning, I can never hope to make you believe impossible things!—so you will see why I accepted the call when it came as an imperative summons. I couldn't have stayed away after he sent for me. However much I may have tried not to go, I know that in the end I must have gone. In those days, while I was still hoping to write novels, I used to talk a great deal about "destiny" (I have learned since then how silly all such talk is), and I suppose it was my "destiny" to be caught in the web of Roland Medwick's personality. But I am not the first nurse to grow love-sick about a doctor who never gave her a thought.

"I am glad you got the call, Margaret. It may mean a great deal to you. Only try not to be too emotional." I remember that Miss Hemphill was holding a bit of rose-geranium in her hand while she spoke—one of the patients had given it to her from a pot she kept in her room, and the scent of the flower is still in my nostrils—or my memory. Since then—oh, long since then—I have wondered if she also had been caught in the web.

"I wish I knew more about the case." I was pressing for light. "Have you ever seen Mrs. Maradick?"

"Oh, dear, yes. They have been married only a little over a year, and in the beginning she used to come sometimes to the hospital and wait outside while the doctor made his visits. She was a very sweet-looking woman then —not exactly pretty, but fair and slight, with the loveliest smile, I think, I have ever seen. In those first months she was so much in love that we used to laugh about it among ourselves. To see her face light up when the doctor came out of the hospital and crossed the pavement to his car, was as good as a play. We never tired of watching her—I wasn't superintendent then, so I had more time to look out of the window while I was on day duty. Once or twice she brought her little girl in to see one of the patients. The child was so much like her that you would have known them anywhere for mother and daughter."

I had heard that Mrs. Maradick was a widow, with one child, when she first met the doctor, and I asked now, still seeking an illumination I had not found, "There was a great deal of money, wasn't there?"

"A great fortune. If she hadn't been so attractive, people would have said, I suppose, that Doctor Maradick married her for her money. Only," she appeared to make an effort of memory, "I believe I've heard somehow that it was all left in trust away from Mrs. Maradick if she married again. I can't, to save my life, remember just how it was; but it was a queer will, I know, and Mrs. Maradick wasn't to come into the money unless the child didn't live to grow up. The pity of it——"

A young nurse came into the office to ask for something —the keys, I think, of the operating-room, and Miss Hemphill broke off inconclusively as she hurried out of the door. I was sorry that she left off just when she did. Poor Mrs. Maradick! Perhaps I was too emotional, but even before I saw her I had begun to feel her pathos and her strangeness.

My preparations took only a few minutes. In those days I always kept a suitcase packed and ready for sudden calls; and it was not yet six o'clock when I turned from Tenth Street into Fifth Avenue, and stopped for a minute, before ascending the steps, to look at the house in which Doctor Maradick lived. A fine rain was falling, and I remember thinking, as I turned the corner, how depressing the weather must be for Mrs. Maradick. It was an old house, with damp-looking walls (though that may have been because of the rain) and a spindle-shaped iron railing which ran up the stone steps to the black door, where I noticed a dim flicker through the old-fashioned fanlight. Afterwards I discovered that Mrs. Maradick had been born in the house—her maiden name was Calloran—and that she had never wanted to live anywhere else. She was a woman—this I found out when I knew her better—of strong attachments to both persons and places; and though Doctor Maradick had tried to persuade her to move uptown after her marriage, she had clung, against his wishes, to the old house in lower Fifth Avenue. I dare say she was obstinate about it in spite of her gentleness and her passion for the doctor. Those sweet, soft women, especially when they have always been rich, are sometimes amazingly obstinate. I have nursed so many of them since —women with strong affections and weak intellects—that I have come to recognize the type as soon as I set eyes upon it.

My ring at the bell was answered after a little delay, and when I entered the house I saw that the hall was quite dark except for the waning glow from an open fire which burned in the library. When I gave my name, and added that I was the night nurse, the servant appeared to think my humble presence unworthy of illumination. He was an old negro butler, inherited perhaps from Mrs. Maradick's mother, who, I learned afterwards, was from South Carolina; and while he passed me on his way up the staircase, I heard him vaguely muttering that he "wa'n't gwinter tu'n on dem lights twel de chile had done playin'."

To the right of the hall, the soft glow drew me into the library, and crossing the threshold timidly, I stooped to dry my wet coat by the fire. As I bent there, meaning to start up at the first sound of a footstep, I thought how cosy the room was after the damp walls outside to which some bared creepers were clinging; and I was watching the strange shapes and patterns the firelight made on the old Persian rug, when the lamps of a slowly turning motor flashed on me through the white shades at the window. Still dazzled by the glare, I looked round in the dimness and saw a child's ball of red and blue rubber roll towards me out of the gloom of the adjoining room. A moment later, while I made a vain attempt to capture the toy as it spun past me, a little girl darted airily, with peculiar lightness and grace, through the doorway, and stopped quickly, as if in surprise at the sight of a stranger. She was a small child—so small and slight that her footsteps made no sound on the polished floor of the threshold; and I remember thinking while I looked at her that she had the gravest and sweetest face I had ever seen. She couldn't—I decided this afterwards—have been more than six or seven years old, yet she stood there with a curious prim dignity, like the dignity of an elderly person, and gazed up at me with enigmatical eyes. She was dressed in Scotch plaid, with a bit of red ribbon in her hair, which was cut in a fringe over her forehead and hung very straight to her shoulders. Charming as she was, from her uncurled brown hair to the white socks and black slippers on her little feet, I recall most vividly the singular look in her eyes, which appeared in the shifting light to be of an indeterminate colour. For the odd thing about this look was that it was not the look of childhood at all. It was the look of profound experience, of bitter knowledge.

"Have you come for your ball?" I asked; but while the friendly question was still on my lips, I heard the servant returning. In my confusion I made a second in-effectual grasp at the plaything, which had rolled away from me into the dusk of the drawing-room. Then, as I raised my head, I saw that the child also had slipped from the room; and without looking after her I followed the old negro into the pleasant study above, where the great surgeon awaited me.

Ten years ago, before hard nursing had taken so much out of me, I blushed very easily, and I was aware at the moment when I crossed Doctor Maradick's study that my cheeks were the colour of peonies. Of course, I was a fool —no one knows this better than I do—but I had never been alone, even for an instant, with him before, and the man was more than a hero to me, he was—there isn't any reason now why I should blush over the confession— almost a god. At that age I was mad about the wonders of surgery, and Roland Maradick in the operating-room was magician enough to have turned an older and more sensible head than mine. Added to his great reputation and his marvelous skill, he was, I am sure of this, the most splendid-looking man, even at forty-five, that one could imagine. Had he been ungracious—had he been positively rude to me, I should still have adored him; but when he held out his hand, and greeted me in the charm-ing way he had with women, I felt that I would have died for him. It is no wonder that a saying went about the hospital that every woman he operated on fell in love with him. As for the nurses—well, there wasn't a single one of them who had escaped his spell—not even Miss Hemphill, who could have been scarcely a day under fifty.

"I am glad you could come, Miss Randolph. You were with Miss Hudson last week when I operated?"

I bowed. To save my life I couldn't have spoken without blushing the redder.

"I noticed your bright face at the time. Brightness, I think, is what Mrs. Maradick needs. She finds her day nurse depressing." His eyes rested so kindly upon me that I have suspected since that he was not entirely unaware of my worship. It was a small thing, heaven knows, to flatter his vanity—a nurse just out of a training-school—but to some men no tribute is too insignificant to give pleasure.

"You will do your best, I am sure." He hesitated an instant—just long enough for me to perceive the anxiety beneath the genial smile on his face—and then added gravely, "We wish to avoid, if possible, having to send her away."

I could only murmur in response, and after a few carefully chosen words about his wife's illness, he rang the bell and directed the maid to take me upstairs to my room. Not until I was ascending the stairs to the third storey did it occur to me that he had really told me nothing. I was as perplexed about the nature of Mrs. Maradick's malady as I had been when I entered the house.

I found my room pleasant enough. It had been arranged —at Doctor Maradick's request, I think—that I was to sleep in the house, and after my austere little bed at the hospital, I was agreeably surprised by the cheerful look of the apartment into which the maid led me. The walls were papered in roses, and there were curtains of flowered chintz at the window, which looked down on a small formal garden at the rear of the house. This the maid told me, for it was too dark for me to distinguish more than a marble fountain and a fir-tree, which looked old, though I afterwards learned that it was replanted almost every season.

In ten minutes I had slipped into my uniform and was ready to go to my patient; but for some reason—to this day I have never found out what it was that turned her against me at the start—Mrs. Maradick refused to receive me. While I stood outside her door I heard the day nurse trying to persuade her to let me come in. It wasn't any use, however, and in the end I was obliged to go back to my room and wait until the poor lady got over her whim and consented to see me. That was long after dinner—it must have been nearer eleven than ten o'clock—and Miss Peterson was quite worn out by the time she came for me.

"I'm afraid you'll have a bad night," she said as we went downstairs together. That was her way, I soon saw, to expect the worst of everything and everybody.

"Does she often keep you up like this?"

"Oh, no, she is usually very considerate. I never knew a sweeter character. But she still has this hallucination——"

Here again, as in the scene with Doctor Maradick, I felt that the explanation had only deepened the mystery. Mrs. Maradick's hallucination, whatever form it assumed, was evidently a subject for evasion and subterfuge in the household. It was on the tip of my tongue to ask, "What is her hallucination?"—but before I could get the words past my lips we had reached Mrs. Maradick's door, and Miss Peterson motioned me to be silent. As the door opened a little way to admit me, I saw that Mrs. Maradick was already in bed, and that the lights were out except for a night-lamp burning on a candle-stand beside a book and a carafe of water.

"I won't go in with you," said Miss Peterson in a whisper; and I was on the point of stepping over the threshold when I saw the little girl, in the dress of Scotch plaid, slip by me from the dusk of the room into the electric light of the hall. She held a doll in her arms, and as she went by she dropped a doll's work-basket in the doorway. Miss Peterson must have picked up the toy, for when I turned in a minute to look for it I found that it was gone. I remember thinking that it was late for a child to be up—she looked delicate, too—but, after all, it was no business of mine, and four years in a hospital had taught me never to meddle in things that do not concern me. There is nothing a nurse learns quicker than not to try to put the world to rights in a day.

When I crossed the floor to the chairs by Mrs. Maradick's bed, she turned over on her side and looked at me with the sweetest and saddest smile.

"You are the night nurse," she said in a gentle voice; and from the moment she spoke I knew that there was nothing hysterical or violent about her mania—or hallucination, as they called it. "They told me your name, but I have forgotten it."

"Randolph—Margaret Randolph." I liked her from the start, and I think she must have seen it.

"You look very young, Miss Randolph."

"I am twenty-two, but I suppose I don't look quite my age. People usually think I am younger."

For a minute she was silent, and while I settled myself in the chair by the bed, I thought how strikingly she resembled the little girl I had seen first in the afternoon, and then leaving her room a few moments before. They had the same small, heart-shaped faces, coloured ever so faintly; the same straight, soft hair, between brown and flaxen; and the same large, grave eyes, set very far apart under arched eyebrows. What surprised me most, however, was that they both looked at me with that enigmatical and vaguely wondering expression—only in Mrs. Maradick's face the vagueness seemed to change now and then to a definite fear—a flash, I had almost said, of startled horror.

I sat quite still in my chair, and until the time came for Mrs. Maradick to take her medicine not a word passed between us. Then, when I bent over her with the glass in my hand, she raised her head from the pillow and said in a whisper of suppressed intensity:

"You look kind. I wonder if you could have seen my little girl?"

As I slipped my arm under the pillow I tried to smile cheerfully down on her. "Yes, I've seen her twice. I'd know her anywhere by her likeness to you."

A glow shone in her eyes, and I thought how pretty she must have been before illness took the life and animation out of her features. "Then I know you're good." Her voice was so strained and low that I could barely hear it. "If you weren't good you couldn't have seen her."

I thought this queer enough, but all I answered was, "She looked delicate to be sitting up so late."

A quiver passed over her thin features, and for a minute I thought she was going to burst into tears. As she had taken the medicine, I put the glass back on the candle-stand, and bending over the bed, smoothed the straight brown hair, which was as fine and soft as spun silk, back from her forehead. There was something about her—I don't know what it was—that made you love her as soon as she looked at you.

"She always had that light and airy way, though she was never sick a day in her life," she answered calmly after a pause. Then, groping for my hand, she whispered passionately, "You must not tell him—you must not tell any one that you have seen her!"

"I must not tell any one?" Again I had the impression that had come to me first in Doctor Maradick's study, and afterwards with Miss Peterson on the staircase, that I was seeking a gleam of light in the midst of obscurity.

"Are you sure there isn't any one listening—that there isn't any one at the door?" she asked, pushing aside my arm and raising herself on the pillows.

"Quite, quite sure. They have put out the lights in the hall."

"And you will not tell him? Promise me that you will not tell him." The startled horror flashed from the vague wonder of her expression. "He doesn't like her to come back, because he killed her."

"Because he killed her!" Then it was that light burst on me in a blaze. So this was Mrs. Maradick's hallucination! She believed that her child was dead—the little girl I had seen with my own eyes leaving her room; and she believed that her husband—the great surgeon we worshipped in the hospital—had murdered her. No wonder

they veiled the dreadful obsession in mystery! No wonder
that even Miss Peterson had not dared to drag the horrid
thing out into the light! It was the kind of hallucination
one simply couldn't stand having to face.

"There is no use telling people things that nobody believes," she resumed slowly, still holding my hand in a
grasp that would have hurt me if her fingers had not been
so fragile. "Nobody believes that he killed her. Nobody
believes that she comes back every day to the house. Nobody believes—and yet you saw her——"

"Yes, I saw her—but why should your husband have
killed her?" I spoke soothingly, as one would speak to a
person who was quite mad. Yet she was not mad, I could
have sworn this while I looked at her.

For a moment she moaned inarticulately, as if the horror of her thoughts were too great to pass into speech.
Then she flung out her thin, bare arm with a wild gesture.

"Because he never loved me!" she said. "He never loved
me!"

"But he married you," I urged gently while I stroked
her hair. "If he hadn't loved you, why should he have
married you?"

"He wanted the money—my little girl's money. It all
goes to him when I die."

"But he is rich himself. He must make a fortune from
his profession."

"It isn't enough. He wanted millions." She had grown
stern and tragic. "No, he never loved me. He loved someone else from the beginning—before I knew him."

It was quite useless, I saw, to reason with her. If she
wasn't mad, she was in a state of terror and despondency
so black that it had almost crossed the border-line into
madness. I thought once that I would go upstairs and
bring the child down from her nursery; but, after a moment's hesitation, I realized that Miss Peterson and Doctor Maradick must have long ago tried all these measures.
Clearly, there was nothing to do except soothe and quiet

her as much as I could; and this I did until she dropped into a light sleep which lasted well into the morning.

By seven o'clock I was worn out—not from work but from the strain on my sympathy—and I was glad, indeed, when one of the maids came in to bring me an early cup of coffee. Mrs. Maradick was still sleeping—it was a mixture of bromide and chloral I had given her—and she did not wake until Miss Peterson came on duty an hour or two later. Then, when I went downstairs, I found the dining-room deserted except for the old housekeeper, who was looking over the silver. Doctor Maradick, she explained to me presently, had his breakfast served in the morning-room on the other side of the house.

"And the little girl? Does she take her meals in the nursery?"

She threw me a startled glance. Was it, I questioned afterwards, one of distrust or apprehension?

"There isn't any little girl. Haven't you heard?"

"Heard? No. Why, I saw her only yesterday."

The look she gave me—I was sure of it now—was full of alarm.

"The little girl—she was the sweetest child I ever saw —died just two months ago of pneumonia."

"But she couldn't have died." I was a fool to let this out, but the shock had completely unnerved me. "I tell you I saw her yesterday."

The alarm in her face deepened. "That is Mrs. Maradick's trouble. She believes that she still sees her."

"But don't you see her?" I drove the question home bluntly.

"No." She set her lips tightly. "I never see anything."

So I had been wrong, after all, and the explanation, when it came, only accentuated the terror. The child was dead—she had died of pneumonia two months ago—and yet I had seen her, with my own eyes, playing ball in the library; I had seen her slipping out of her mother's room, with her doll in her arms.

"Is there another child in the house? Could there be a

child belonging to one of the servants?" A gleam had shot through the fog in which I was groping.

"No, there isn't any other. The doctors tried bringing one once, but it threw the poor lady into such a state she almost died of it. Besides, there wouldn't be any other child as quiet and sweet-looking as Dorothea. To see her skipping along in her dress of Scotch plaid used to make me think of a fairy, though they say that fairies wear nothing but white or green."

"Has any one else seen her—the child, I mean—any of the servants?"

"Only old Gabriel, the coloured butler, who came with Mrs. Maradick's mother from South Carolina. I've heard that negroes often have a kind of second sight—though I don't know that that is just what you would call it. But they seem to believe in the supernatural by instinct, and Gabriel is so old and doty—he does no work except answer the door-bell and clean the silver—that nobody pays much attention to anything that he sees——"

"Is the child's nursery kept as it used to be?"

"Oh, no. The doctor had all the toys sent to the children's hospital. That was a great grief to Mrs. Maradick; but Doctor Brandon thought, and all the nurses agreed with him, that it was best for her not to be allowed to keep the room as it was when Dorothea was living."

"Dorothea? Was that the child's name?"

"Yes, it means the gift of God, doesn't it? She was named after the mother of Mrs. Maradick's first husband, Mr. Ballard. He was the grave, quiet kind—not the least like the doctor."

I wondered if the other dreadful obsession of Mrs. Maradick's had drifted down through the nurses or the servants to the housekeeper; but she said nothing about it, and since she was, I suspected, a garrulous person, I thought it wiser to assume that the gossip had not reached her.

A little later, when breakfast was over and I had not yet gone upstairs to my room, I had my first interview with Doctor Brandon, the famous alienist who was in charge of the case. I had never seen him before, but from the first moment that I looked at him I took his measure almost by intuition. He was, I suppose, honest enough—I have always granted him that, bitterly as I have felt towards him. It wasn't his fault that he lacked red blood in his brain, or that he had formed the habit, from long association with abnormal phenomena, of regarding all life as a disease. He was the sort of physician—every nurse will understand what I mean—who deals instinctively with groups instead of with individuals. He was long and solemn and very round in the face; and I hadn't talked to him ten minutes before I knew he had been educated in Germany, and that he had learned over there to treat every emotion as a pathological manifestation. I used to wonder what he got out of life—what any one got out of life who had analyzed away everything except the bare structure.

When I reached my room at last, I was so tired that I could barely remember either the questions Doctor Brandon had asked or the directions he had given me. I fell asleep, I know, almost as soon as my head touched the pillow; and the maid who came to inquire if I wanted luncheon decided to let me finish my nap. In the afternoon, when she returned with a cup of tea, she found me still heavy and drowsy. Though I was used to night nursing, I felt as if I had danced from sunset to daybreak. It was fortunate, I reflected, while I drank my tea, that every case didn't wear on one's sympathies as acutely as Mrs. Maradick's hallucination had worn on mine.

Through the day I did not see Doctor Maradick; but at seven o'clock when I came up from my early dinner on my way to take the place of Miss Peterson, who had kept on duty an hour later than usual, he met me in the hall and asked me to come into his study. I thought him handsomer than ever in his evening clothes, with a white flower in his buttonhole. He was going to some public dinner, the housekeeper told me, but, then, he was always going somewhere. I believe he didn't dine at home a single evening that winter.

"Did Mrs. Maradick have a good night?" He had closed the door after us, and turning now with the question, he smiled kindly, as if he wished to put me at ease in the beginning.

"She slept very well after she took the medicine. I gave her that at eleven o'clock."

For a minute he regarded me silently, and I was aware that his personality—his charm—was focussed upon me. It was almost as if I stood in the centre of converging rays of light, so vivid was my impression of him.

"Did she allude in any way to her—to her hallucination?" he asked.

How the warning reached me—what invisible waves of sense-perception transmitted the message—I have never known; but while I stood there, facing the splendour of the doctor's presence, every intuition cautioned me that the time had come when I must take sides in the household. While I stayed there I must stand either with Mrs. Maradick or against her.

"She talked quite rationally," I replied after a moment.

"What did she say?"

"She told me how she was feeling, that she missed her child, and that she walked a little every day about her room."

His face changed—how I could not at first determine. "Have you seen Doctor Brandon?"

"He came this morning to give me his directions."

"He thought her less well to-day. He has advised me to send her to Rosedale."

I have never, even in secret, tried to account for Doctor Maradick. He may have been sincere. I tell only what I know—not what I believe or imagine—and the human is sometimes as inscrutable, as inexplicable, as the supernatural.

While he watched me I was conscious of an inner struggle, as if opposing angels warred somewhere in the depths of my being. When at last I made my decision, I was acting less from reason, I knew, than in obedience to the pressure of some secret current of thought. Heaven knows, even then, the man held me captive while I defied him.

"Doctor Maradick," I lifted my eyes for the first time frankly to his, "I believe that your wife is as sane as I am—or as you are."

He started. "Then she did not talk freely to you?"

"She may be mistaken, unstrung, piteously distressed in mind"—I brought this out with emphasis—"but she is not—I am willing to stake my future on it—a fit subject for an asylum. It would be foolish—it would be cruel to send her to Rosedale."

"Cruel, you say?" A troubled look crossed his face, and his voice grew very gentle. "You do not imagine that I could be cruel to her?"

"No, I do not think that." My voice also had softened.

"We will let things go on as they are. Perhaps Doctor Brandon may have some other suggestion to make." He drew out his watch and compared it with the clock —nervously, I observed, as if his action were a screen for his discomfiture or perplexity. "I must be going now. We will speak of this again in the morning."

But in the morning we did not speak of it, and during the month that I nursed Mrs. Maradick I was not called again into her husband's study. When I met him in the hall or on the staircase, which was seldom, he was as charming as ever; yet, in spite of his courtesy, I had a persistent feeling that he had taken my measure on that evening, and that he had no further use for me.

As the days went by Mrs. Maradick seemed to grow stronger. Never, after our first night together, had she mentioned the child to me; never had she alluded by so much as a word to her dreadful charge against her husband. She was like any woman recovering from a great sorrow, except that she was sweeter and gentler. It is no wonder that everyone who came near her loved her; for there was a mysterious loveliness about her like the mystery of light, not of darkness. She was, I have always thought, as much of an angel as it is possible for a woman to be on this earth. And yet, angelic as she was, there were times when it seemed to me that she both hated and feared her husband. Though he never entered her room while I was there, and I never heard his name on her lips until an hour before the end, still I could tell by the look of terror in her face whenever his step passed down the hall that her very soul shivered at his approach.

During the whole month I did not see the child again, though one night, when I came suddenly into Mrs. Maradick's room, I found a little garden, such as children make out of pebbles and bits of box, on the window-sill. I did not mention it to Mrs. Maradick, and a little later, as the maid lowered the shades, I noticed that the garden had vanished. Since then I have often wondered if the child were invisible only to the rest of us, and if her mother still saw her. But there was no way of finding out except by questioning, and Mrs. Maradick was so well and patient that I hadn't the heart to question. Things couldn't have been better with her than they were, and I was beginning to tell myself that she might soon go out for an airing, when the end came so suddenly.

It was a mild January day—the kind of day that brings the foretaste of spring in the middle of winter, and when I came downstairs in the afternoon, I stopped a minute by the window at the end of the hall to look down on the box maze in the garden. There was an old fountain, bearing two laughing boys in marble, in the centre of the gravelled walk, and the water, which had been turned on that morning for Mrs. Maradick's pleasure, sparkled now like silver as the sunlight splashed over it. I had never before felt the air quite so soft and spring-like in January; and I thought, as I gazed down on the garden, that it would be a good idea for Mrs. Maradick to go out and bask for an hour or so in the sunshine. It seemed strange to me that she was never allowed to get any fresh air except the air that came through her windows.

When I went into her room, however, I found that she had no wish to go out. She was sitting, wrapped in shawls, by the open window, which looked down on the fountain; and as I entered she glanced up from a little book she was reading. A pot of daffodils stood on the window-sill —she was very fond of flowers and we tried always to keep some growing in her room.

"Do you know what I am reading, Miss Randolph?" she asked in her soft voice; and she read aloud a verse while I went over to the candle-stand to measure out a dose of medicine.

" 'If thou hast two loaves of bread, sell one and buy daffodils, for bread nourisheth the body, but daffodils delight the soul.' That is very beautiful, don't you think so?"

I said "Yes," that it was beautiful; and then I asked her if she wouldn't go downstairs and walk about in the garden.

"He wouldn't like it," she answered; and it was the first time she had mentioned her husband to me since the night I came to her. "He doesn't want me to go out."

I tried to laugh her out of the idea; but it was no use, and after a few minutes I gave up and began talking of other things. Even then it did not occur to me that her fear of Doctor Maradick was anything but a fancy. I could see, of course, that she wasn't out of her head; but sane persons, I knew, sometimes have unaccountable prejudices, and I accepted her dislike as a mere whim or aversion. I did not understand then and—I may as well confess this before the end comes—I do not understand any better to-day. I am writing down the things I actually saw, and I repeat that I have never had the slightest twist in the direction of the miraculous.

The afternoon slipped away while we talked—she talked brightly when any subject came up that interested her—and it was the last hour of day—that grave, still hour when the movement of life seems to droop and falter for a few precious minutes—that brought us the thing I had dreaded silently since my first night in the house. I remember that I had risen to close the window, and was leaning out for a breath of the mild air, when there was the sound of steps, consciously softened, in the hall out-side, and Doctor Brandon's usual knock fell on my ears. Then, before I could cross the room, the door opened, and the doctor entered with Miss Peterson. The day nurse, I knew, was a stupid woman; but she had never appeared to me so stupid, so armoured and encased in her professional manner, as she did at that moment.

"I am glad to see that you are taking the air." As Doctor Brandon came over to the window, I wondered maliciously what devil of contradictions had made him a distinguished specialist in nervous diseases.

"Who was the other doctor you brought this morning?" asked Mrs. Maradick gravely; and that was all I ever heard about the visit of the second alienist.

"Someone who is anxious to cure you." He dropped into a chair beside her and patted her hand with his long, pale fingers. "We are so anxious to cure you that we want to send you away to the country for a fortnight or so. Miss Peterson has come to help you to get ready, and I've kept my car waiting for you. There couldn't be a nicer day for a trip, could there?"

The moment had come at last. I knew at once what he meant, and so did Mrs. Maradick. A wave of colour flowed and ebbed in her thin cheeks, and I felt her body quiver when I moved from the window and put my arms on her shoulders. I was aware again, as I had been aware that evening in Doctor Maradick's study, of a current of thought that beat from the air around into my brain. Though it cost me my career as a nurse and my reputation for sanity, I knew that I must obey that invisible warning.

"You are going to take me to an asylum," said Mrs. Maradick.

He made some foolish denial or evasion; but before he had finished I turned from Mrs. Maradick and faced him impulsively. In a nurse this was flagrant rebellion, and I realized that the act wrecked my professional future. Yet I did not care—I did not hesitate. Something stronger than I was driving me on.

"Doctor Brandon," I said, "I beg you—I implore you to wait until to-morrow. There are things I must tell you."

A queer look came into his face, and I understood, even in my excitement, that he was mentally deciding in which group he should place me—to which class of morbid manifestations I must belong.

"Very well, very well, we will hear everything," he replied soothingly; but I saw him glance at Miss Peterson, and she went over to the wardrobe for Mrs. Maradick's fur coat and hat.

Suddenly, without warning, Mrs. Maradick threw the shawls away from her, and stood up. "If you send me away," she said, "I shall never come back. I shall never live to come back."

The grey of twilight was just beginning, and while she stood there, in the dusk of the room, her face shone out as pale and flower-like as the daffodils on the window-sill. "I cannot go away!" she cried in a sharper voice. "I cannot go away from my child!"

I saw her face clearly; I heard her voice; and then— the horror of the scene sweeps back over me!—I saw the door open slowly and the little girl run across the room to her mother. I saw the child lift her little arms, and I saw the mother stoop and gather her to her bosom. So closely locked were they in that passionate embrace that their forms seemed to mingle in the gloom that enveloped them.

"After this can you doubt?" I threw out the words almost savagely—and then, when I turned from the mother and child to Doctor Brandon and Miss Peterson, I knew breathlessly—oh, there was a shock in the discovery!— that they were blind to the child. Their blank faces revealed the consternation of ignorance, not of conviction. They had seen nothing except the vacant arms of the mother and the swift, erratic gesture with which she stooped to embrace some invisible presence. Only my vision—and I have asked myself since if the power of sympathy enabled me to penetrate the web of material fact and see the spiritual form of the child—only my vision was not blinded by the clay through which I looked.

"After this can you doubt?" Doctor Brandon had flung my words back to me. Was it his fault, poor man, if life had granted him only the eyes of flesh? Was it his fault if he could see only half of the thing there before him?

But they couldn't see, and since they couldn't see I realized that it was useless to tell them. Within an hour they took Mrs. Maradick to the asylum; and she went quietly, though when the time came for parting from me she showed some faint trace of feeling. I remember that at the last, while we stood on the pavement, she lifted her black veil, which she wore for the child, and said: "Stay with her, Miss Randolph, as long as you can. I shall never come back."

Then she got into the car and was driven off, while I stood looking after her with a sob in my throat. Dreadful as I felt it to be, I didn't, of course, realize the full horror of it, or I couldn't have stood there quietly on the pavement. I didn't realize it, indeed, until several months afterwards when word came that she had died in the asylum. I never knew what her illness was, though I vaguely recall that something was said about "heart failure"—a loose enough term. My own belief is that she died simply of the terror of life.

To my surprise Doctor Maradick asked me to stay on as his office nurse after his wife went to Rosedale; and when the news of her death came there was no suggestion of my leaving. I don't know to this day why he wanted me in the house. Perhaps he thought I should have less opportunity to gossip if I stayed under his roof; perhaps he still wished to test the power of his charm over me. His vanity was incredible in so great a man. I have seen him flush with pleasure when people turned to look at him in the street, and I know that he was not above playing on the sentimental weakness of his patients. But he was magnificent, heaven knows! Few men, I imagine, have been the objects of so many foolish infatuations.

The next summer Doctor Maradick went abroad for two months, and while he was away I took my vacation in Virginia. When we came back the work was heavier than ever—his reputation by this time was tremendous—and my days were so crowded with appointments, and hurried flittings to emergency cases, that I had scarcely a minute left in which to remember poor Mrs. Maradick. Since the afternoon when she went to the asylum the child had not been in the house; and at last I was beginning to persuade myself that the little figure had been an optical illusion—the effect of shifting lights in the gloom of the old rooms—not the apparition I had once believed it to be. It does not take long for a phantom to fade from the memory—especially when one leads the active and methodical life I was forced into that winter. Perhaps— who knows?—(I remember telling myself) the doctors may have been right, after all, and the poor lady may have actually been out of her mind. With this view of the past, my judgment of Doctor Maradick insensibly altered. It ended, I think, in my acquitting him altogether. And then, just as he stood clear and splendid in my verdict of him, the reversal came so precipitately that I grow breathless now whenever I try to live it over again. The violence of the next turn in affairs left me, I often fancy, with a perpetual dizziness of the imagination.

It was in May that we heard of Mrs. Maradick's death, and exactly a year later, on a mild and fragrant afternoon, when the daffodils were blooming in patches around the old fountain in the garden, the housekeeper came into the office, where I lingered over some accounts, to bring me news of the doctor's approaching marriage.

"It is no more than we might have expected," she concluded rationally. "The house must be lonely for him—he is such a sociable man. But I can't help feeling," she brought out slowly after a pause in which I felt a shiver pass over me, "I can't help feeling that it is hard for that other woman to have all the money poor Mrs. Maradick's first husband left her."

"There is a great deal of money, then?" I asked curiously.

"A great deal." She waved her hand, as if words were futile to express the sum. "Millions and millions!"

"They will give up this house, of course?"

"That's done already, my dear. There won't be a brick left of it by this time next year. It's to be pulled down and an apartment-house built on the ground."

Again the shiver passed over me. I couldn't bear to think of Mrs. Maradick's old home falling to pieces.

"You didn't tell me the name of the bride," I said. "Is she someone he met while he was in Europe?"

"Dear me, no! She is the very lady he was engaged to before he married Mrs. Maradick, only she threw him over, so people said, because he wasn't rich enough. Then she married some lord or prince from over the water; but there was a divorce, and now she has turned again to her old lover. He is rich enough now, I guess, even for her!"

It was all perfectly true, I suppose; it sounded as plausible as a story out of a newspaper; and yet while she told me I felt, or dreamed that I felt, a sinister, an impalpable hush in the air. I was nervous, no doubt; I was shaken by the suddenness with which the housekeeper had sprung her news on me; but as I sat there I had quite vividly an impression that the old house was listening— that there was a real, if invisible, presence somewhere in the room or the garden. Yet, when an instant afterwards I glanced through the long window which opened down to the brick terrace, I saw only the faint sunshine over the deserted garden, with its maze of box, its marble fountain, and its patches of daffodils.

The housekeeper had gone—one of the servants, I think, came for her—and I was sitting at my desk when the words of Mrs. Maradick on that last evening floated into my mind. The daffodils brought her back to me; for I thought, as I watched them growing, so still and golden in the sunshine, how she would have enjoyed them. Almost unconsciously I repeated the verse she had read to me:

"If thou hast two loaves of bread, sell one and buy daffodils"—and it was at this very instant, while the words were still on my lips, that I turned my eyes to the box maze, and saw the child skipping rope along the gravelled path to the fountain. Quite distinctly, as clear as day, I saw her come, with what children call the dancing step, between the low box borders to the place where the daffodils bloomed by the fountain. From her straight brown hair to her frock of Scotch plaid and her little feet, which twinkled in white socks and black slippers over the turning rope, she was as real to me as the ground on which she trod or the laughing marble boys under the splashing water. Starting up from my chair, I made a single step to the terrace. If I could only reach her— only speak to her—I felt that I might at last solve the mystery. But with the first flutter of my dress on the terrace, the airy little form melted into the quiet dusk of the maze. Not a breath stirred the daffodils, not a shadow passed over the sparkling flow of the water; yet, weak and shaken in every nerve, I sat down on the brick step of the terrace and burst into tears. I must have known that something terrible would happen before they pulled down Mrs. Maradick's home.

The doctor dined out that night. He was with the lady he was going to marry, the housekeeper told me; and it must have been almost midnight when I heard him come in and go upstairs to his room. I was downstairs because I had been unable to sleep, and the book I wanted to finish I had left that afternoon in the office. The book—I can't remember what it was—had seemed to me very exciting when I began it in the morning; but after the visit of the child I found the romantic novel as dull as a treatise on nursing. It was impossible for me to follow the lines, and I was on the point of giving up and going to bed, when Doctor Maradick opened the front door with his latch-key and went up the staircase. "There can't be a bit of truth in it." I thought over and over again as I listened to his even step ascending the stairs. "There can't be a bit of truth in it." And yet, though I assured myself that "there couldn't be a bit of truth in it," I shrank, with a creepy sensation, from going through the house to my room in the third storey. I was tired out after a hard day, and my nerves must have reacted morbidly to the silence and the darkness. For the first time in my life I knew what it was to be afraid of the unknown, of the unseen; and while I bent over my book, in the glare of the electric light, I became conscious presently that I was straining my senses for some sound in the spacious emptiness of the rooms overhead. The noise of a passing motor-car in the street jerked me back from the intense hush of expectancy; and I can recall the wave of relief that swept over me as I turned to my book again and tried to fix my distracted mind on its pages.

I was still sitting there when the telephone on my desk rang, with what seemed to my overwrought nerves a startling abruptness, and the voice of the superintendent told me hurriedly that Doctor Maradick was needed at the hospital. I had become so accustomed to these emergency calls in the night that I felt reassured when I had rung up the doctor in his room and had heard the hearty sound of his response. He had not yet undressed, he said, and would come down immediately while I ordered back his car, which must just have reached the garage.

"I'll be with you in five minutes!" he called as cheerfully as if I had summoned him to his wedding.

I heard him cross the floor of his room; and before he could reach the head of the staircase, I opened the door and went out into the hall in order that I might turn on the light and have his hat and coat waiting. The electric button was at the end of the hall, and as I moved towards it, guided by the glimmer that fell from the landing above, I lifted my eyes to the staircase, which climbed dimly, with its slender mahogany balustrade, as far as the third storey. Then it was, at the very moment when the doctor, humming gaily, began his quick descent of the steps, that I distinctly saw—I will swear to this on my death-bed—a child's skipping-rope lying loosely coiled, as if it had dropped from a careless little hand, in the bend of the staircase. With a spring I had reached the electric button, flooding the hall with light; but as I did so, while my arm was still outstretched behind me, I heard the humming voice change to a cry of surprise or terror, and the figure on the staircase tripped heavily and stumbled with groping hands into emptiness. The scream of warning died in my throat while I watched him pitch forward down the long flight of stairs to the floor at my feet. Even before I bent over him, before I wiped the blood from his brow and felt for his silent heart, I knew that he was dead.

Something—it may have been, as the world believes, a misstep in the dimness, or it may have been, as I am ready to bear witness, an invisible judgment—something had killed him at the very moment when he most wanted to live.

Edwin Arlington Robinson

FLAMMONDE

THE man Flammonde, from God knows where,
With firm address and foreign air,
With news of nations in his talk
And something royal in his walk,
With glint of iron in his eyes,
But never doubt, nor yet surprise,
Appeared, and stayed, and held his head
As one by kings accredited.

Erect, with his alert repose
About him, and about his clothes,
He pictured all tradition hears
Of what we owe to fifty years.
His cleansing heritage of taste
Paraded neither want nor waste;
And what he needed for his fee
To live, he borrowed graciously.

He never told us what he was,
Or what mischance, or other cause,
Had banished him from better days
To play the Prince of Castaways.
Meanwhile he played surpassing well
A part, for most, unplayable;
In fine, one pauses, half afraid
To say for certain that he played.

For that, one may as well forego
Conviction as to yes or no;
Nor can I say just how intense
Would then have been the difference
To several, who, having striven
In vain to get what he was given,

Would see the stranger taken on
By friends not easy to be won.

Moreover, many a malcontent
He soothed and found munificent;
His courtesy beguiled and foiled
Suspicion that his years were soiled;
His mien distinguished any crowd,
His credit strengthened when he bowed;
And women, young and old, were fond
Of looking at the man Flammonde.

There was a woman in our town
On whom the fashion was to frown;
But while our talk renewed the tinge
Of a long-faded scarlet fringe,
The man Flammonde saw none of that,
And what he saw we wondered at—
That none of us, in her distress,
Could hide or find our littleness.

There was a boy that all agreed
Had shut within him the rare seed
Of learning. We could understand,
But none of us could lift a hand.
The man Flammonde appraised the youth,
And told a few of us the truth;
And thereby, for a little gold,
A flowered future was unrolled.

There were two citizens who fought
For years and years, and over nought;
They made life awkward for their friends,
And shortened their own dividends.
The man Flammonde said what was wrong
Should be made right; nor was it long
Before they were again in line,
And had each other in to dine.

And these I mention are but four
Of many out of many more.
So much for them. But what of him—
So firm in every look and limb?
What small satanic sort of kink
Was in his brain? What broken link
Withheld him from the destinies
That came so near to being his?

What was he, when we came to sift
His meaning, and to note the drift
Of incommunicable ways
That make us ponder while we praise?
Why was it that his charm revealed
Somehow the surface of a shield?
What was it that we never caught?
What was he, and what was he not?

How much it was of him we met
We cannot ever know; nor yet
Shall all he gave us quite atone
For what was his, and his alone;
Nor need we now, since he knew best,
Nourish an ethical unrest;
Rarely at once will nature give
The power to be Flammonde and live.

We cannot know how much we learn
From those who never will return,
Until a flash of unforeseen
Remembrance falls on what has been.
We've each a darkening hill to climb;
And this is why, from time to time
In Tilbury Town, we look beyond
Horizons for the man Flammonde.

Hugh Walpole

THE SILVER MASK

Miss sonia herries, coming home from a dinner-party at the Westons', heard a voice at her elbow.

"If you please—only a moment——"

She had walked from the Westons' flat because it was only three streets away, and now she was only a few steps from her door, but it was late, there was no one about and the King's Road rattle was muffled and dim.

"I am afraid I can't——" she began. It was cold, and the wind nipped her cheeks.

"If you would only——" he went on.

She turned and saw one of the handsomest young men possible. He was the handsome young man of all romantic stories, tall, dark, pale, slim, distinguished—oh! everything!—and he was wearing a shabby blue suit and shivering with the cold just as he should have been.

"I'm afraid I can't——" she repeated, beginning to move on.

"Oh, I know," he interrupted quickly. "Everyone says the same, and quite naturally. I should if our positions were reversed. But I *must* go on with it. I *can't* go back to my wife and baby with simply nothing. We have no fire, no food, nothing except the ceiling we are under. It is my fault, all of it. I don't want your pity, but I *have* to attack your comfort."

He trembled. He shivered as though he were going to fall. Involuntarily she put out her hand to steady him. She touched his arm and felt it quiver under the thin sleeve.

"It's all right . . ." he murmured. "I'm hungry . . . I can't help it."

She had had an excellent dinner. She had drunk perhaps just enough to lead to recklessness—in any case, before she realised it, she was ushering him in, through

445

her dark-blue painted door. A crazy thing to do! Nor was it as though she were too young to know any better, for she was fifty if she was a day and, although sturdy of body and as strong as a horse (except for a little unsteadiness of the heart), intelligent enough to be thin, neurotic and abnormal; but she was none of these.

Although intelligent she suffered dreadfully from impulsive kindness. All her life she had done so. The mistakes that she had made—and there had been quite a few —had all arisen from the triumph of her heart over her brain. She knew it—how well she knew it!—and all her friends were for ever dinning it into her. When she reached her fiftieth birthday she said to herself, "Well, now at last I'm too old to be foolish any more." And here she was, helping an entirely unknown young man into her house at dead of night, and he in all probability the worst sort of criminal.

Very soon he was sitting on her rose-coloured sofa, eating sandwiches and drinking a whisky and soda. He seemed to be entirely overcome by the beauty of her possessions. "If he's acting he's doing it very well," she thought to herself. But he had taste and he had knowledge. He knew that the Utrillo was an early one, the only period of importance in that master's work, he knew that the two old men talking under a window belonged to Sickert's "Middle Italian," he recognised the Dobson head and the wonderful green bronze Elk of Carl Milles.

"You are an artist," she said. "You paint?"

"No, I am a pimp, a thief, a what you like—anything bad," he answered fiercely. "And now I must go," he added, springing up from the sofa.

He seemed most certainly invigorated. She could scarcely believe that he was the same young man who only half an hour before had had to lean on her arm for support. And he was a gentleman. Of that there could be no sort of question. And he was astoundingly beautiful in the spirit of a hundred years ago, a young Byron, a young Shelley, not a young Ramón Novarro or a young Ronald Colman.

Well, it was better that he should go, and she did hope (for his own sake rather than hers) that he would not demand money and threaten a scene. After all, with her snow-white hair, firm broad chin, firm broad body, she did not look like someone who could be threatened. He had not apparently the slightest intention of threatening her. He moved towards the door.

"Oh!" he murmured with a little gasp of wonder. He had stopped before one of the loveliest things that she had—a mask in silver of a clown's face, the clown smiling, gay, joyful, not hinting at perpetual sadness as all clowns are traditionally supposed to do. It was one of the most successful efforts of the famous Sorat, greatest living master of Masks.

"Yes. Isn't that lovely?" she said. "It was one of Sorat's earliest things, and still, I think, one of his best."

"Silver is the right material for that clown," he said.

"Yes, I think so too," she agreed. She realised that she had asked him nothing about his troubles, about his poor wife and baby, about his past history. It was better perhaps like this.

"You have saved my life," he said to her in the hall. She had in her hand a pound note.

"Well," she answered cheerfully, "I was a fool to risk a strange man in my house at this time of night—or so my friends would tell me. But such an old woman like me —where's the risk?"

"I could have cut your throat," he said quite seriously.

"So you could," she admitted. "But with horrid consequences to yourself."

"Oh no," he said. "Not in these days. The police are never able to catch anybody."

"Well, good-night. Do take this. It can get you some warmth at least."

He took the pound. "Thanks," he said carelessly. Then at the door he remarked: "That mask. The loveliest thing I ever saw."

When the door had closed and she went back into the sitting-room she sighed:

"What a good-looking young man!" Then she saw that her most beautiful white jade cigarette-case was gone. It had been lying on the little table by the sofa. She had seen it just before she went into the pantry to cut the sandwiches. He had stolen it. She looked everywhere. No, undoubtedly he had stolen it.

"What a good-looking young man!" she thought as she went up to bed.

Sonia Herries was a woman of her time in that outwardly she was cynical and destructive while inwardly she was a creature longing for affection and appreciation. For though she had white hair and was fifty she was outwardly active, young, could do with little sleep and less food, could dance and drink cocktails and play bridge to the end of all time. Inwardly she cared for neither cocktails nor bridge. She was above all things maternal and she had a weak heart, not only a spiritual weak heart but also a physical one. When she suffered, must take her drops, lie down and rest, she allowed no one to see her. Like all the other women of her period and manner of life she had a courage worthy of a better cause.

She was a heroine for no reason at all.

But, beyond everything else, she was maternal. Twice at least she would have married had she loved enough, but the man she had really loved had not loved her (that was twenty-five years ago), so she had pretended to despise matrimony. Had she had a child her nature would have been fulfilled; as she had not had that good fortune she had been maternal (with outward cynical indifference) to numbers of people who had made use of her, sometimes laughed at her, never deeply cared for her. She was named "a jolly good sort," and was always "just outside" the real life of her friends. Her Herries relations, Rockages and Cards and Newmarks, used her to take odd places at table, to fill up spare rooms at house-parties, to make purchases for them in London, to talk to when things went wrong with them or people abused them. She was a very lonely woman.

She saw her young thief for the second time a fortnight later. She saw him because he came to her house one evening when she was dressing for dinner.

"A young man at the door," said her maid Rose.

"A young man? Who?" But she knew.

"I don't know, Miss Sonia. He won't give his name."

She came down and found him in the hall, the cigarette-case in his hand. He was wearing a decent suit of clothes, but he still looked hungry, haggard, desperate and incredibly handsome. She took him into the room where they had been before. He gave her the cigarette-case. "I pawned it," he said, his eyes on the silver mask.

"What a disgraceful thing to do!" she said. "And what are you going to steal next?"

"My wife made some money last week," he said. "That will see us through for a while."

"Do you never do any work?" she asked him.

"I paint," he answered. "But no one will touch my pictures. They are not modern enough."

"You must show me some of your pictures," she said, and realised how weak she was. It was not his good looks that gave him his power over her, but something both helpless and defiant, like a wicked child who hates his mother but is always coming to her for help.

"I have some here," he said, went into the hall, and returned with several canvases. He displayed them. They were very bad—sugary landscapes and sentimental figures.

"They are very bad," she said.

"I know they are. You must understand that my æsthetic taste is very fine. I appreciate only the best things in art, like your cigarette-case, that mask there, the Utrillo. But I can paint nothing but these. It is very exasperating." He smiled at her.

"Won't you buy one?" he asked her.

"Oh, but I don't want one," she answered. "I should have to hide it." She was aware that in ten minutes her guests would be here.

"Oh, do buy one."

"No, but of course not——"

"Yes, please." He came nearer and looked up into her broad kindly face like a beseeching child.

"Well. . . how much are they?"

"This is twenty pounds. This twenty-five——"

"But how absurd! They are not worth anything at all."

"They may be one day. You never know with modern pictures."

"I am quite sure about these."

"Please buy one. That one with the cows is not so bad."

She sat down and wrote a cheque.

"I'm a perfect fool. Take this, and understand I never want to see you again. Never! You will never be admitted. It is no use speaking to me in the street. If you bother me I shall tell the police."

He took the cheque with quiet satisfaction, held out his hand and pressed hers a little.

"Hang that in the right light and it will not be so bad——"

"You want new boots," she said. "Those are terrible."

"I shall be able to get some now," he said and went away.

All that evening while she listened to the hard and crackling ironies of her friends she thought of the young man. She did not know his name. The only thing that she knew about him was that by his own confession he was a scoundrel and had at his mercy a poor young wife and a starving child. The picture that she formed of these three haunted her. It had been, in a way, honest of him to return the cigarette-case. Ah, but he knew, of course, that did he not return it he could never have seen her again. He had discovered at once that she was a splendid source of supply, and now that she had bought one of his wretched pictures—— Nevertheless he could not be altogether bad. No one who cared so passionately for beautiful things could be quite worthless. The way that he had gone straight to the silver mask as soon as he entered the room and gazed at it as though with his very soul! And, sitting at her dinner-table, uttering the most cynical sen-

timents, she was all softness as she gazed across to the
wall upon whose pale surface the silver mask was hanging. There was, she thought, a certain look of the young
man in that jolly shining surface. But where? The clown's
cheek was fat, his mouth broad, his lips thick—and yet,
and yet——

For the next few days as she went about London she
looked in spite of herself at the passers-by to see whether
he might not be there. One thing she soon discovered, that
he was very much more handsome than anyone else whom
she saw. But it was not for his handsomeness that he
haunted her. It was because he wanted her to be kind to
him, and because she wanted—oh, so terribly—to be kind
to someone!

The silver mask, she had the fancy, was gradually
changing, the rotundity thinning, some new light coming
into the empty eyes. It was most certainly a beautiful
thing.

Then, as unexpectedly as on the other occasions, he
appeared again. One night as she, back from a theatre
smoking one last cigarette, was preparing to climb the
stairs to bed, there was a knock on the door. Everyone
of course rang the bell—no one attempted the old-
fashioned knocker shaped like an owl that she had bought,
one idle day, in an old curiosity shop. The knock made
her sure that it was he. Rose had gone to bed, so she went
herself to the door. There he was—and with him a young
girl and a baby. They all came into the sitting-room and
stood awkwardly by the fire. It was at that moment when
she saw them in a group by the fire that she felt her first
sharp pang of fear. She knew suddenly how weak she was
—she seemed to be turned to water at sight of them, she,
Sonia Herries, fifty years of age, independent and strong,
save for that little flutter of the heart—yes, turned to
water! She was afraid as though someone had whispered a
warning in her ear.

The girl was striking, with red hair and a white face, a
thin graceful little thing. The baby, wrapped in a shawl,
was soaked in sleep. She gave them drinks and the re-

mainder of the sandwiches that had been put there for herself. The young man looked at her with his charming smile.

"We haven't come to cadge anything this time," he said. "But I wanted you to see my wife and I wanted her to see some of your lovely things."

"Well," she said sharply, "you can only stay a minute or two. It's late. I'm off to bed. Besides, I told you not to come here again."

"Ada made me," he said, nodding at the girl. "She was so anxious to see you."

The girl never said a word but only stared sulkily in front of her.

"All right. But you must go soon. By the way, you've never told me your name."

"Henry Abbott, and that's Ada, and the baby's called Henry too."

"All right. How have you been getting on since I saw you?"

"Oh, fine! Living on the fat of the land." But he soon fell into silence and the girl never said a word. After an intolerable pause Sonia Herries suggested that they should go. They didn't move. Half an hour later she insisted. They got up. But, standing by the door, Henry Abbott jerked his head towards the writing-desk.

"Who writes your letters for you?"

"Nobody. I write them myself."

"You ought to have somebody. Save a lot of trouble. I'll do them for you."

"Oh no, thank you. That would never do. Well, good-night, good-night——"

"Of course I'll do them for you. And you needn't pay me anything either. Fill up my time."

"Nonsense . . . good-night, good-night." She closed the door on them. She could not sleep. She lay there thinking of him. She was moved, partly by a maternal tenderness for them that warmed her body (the girl and the baby had looked so helpless sitting there), partly by a shiver of apprehension that chilled her veins. Well, she

hoped that she would never see them again. Or did she?
Would she not to-morrow, as she walked down Sloane
Street, stare at everyone to see whether by chance that
was he?

Three mornings later he arrived. It was a wet morning
and she had decided to devote it to the settling of accounts. She was sitting there at her table when Rose
showed him in.

"I've come to do your letters," he said.

"I should think not," she said sharply. "Now, Henry
Abbott, out you go. I've had enough——"

"Oh no, you haven't," he said, and sat down at her
desk.

She would be ashamed for ever, but half an hour later
she was seated in the corner of the sofa telling him what
to write. She hated to confess it to herself, but she liked
to see him sitting there. He was company for her, and to
whatever depths he might by now have sunk, he was most
certainly a gentleman. He behaved very well that morning; he wrote an excellent hand. He seemed to know just
what to say.

A week later she said, laughing, to Amy Weston: "My
dear, would you believe it? I've had to take on a secretary. A very good-looking young man—but you needn't
look down your nose. You know that good-looking young
men are nothing to *me*—and he does save me endless
bother."

For three weeks he behaved very well, arriving punctually, offering her no insults, doing as she suggested about
everything. In the fourth week, about a quarter to one on
a day, his wife arrived. On this occasion she looked astonishingly young, sixteen perhaps. She wore a simple grey
cotton dress. Her red bobbed hair was strikingly vibrant
about her pale face.

The young man already knew that Miss Herries was
lunching alone. He had seen the table laid for one with its
simple appurtenances. It seemed to be very difficult not
to ask them to remain. She did, although she did not wish
to. The meal was not a success. The two of them together

were tiresome, for the man said little when his wife was
there, and the woman said nothing at all. Also the pair
of them were in a way sinister.

She sent them away after luncheon. They departed
without protest. But as she walked, engaged on her shopping that afternoon, she decided that she must rid herself
of them, once and for all. It was true that it had been
rather agreeable having him there; his smile, his wicked
humorous remarks, the suggestion that he was a kind of
malevolent gamin who preyed on the world in general
but spared her because he liked her—all this had attracted her—but what really alarmed her was that during all these weeks he had made no request for money,
made indeed no request for anything. He must be piling
up a fine account, must have some plan in his head with
which one morning he would balefully startle her! For a
moment there in the bright sunlight, with the purr of the
traffic, the rustle of the trees about her, she saw herself
in surprising colour. She was behaving with a weakness
that was astonishing. Her stout, thick-set, resolute body,
her cheery rosy face, her strong white hair—all these
disappeared, and in their place, there almost clinging for
support to the Park railings, was a timorous little old
woman with frightened eyes and trembling knees. What
was there to be afraid of? She had done nothing wrong.
There were the police at hand. She had never been a
coward before. She went home, however, with an odd impulse to leave her comfortable little house in Walpole
Street and hide herself somewhere, somewhere that no one
could discover.

That evening they appeared again, husband, wife and
baby. She had settled herself down for a cosy evening
with a book and an "early to bed." There came the knock
on the door.

On this occasion she was most certainly firm with them.
When they were gathered in a little group she got up and
addressed them.

"Here is five pounds," she said, "and this is the end.

If one of you shows his or her face inside this door again I call the police. Now go."

The girl gave a little gasp and fell in a dead faint at her feet. It was a perfectly genuine faint. Rose was summoned. Everything possible was done.

"She has simply not had enough to eat," said Henry Abbott. In the end (so determined and resolved was the faint) Ada Abbott was put to bed in the spare room and a doctor was summoned. After examining her he said that she needed rest and nourishment. This was perhaps the critical moment of the whole affair. Had Sonia Herries been at this crisis properly resolute and bundled the Abbott family, faint and all, into the cold unsympathising street, she might at this moment be a hale and hearty old woman enjoying bridge with her friends. It was, however, just here that her maternal temperament was too strong for her. The poor young thing lay exhausted, her eyes closed, her cheeks almost the colour of her pillow. The baby (surely the quietest baby ever known) lay in a cot beside the bed. Henry Abbott wrote letters to dictation downstairs. Once Sonia Herries, glancing up at the silver mask, was struck by the grin on the clown's face. It seemed to her now a thin sharp grin—almost derisive.

Three days after Ada Abbott's collapse there arrived her aunt and her uncle, Mr. and Mrs. Edwards. Mr. Edwards was a large red-faced man with a hearty manner and a bright waistcoat. He looked like a publican. Mrs. Edwards was a thin sharp-nosed woman with a bass voice. She was very, very thin, and wore a large old-fashioned brooch on her flat but emotional chest. They sat side by side on the sofa and explained that they had come to enquire after Ada, their favourite niece. Mrs. Edwards cried, Mr. Edwards was friendly and familiar. Unfortunately Mrs. Weston and a friend came and called just then. They did not stay very long. They were frankly amazed at the Edwards couple and deeply startled by Henry Abbott's familiarity. Sonia Herries could see that they drew the very worst conclusions.

A week later Ada Abbott was still in bed in the upstairs room. It seemed to be impossible to move her. The Edwardses were constant visitors. On one occasion they brought Mr. and Mrs. Harper and their girl Agnes. They were profusely apologetic, but Miss Herries would understand that "with the interest they took in Ada it was impossible to stay passive." They all crowded into the spare bedroom and gazed at the pale figure with the closed eyes sympathetically.

Then two things happened together. Rose gave notice and Mrs. Weston came and had a frank talk with her friend. She began with that most sinister opening: "I think you ought to know, dear, what everyone is saying——" What everyone was saying was that Sonia Herries was living with a young ruffian from the streets, young enough to be her son.

"You must get rid of them all and at once," said Mrs. Weston, "or you won't have a friend left in London, darling."

Left to herself, Sonia Herries did what she had not done for years, she burst into tears. What had happened to her? Not only had her will and determination gone but she felt most unwell. Her heart was bad again; she could not sleep; the house, too, was tumbling to pieces. There was dust over everything. How was she ever to replace Rose? She was living in some horrible nightmare. This dreadful handsome young man seemed to have some authority over her. Yet he did not threaten her. All he did was to smile. Nor was she in the very least in love with him. This must come to an end or she would be lost.

Two days later, at tea-time, her opportunity arrived. Mr. and Mrs. Edwards had called to see how Ada was; Ada was downstairs at last, very weak and pale. Henry Abbott was there, also the baby. Sonia Herries, although she was feeling dreadfully unwell, addressed them all with vigour. She especially addressed the sharp-nosed Mrs. Edwards.

"You must understand," she said. "I don't want to be unkind, but I have my own life to consider. I am a very busy woman, and this has all been forced on me. I don't want to seem brutal. I'm glad to have been of some assistance to you, but I think Mrs. Abbott is well enough to go home now——and I wish you all good-night."

"I am sure," said Mrs. Edwards, looking up at her from the sofa, "that you've been kindness itself, Miss Herries. Ada recognises it, I'm sure. But to move her now would be to kill her, that's all. Any movement and she'll drop at your feet."

"We have nowhere to go," said Henry Abbott.

"But, Mrs. Edwards——" began Miss Herries, her anger rising.

"We have only two rooms," said Mrs. Edwards quietly. "I'm sorry, but just now, what with my husband coughing all night——"

"Oh, but this is monstrous!" Miss Herries cried. "I have had enough of this. I have been generous to a degree——"

"What about my pay," said Henry, "for all these weeks?"

"Pay! Why of course——" Miss Herries began. Then she stopped. She realised several things. She realised that she was alone in the house, the cook having departed that afternoon. She realised that none of them had moved. She realised that her "things"—the Sickert, the Utrillo, the sofa—were alive with apprehension. She was fearfully frightened of their silence, their immobility. She moved towards her desk, and her heart turned, squeezed itself dry, shot through her body the most dreadful agony.

"Please," she gasped. "In the drawer—the little green bottle—oh, quick! Please, please!"

The last thing of which she was aware was the quiet handsome features of Henry Abbott bending over her.

When, a week later, Mrs. Weston called, the girl, Ada Abbott, opened the door to her.

"I came to enquire for Miss Herries," she said. "I haven't seen her about. I have telephoned several times and received no answer."

"Miss Herries is very ill."

"Oh, I'm so sorry. Can I not see her?"

Ada Abbott's quiet gentle tones were reassuring her. "The doctor does not wish her to see anyone at present. May I have your address? I will let you know as soon as she is well enough."

Mrs. Weston went away. She recounted the event. "Poor Sonia, she's pretty bad. They seem to be looking after her. As soon as she's better we'll go and see her."

The London life moves swiftly. Sonia Herries had never been of very great importance to anyone. Herries relations enquired. They received a very polite note assuring them that so soon as she was better——

Sonia Herries was in bed, but not in her own room. She was in the little attic bedroom but lately occupied by Rose the maid. She lay at first in a strange apathy. She was ill. She slept and woke and slept again. Ada Abbott, sometimes Mrs. Edwards, sometimes a woman she did not know, attended to her. They were all very kind. Did she need a doctor? No, of course she did not need a doctor, they assured her. They would see that she had everything that she wanted.

Then life began to flow back into her. Why was she in this room? Where were her friends? What was this horrible food that they were bringing her? What were they doing here, these women?

She had a terrible scene with Ada Abbott. She tried to get out of bed. The girl restrained her—and easily, for all the strength seemed to have gone from her bones. She protested, she was as furious as her weakness allowed her, then she cried. She cried most bitterly. Next day she was alone and she crawled out of bed; the door was locked; she beat on it. There was no sound but her beating. Her heart was beginning again that terrible strangled throb. She crept back into bed. She lay there, weakly, feebly crying. When Ada arrived with some bread, some soup, some water, she demanded that the door should be unlocked, that she should get up, have her bath, come downstairs to her own room.

"You are not well enough," Ada said gently.

"Of course I am well enough. When I get out I will have you put in prison for this——"

"Please don't get excited. It is so bad for your heart."

Mrs. Edwards and Ada washed her. She had not enough to eat. She was always hungry.

Summer had come. Mrs. Weston went to Etretat. Everyone was out of town.

"What's happened to Sonia Herries?" Mabel Newmark wrote to Agatha Benson. "I haven't seen her for ages. . . ."

But no one had time to enquire. There were so many things to do. Sonia was a good sort, but she had been nobody's business. . . .

Once Henry Abbott paid her a visit. "We are doing everything we can for you. It is lucky we were around when you were so ill. You had better sign these papers. Someone must look after your affairs until you are better. You will be downstairs in a week or two."

Looking at him with wide-open terrified eyes, Sonia Herries signed the papers.

The first rains of autumn lashed the streets. In the sitting-room the gramophone was turned on. Ada and young Mr. Jackson, Maggie Trent and stout Harry Bennett were dancing. All the furniture was flung against the walls. Mr. Edwards drank his beer; Mrs. Edwards was toasting her toes before the fire.

Henry Abbott came in. He had just sold the Utrillo. His arrival was greeted with cheers.

He took the silver mask from the wall and went upstairs. He climbed to the top of the house, entered, switched on the naked light.

"Oh! Who—what——?" A voice of terror came from the bed.

"It's all right," he said soothingly. "Ada will be bringing your tea in a minute."

He had a hammer and nail and hung the silver mask on the speckled, mottled wall-paper where Miss Herries could see it.

"I know you're fond of it," he said. "I thought you'd like it to look at."

She made no reply. She only stared.

"You'll want something to look at," he went on. "You're too ill, I'm afraid, ever to leave this room again. So it'll be nice for you. Something to look at."

He went out, gently closing the door behind him.

BRACKENBURN,
October 21, 1930

Booth Tarkington

THE FASCINATING STRANGER

Mr. GEORGE TUTTLE, reclining at ease in his limousine, opened one eye just enough to perceive that daylight had reached his part of the world, then closed that eye, and murmured languidly. What he said, however, was not, "Home, Parker," or "To the club, Eugene"; this murmur of his was not only languid but plaintive. A tear appeared upon the lower lid of the eye that had opened, for it was a weak and drowsy eye, and after hours of solid darkness the light fretted it. Moreover, the tear, as a greeting to the new day, harmonized perfectly with Mr. Tuttle's murmur, which was so little more than a husky breathing that only an acute ear close by could have caught it: "Oh, Gosh!" Then he turned partly over, shifting his body so as to lie upon his left side among the shavings that made his limousine such a comfortable bedroom.

After thousands of years of wrangling, economists still murder one another to emphasize varying ideas of what constitutes the ownership of anything; and some people (the most emphatic of all) maintain that everybody owns everything, which is obviously the same as saying that nobody owns anything, especially his own right hand. So it may be a little hasty to speak of this limousine, in which Mr. Tuttle lay finishing his night's sleep, as belonging to him in particular; but he was certainly the only person who had the use of it, and no other person in the world believed himself to be its owner. A doubt better founded may rest upon a definition of the word "limousine"; for Mr. Tuttle's limousine was not an automobile; it had no engine, no wheels, no steeringgear; neither had it cushions nor glass; yet Mr. Tuttle thought of it and spoke of it as his limousine, and took some pleasure in such thinking and speaking.

Definitely, it was what is known as a "limousine body"

461

in an extreme but permanent state of incompletion. That is to say, the wooden parts of a "limousine body" had been set up, put together on a "buck," or trestle, and then abandoned with apparently the same abruptness and finality that marked the departure of the Pompeiian baker who hurried out of his bakery and left his bread two thousand years in the oven. So sharply the "post-war industrial depression" had struck the factory, that the workmen seemed to have run for their lives from the place, leaving everything behind them just as it happened to be at the moment of panic. And then, one cold evening, eighteen months afterward, the excavator, Tuttle, having dug within the neighbouring city dump-heap to no profitable result, went to explore the desert spaces where once had been the bustling industries, and found this body of a limousine, just as it had been abandoned by the workmen fleeing from ruin. He furnished it plainly with simple shavings and thus made a home.

His shelter was double, for this little house of his itself stood indoors, under a roof that covered acres. When the watery eye of Mr. Tuttle opened, it beheld a room vaster than any palace hall, and so littered with unaccountable other automobile bodies in embryo that their shapes grew vague and small in the distance. But nothing living was here except himself; what leather had been in the great place was long since devoured, and the rats had departed. A night-watchman, paid by the receiver-in-bankruptcy, walked through the long shops once or twice a night, swinging a flashlight; but he was unaware of the tenant, and usually Mr. Tuttle, in slumber, was unaware of him.

The watery eye, having partly opened and then wholly closed, remained closed for another hour. All round about, inside and outside the great room, there was silence; for beyond these shops there were only other shops and others and others, covering square miles, and all as still as a village midnight. They were as quiet as that every day in the week; but on weekdays the cautious Tuttle usually went out rather early, because sometimes a clerk from the receiver's office dawdled about the place with a notebook.

To-day was Sunday; no one would come; so he slept as
long as he could.

His reasons were excellent as reasons, though immoral
at the source;—that is to say, he should not have had
such reasons. He was not well, and sleep is healing; his
reasons for sleeping were therefore good: but he should
not have been unwell; his indisposition was produced by
sin; he had broken the laws of his country and had drunk
of illegal liquor, atrocious in quality; his reasons for sleeping were therefore bad. His sleep was not a good sleep.

From time to time little manifestations proved its gross
character; he lay among the shavings like a fat grampus
basking in sea-foam, and he breathed like one; but sometimes his mouth would be pushed upward in misdirected
expansions; his cheeks would distend, and then suddenly
collapse, after explosion. Lamentable sounds came from
within his corrugated throat, and from deeper tubes; a
shoulder now and then jumped suddenly; and his upper
ear, long and soiled, frequently twitched enough to move
the curl of shaving that lay upon it. For a time one of his
legs trembled violently; then of its own free will and without waking him, it bent and straightened repeatedly,
using the motions of a leg that is walking and confident
that it is going somewhere. Having arrived at its destination, it rested; whereupon its owner shivered, and,
thinking he pulled a blanket higher about his shoulders,
raked a few more shavings upon him. Finally, he woke,
and still keeping his eyes closed, stroked his beard.

It was about six weeks old and no uncommon ornament
with Mr. Tuttle; for usually he wore either a beard or
something on the way to become one; he was indifferent
which, though he might have taken pride in so much
originality in an over-razored age. His round and somewhat oily head, decorated with this beard upon a face a
little blurred by puffiness, was a relic; the last survival
of a type of head long ago gloriously portrayed and set
before a happy public by that adept in the most perishable of the arts, William Hoey. Mr. Tuttle was heavier in
body than the blithe comedian's creation, it is true; he

was incomparably slower in wit and lower in spirits, yet he might well enough have sat for the portrait of an older brother of Mr. Hoey's masterpiece, "Old Hoss."

Having stroked his beard with a fat and dingy hand, he uttered detached guttural complaints in Elizabethan monosyllables, followed these with sighing noises; then, at the instigation of some abdominal feeling of horror, shuddered excessively, opened his eyes to a startled wideness and abruptly sat up in his bed. To the interior of his bosky ear, just then, was borne the faint religious sound of church bells chiming in a steeple miles away in the centre of the city, and he was not pleased. An expression of disfavour slightly altered the contours of his face; he muttered defiantly, and decided to rise and go forth.

Nothing could have been simpler. The April night had been chilly, and he had worn his shoes; no nightgear had to be exchanged for other gaments;—in fact no more was to be done than to step out of the limousine. He did so, taking his greenish and too plastic "Derby" hat with him; and immediately he stood forth upon the factory floor as well equipped to face the public as ever. Thus, except for several safety-pins, glinting too brightly where they might least have been expected, he was a most excellent specimen of the protective coloration exhibited by man; for man has this instinct, undoubtedly. On the bright beaches by the sea, how gaily he conforms is to be noted by the dullest observer; in the autumnal woods man goes dull green and dead leaf brown; and in the smoky city all men, inside and out, are the colour of smoke. Mr. Tuttle stood forth, the colour of the grimy asphalt streets on which he lived; and if at any time he had chosen to rest in a gutter, no extraneous tint would have hinted of his presence.

Not far from him was a faucet over a sink; and he went to it, but not for the purpose of altering his appearance. Lacking more stimulating liquid, it was the inner man that wanted water; and he set his mouth to the faucet, drinking long, but not joyously. Then he went out to the sunshine of that spring morning, with the whole world before him, and his the choice of what to do with it.

He chose to walk toward the middle part of the city, the centre of banking and trade; but he went slowly, his eye wandering over the pavement; and so, before long, he decided to smoke. He was near the great building of the railway station at the time, and, lighting what was now his cigarette (for he had a match of his own) he leaned back against a stone pilaster, smoked and gazed unfavourably upon the taxicabs in the open square before the station.

As he stood thus, easing his weight against the stone and musing, he was hailed by an acquaintance, a tall negro, unusually limber at the knees and naïvely shabby in dress, but of amiable expression and soothing manners.

"How do, Mist' Tuttle," he said genially, in a light tenor voice. "How the worl' treatin' you vese days, Mist' Tuttle? I hope evathing movin' the ri' way to please you nicely."

Mr. Tuttle shook his head. "Yeh!" he returned sarcastically. "Seems like it, don't it! Look at 'em, I jest ast you! *Look* at 'em!"

"Look at who?"

"At them taxicabs," Mr. Tuttle replied, with sudden heat. "That's a nice sight fer decent people to haf to look at!" And he added, with rancour: "On a Sunday, too!"

"Well, you take them taxicabs now," the negro said, mildly argumentative, "an' what hurt they doin' to nobody to jes' look at 'em, Mist' Tuttle? I fine myse'f in some difficulty to git the point of what you was a-settin' you'se'f to point out, Mist' Tuttle. What make you so industrious 'gains them taxicabs?"

"I'll tell you soon enough," Mr. Tuttle said ominously. "I reckon if they's a man alive in this here world to-day, I'm the one 't can tell you jest exackly what I got against them taxicabs. In the first place, take and look where the United States stood twenty years ago, when they wasn't any o' them things, and then take and look where the

United States stands to-day, when it's full of 'em! I don't ast you to take my word fer it; I only ast you to use your own eyes and take and look around you and see where the United States stands to-day and what it's comin' to!"

But the coloured man's perplexity was not dispelled; he pushed back his ancient soft hat in order to assist his brain, but found the organ still unstimulated after adjacent friction, and said plaintively: "I cain' seem to grasp jes' whur you aiminin' at. What you say the United States comin' to?"

"Why, nowhere at all!" Mr. Tuttle replied grimly. "This country's be'n all ruined up. You take and look at what's left of it, and what's the use of it? I jest ast you the one simple question: What's the use of it? Jest tell me that, Bojus."

"You got me, Cap'n!" Bojus admitted. "I doe' know what you aiminin' to say 't all! What *do* all them taxi-cabs do?"

"Do?" his friend repeated hotly. "Wha'd they do? You take and look at this city. You know how many people it's got in it?"

"No, I don't, Mist' Tuttle. Heap of 'em, though!"

"Heap? I sh'd say they was! They's hunderds and hunderds and hunderds o' thousand men, women and chuldern in this city; you know that as well as I do, Bojus. Well, with all the hunderds o' thousands o' men, women and chuldern in this city, I ast you, how many livery-stables has this city got in it?"

"Livvy-stables, Mist' Tuttle? Lemme see. I ain't made the observation of no livvy-stable fer long time."

Tuttle shook a soiled finger at him severely. "You ain't answered my question. Didn't you hear me? I ast you the simple question: How many livery-stables is they?"

"Well, I ain't *see* none lately; I guess I doe' know, Cap'n."

"Then I'll tell you," said Tuttle fiercely. "They ain't *any!* What's more, I'll bet twenty thousand dollars they ain't five livery-stables left in the whole United States! That's a nice thing, ain't it!"

Bojus looked at him inquiringly, still rather puzzled. "You interust you'se'f in livvy-stables, Mist' Tuttle?"

At this Mr. Tuttle looked deeply annoyed; then he thought better of it and smiled tolerantly. "Listen here," he said. "You listen, my friend, and I'll tell you something 't's worth any man's while to try and understand the this-and-that of it. I grew up in the livery-stable business, and I guess if they's a man alive to-day, why, I know more about the livery-stable business than all the rest the men, women and chuldern in this city put together."

"Yes, suh. You own a livvy-stable one time, Mist' Tuttle?"

"I didn't exackly own one," said the truthful Tuttle, "but that's the business I grew up in. I'm a horse man, and I like to sleep around a horse. I drove a hack for the old B. P. Thomas Livery and Feed Company more than twenty years, off and on;—off and on, I did. I was a horse man all my life and I was in the horse business. I could go anywhere in the United States and I didn't haf to carry no money with me when I travelled; I could go into any town on the map and make all the money I'd care to handle. I'd never go to a boarding-house. What's the use of a hired room and all the useless fixin's in it they stick you fer? No man that's got the gumption of a man wants to waste his money like that when they's a whole nice livery-stable to sleep in. You take some people—women, most likely!—and they get finicky and say it makes you kind of smell. 'Oh, don't come near *me!*' they'll say. Now, what kind of talk is that? You take me, why, I *like* to smell like a horse."

"Yes, suh," said Bojus. "Hoss smell ri' pleasan' smell."

"Well, I should *say* it is!" Mr. Tuttle agreed emphatically. "But you take a taxicab, all you ever git a chance to smell, it's burnt grease and gasoline. Yes, sir, that's what you got to smell of if you run one o' them things. Nice fer a man to carry around on him, ain't it?" He laughed briefly, in bitterness; and continued: "No, sir; the first time I ever laid eyes on one, I hollered, 'Git a horse!' but if you was to holler that at one of 'em to-day, the feller'd prob'ly answer, 'Where 'm I goin' to git one?' I ain't seen a horse I'd be willin' to *call* a horse, not fer I don't know how long!"

"No, suh," Bojus assented. "I guess so. Man go look fer good hoss he fine mighty fewness of 'em. I guess automobile put hoss out o' business—an' hoss man, too, Mist' Tuttle."

"Yes, sir, I guess it did! First four five years, when them things come in, why, us men in the livery-stable business, we jest laughed at 'em. Then, by and by, one or two stables begun keepin' a few of 'em to hire. Perty soon after that they all wanted 'em, and a man had to learn to run one of 'em or he was liable to lose his livin'. They kep' gittin' worse and worse—and then, my goodness! didn't even the undertakers go and git 'em? 'Well,' I says, 'I give up! *I* give up!' I says. 'Men in this business that's young enough and ornery enough,' I says, 'why, they can go ahead and learn to run them things. I can git along nice with a horse,' I says. 'A horse knows what you say to him, but I ain't goin' to try and talk to no engine!' "

He paused, frowning, and applied the flame of a match to the half-inch of cigarette that still remained to him. "Them things ought to be throwed in the ocean," he said. "That's what *I'd* do with 'em!"

"You doe' like no automobile?" Bojus inquired. "You take you' enjoyment some way else, I guess, Mist' Tuttle."

"There's jest one simple question I want to ast you," Mr. Tuttle said. "S'pose a man's been drinkin' a little; well, he can git along with a horse all right—like as not a horse'll take him right on back home to the stable—but where's one o' *them* things liable to take him?"

"Jail," Bojus suggested.

"Yes, sir, or right over the bank into some creek, maybe. I don't want nothin' to do with 'em, and that's what I says from the first. I don't want nothin' to do with 'em, I says, and I've stuck to it." Here he was interrupted by a demand upon his attention, for his cigarette had become too short to be held with the fingers; he inhaled a

final breath of smoke and tossed the tiny fragment away.
"I own one of 'em, though," he said lightly.

At this the eyes of Bojus widened. "You own automobile, Mist' Tuttle?"

"Yes, I got a limousine."

"What!" Bojus cried, and stared the more incredulously. "You got a limousine? Whur you got it?"

"I got it," Mr. Tuttle replied coldly. "That's enough fer me. I got it, but I don't go around in it none."

"What you *do* with it?"

"I use it," said Tuttle, with an air of reticence. "I got my own use fer it. I don't go showin' off like some men."

Bojus was doubtful, yet somewhat impressed, and his incredulous expression lapsed to a vagueness. "No," he said. "Mighty nice to ride roun' in, though. I doe' know where evabody git all the money. Money ain't come knockin' on Bojus' do' beggin' 'Lemme in, honey!' No, suh; the way money act with me, it act like it think I ain' goin' use it right. Money act like I ain't its lovin' frien'!"

He laughed, and Mr. Tuttle smiled condescendingly. "Money don't amount to so much, Bojus," he said. "Anybody can make money!"

"They *kin?*"

"Why, you take a thousand dollars," said Tuttle; "and you take and put it out at compound interest; jest leave it lay and go on about your business—why, it'll pile up and pile up, you can't stop it. You know how much it'd amount to in twenty-five years? More than a million dollars."

"Whur all that million dolluhs come from?"

"It comes from the poor," said Mr. Tuttle solemnly. "That's the way all them rich men git their money, gougin' the poor".

"Well, suh," Bojus inquired reasonably, "what about me? I like git rich, too. Whur's some poor I kin go gouge? I'm willin' to do the gougin' if I kin git the money."

"Money ain't everything," his friend reminded him. "Some day the people o' this country's goin' to raise and take all that money away from them rich robbers. What *right* they got to it? That's what I want to know. We're goin' to take it and divide it among the people that need it."

Bojus laughed cheerfully. "Tell Bojus when you goin' begin dividin'! *He* be on han'!"

"Why, anybody could have all the money he wants, any time," Tuttle continued, rather inconsistently. "Anybody could."

"How anybody goin' git it?"

"I didn't say anybody *was* goin' to; I said anybody *could*."

"How could?"

"Well, you take me," said Tuttle. "Johnny Rockafeller could drive right up here now, if he wanted to. S'pose he did; s'pose he was to drive right up to that curbstone there and s'pose he was to lean out and say, 'Howdy do, Mr. Tuttle. Git right in and set down, and let's take a drive. Now, how much money would you like me to hand you, Mr. Tuttle?' "

"Hoo-*oo!*" cried Bojus in high pleasure, for the sketch seemed beautiful to him; so he amplified it. " 'How much money you be so kine as to invite me to p'litely han' ovuh to you?' *Hoo!* Jom B. Rockfelluh take an' ast *me*, I tell 'im, 'Well, jes han' me out six, sevvum, eight, nine hunnud dolluhs; that'll do fer *this* week, but you come 'roun' *nex'* Sunday an' ast me same. Don't let me ketch you not comin' roun' every Sunday, now!' *Hoo!* I go Mist' Rockfelluh's house to dinnuh; he say, 'What dish I serve you p'litely, Mist' Bojus?' I say, 'Please pass me that big gol' dish o' money an' a scoop, so's I kin fill my soup-plate!' Hoo-*oo!*" He laughed joyously; and then, with some abruptness descended from these roseate heights and looked upon the actual earth. "I reckon Jom B. Rockfelluh ain' stedyin' about how much money you and me like to use, Mist' Tuttle," he concluded. "He ain' comin' roun' *this* Sunday, nohow!"

"No, and I didn't say he was," Mr. Tuttle protested. "I says he *could*, and you certainly know enough to know he *could*, don't you, Bojus?"

"Well," said Bojus, "whyn't he go on ahead an' do it, then? If he kin do it as well as not, what make him all time decide fer *not?* Res' of us willin'!"

"That's jest the trouble," Tuttle complained, with an air of reproof. "You're willin' but you don't use your brains."

"Brains?" said Bojus, and laughed. "Brains ain' goin' make Bojus no money. What I need is a good lawn-mo'. If I could take an' buy me a nice good lawn-mo', I could make all the money I'm a-goin' a need the live-long sum-muh."

"Lawn-mower?" his friend inquired. "You ain't got no house and lot, have you? What you want of a lawn-mower?"

"I awready got a rake," Bojus explained. "If I had a lawn-mo' I could make th'ee, fo', fi' dolluhs a day. See that spring sun settin' up there a-gittin' ready to shine so hot? She's goin' to bring up the grass knee-high, honey, 'less somebody take a lawn-mo' an' cut it down. I kin take a lawn-mo' an' walk 'long all vese resident'al streets; git a dozen jobs a day if I kin do 'em. I truly would like to git me a nice good lawn-mo', but I ain' got no money. I got a diamon' ring, though. I give a diamon' ring fer a good lawn-mo'."

"Diamon' ring?" Mr. Tuttle inquired with some interest. "Le'ss see it."

"Gran' big diamon' ring," Bojus said, and held forth his right hand for inspection. Upon the little finger appeared a gem of notable dimensions, for it was a full quarter of an inch in width, but no one could have called it lustrous; it sparkled not at all. Yet its dimness might have been a temporary condition that cleaning would relieve, and what struck Mr. Tuttle most unfavourably was the fact that it was set in a metal of light colour.

"Why, it ain't even gold," he said. "That's a perty pore sample of a diamon' ring I expect, Bojus. Nobody'd want to wear a diamon' ring with the ring part made o' silver. Truth is, I never see no diamon' ring jest made o' silver, before. Where'd you git it?"

"Al Joles."

"Wha'd you give Al Joles fer it?"

"Nothin'," said Bojus, and laughed. "Al Joles, he come to where my cousin Mamie live, las' Feb'uary an' bo'de with 'er week or so, 'cause he tryin' keep 'way f'm jail. One day he say this city too hot; he got to leave, an' Mamie tuck an' clean up after him an' she foun' this ring in a crack behine the washstan'. Al Joles drop it an' fergit it, I reckon. He had *plenty* rings!"

"I reckon!"

"Al Joles show Mamie fo' watches an' a whole big han'-ful o' diamon' pins and rings an' chains. Say he got 'em in Chicago an' he tuck 'em all with him when he lit out. Mamie she say this ring worf fi', six thousan' dolluhs."

"Then what fer'd she take and give it to you, Bojus?"

"She di'n'," said Bojus. "She tuck an' try to sell it to Hillum's secon' han' joolry sto' an' Hillum say he won' bargain fer it 'count its bein' silvuh. So she trade it to me fer a nice watch chain. I like silvuh ring well as gol' ring. 'S the diamon' counts: diamon' worf fi', six thousan' dolluhs, I ain' carin' what jes' the *ring* part is."

"Well, it's right perty," Tuttle observed, glancing at it with some favour. "I don't hardly expect you could trade it fer no lawn-mower, though. I expect——" But at this moment a symptom of his indisposition interrupted his remarks. A slight internal convulsion caused him to shudder heavily; he fanned his suddenly bedewed forehead with his hat, and seemed to eat an impalpable but distasteful food.

"You feel sick, Mist' Tuttle?" Bojus inquired sympathetically, for his companion's appearance was a little disquieting. "You feel bad?"

"Well, I do," Tuttle admitted feebly. "I eat a hambone yestiddy that up and disagreed on me. I ain't be'n feelin' none too well all morning, if the truth must be told. The fact is, what I need right now—and I need it right bad," he added—"it's a little liquor."

"Yes, suh; I guess so," his friend agreed. "That's somep'n ain' goin' hurt nobody. I be willin' use a little myse'f."

"You know where any is?"

"Don't I!" the negro exclaimed. "I know whur plenty *is*, but the trouble is: How you an' me goin' git it?"

"Where is it?"

"Ri' dow' my cousin Mamie' celluh. My cousin Mamie' celluh plum full o' Whi' Mule. Man say he goin' buy it off her but ain' show up with no money. Early 's mawn' I say, 'Mamie, gi' me little nice smell o' you' nise whisky?' No, suh! Take an' fretten me with a brade-knife! Mad 'cause man ain' paid 'er, I reckon."

"Le'ss go on up there and ast her again," Tuttle suggested. "She might be feelin' in a nicer temper by this time. Me bein' sick, and it's Sunday and all, why, she ought to show some decency about it. Anyways, it wouldn't hurt anything to jest try."

"No, suh, tha's so, Mist' Tuttle," the negro agreed with ready hopefulness. "If she say no, she say no; but if she say yes, we all fix fine! Le'ss go!"

They went up the street, walking rather slowly, as Mr. Tuttle, though eager, found his indisposition increased with any rapidity of movement; then they turned down an alley, followed it to another alley, and at the intersection of that with another, entered a smoke-coloured cottage of small pretensions, though it still displayed in a front window the card of a Red Cross subscriber to the "drive" of 1918.

"Mamie!" Bojus called, when they had closed the door behind them. "Mamie!"

Then, as they heard the response to this call, both of them had the warming sense of sunshine rushing over them: the world grew light and bright and they perceived that luck did not always run against worthy people. Mamie's answer was not in words, yet it was a vocal sound and human: somewhere within her something quickened to the call and endeavoured to speak. Silently they opened the door of her bedroom and looked upon her where she reposed.

She had consoled herself for her disappointments; she was peaceful indeed; and the callers at once understood that for several hours, at least, she could deny them nothing they would ask. They paused but a moment to gaze, and then, without a word of comment upon their incredible good fortune, they exchanged a single hurried glance, and forthwith descended to the cellar.

An hour later they were singing there, in that cool dimness. They sang of romantic love, of maternal sacrifices, of friendship; and this last theme held them longest, for Tuttle prevailed upon his companion to join him many, many times in a nineteenth century tribute to brotherly affection. With their hands resting fondly upon each other's shoulders, they sang over and over:

Comrades, comrades, *ev-er* since we was boys,
Sharing each other's sorrows, sharing each other's joys,
Comrades when manhood was *daw-ning*——

Our own, our native land, somewhat generally lawless in mood of late, has produced few illegal commodities more effective than the ferocious liquid rich in fusel oil and known as White Mule. Given out of the imaginative heart of a race that has a genius for naming things, this perfect name tells everything of the pale liquor it so precisely labels. The silence of the mule is there, the sinister inertia of his apparent complete placidity as he stands in an interval of seeming patience;—for this is the liquor as it rests in the bottle. And the mule's sudden utter violence is there, with a hospital cot as a never-remote contingency for those who misunderstand.

Over-confidence in himself was not a failing of the experienced Tuttle; and he well knew the potencies of the volcanic stuff with which he dealt. His sincere desire was but to rid himself of the indisposition and nervousness that depressed him, and he indulged himself to-day with a lighter hand than usual. He wished to be at ease in body and mind, to be happy and to remain happy; therefore he stopped at the convivial, checking himself firmly, and took a little water. Not so the less calculating Bojus who had nothing of the epicure about him. Half an hour after the two friends had begun to sing "Comrades," Bojus became unmusical in execution, though his impression was that he still sang; and a little later Mr. Tuttle found himself alone, so far as song, conversation and companionship were concerned. Bojus still lived, but had no animation.

His more cautious friend, on the contrary, felt life freshening within him; his physical uncertainties had disappeared from his active consciousness; he was a new man, and said so. "Hah!" he said with great satisfaction and in a much stronger voice than he had dared to use earlier in the day. "I'm a new man!" And he slapped himself on the chest, repeatedly. Optimism came to him; he began to believe that he was at the end of all his troubles, and he decided to return to the fresh air, the sunshine and an interesting world. "Le'ss git outdoors and see what all's goin' *on!*" he said heartily.

But first he took some precautions for the sake of friendship. Fearing that all might not go well with Bojus if Mamie were the first to be stirring and happened to look into her cellar, he went to the top of the stairs and locked the door there upon the inside. Then he came down again and once more proved his moderation by placing only one flask of Mamie's distillation in his pocket. He could have taken much more if he wished, but he sometimes knew when to say no. In fact, he now said it aloud and praised himself a little. "No! No, sir!" he said to some applicant within him. "I know what's good fer you and what ain't. If you take any more you're liable to go make a hog of yourself again. Why, jest look how you felt when you woke up this morning! I'm the man that knows and I'm perty smart, too, if you ever happen to notice! You take and let well enough alone."

He gave a last glance at Bojus, a glance that lingered with some interest upon the peculiar diamond ring; but he decided not to carry it away with him, because Bojus might be overwhelmingly suspicious later. "No, sir," he said. "You come along now and let well enough alone. We want to git out and see what's goin' on all over town!"

The inward pleader consented, he placed a box against the wall, mounted it and showed a fine persistence in overcoming what appeared to be impossibilities as he contrived to wriggle himself through a window narrower than he was. Then, emerging worm-like upon a dirty brick path beside the cottage, he arose brightly and went forth from that quarter of the city.

It suited his new mood to associate himself now with all that was most brilliant and prosperous; and so, at a briskish saunter he walked those streets where stood fine houses in brave lawns. It was now an hour and more after noon, the air was lively yet temperate in the sunshine, and the wealth he saw in calm display about him invigorated him. Shining cars passed by, proud ladies at ease within them; rich little children played about neat nursemaids as they strolled the cement pavements; haughty young men strode along, flashing their walking-sticks; noble big dogs with sparkling collars galloped over the bright grass under tall trees; and with all of this, Tuttle now felt himself congenial, and even intimate. Moreover, he had the conviction that some charming and dramatic adventure was about to befall him; it seemed to be just ahead.

The precise nature of this adventure remained indefinite in his imagination for a time, but gradually the thought of eating (abhorrent to him earlier in the day) again became pleasant, and he sketched some little scenes climaxing in banquets. "One these here millionaires could do it easy as not," he said, speaking only in fancy and not vocally. "One of 'em might jest as well as not look out his big window, see me, and come down his walk and say, 'Step right in, Mr. Tuttle. We got quite a dinner-party to-day, but they's always room fer you, Mr. Tuttle. Now what'd you like to have to eat? Liver and chili and baked beans and ham and eggs and a couple of ice-cold muskmelons? We can open three or four cans o' sardines fer you, too, if you'd like to have 'em. You only got to say the word, Mr. Tuttle.' "

He began to regret Bojus's diamond ring a little; perhaps he could have traded it for a can of sardines at a negro restaurant he knew; but the regret was a slight one; he worried himself little about obtaining food, for people will always give it. However, he did not ask for it among the millionaires, whose servants are sometimes cold-hearted; but turned into an unpretentious cross street and walked a little more slowly, estimating the houses. He had not gone far when he began to smell his dinner.

The odour came from the open front door of a neat white frame house in a yard of fair size; and here, near the steps of the small veranda, a man of sixty and his wife were discussing the progress of a row of tulips about to bloom. Their clothes new-looking, decorous and worn with a little unfamiliarity, told everybody that this man and his wife had been to church; that they dined at two o'clock on Sunday, owned their house, owned a burial lot in the cemetery, paid their bills, and had something comfortable in a safety deposit box. Tuttle immediately walked into the yard, took off his hat and addressed the wife.

"Lady," he said, in a voice hoarser from too much singing than he would have liked to make it, "Lady, I be'n out o' work fer some time back. I took sick, too, and I be'n in the hospital. What I reely wish to ast fer is work, but the state of unemployment in this city is awful bad. I don't ast fer no money; all I want is a chance to work."

"On Sunday?" she said reprovingly. "Of course there isn't any work on Sunday."

Tuttle stepped a little closer to her—a mistake—and looked appealing. "Then how 'm I a-goin' to git no nourishment?" he asked. "If you can't give me no work, I ain't eat nothin' at all since day before yestiddy and I'd be truly thankful if you felt you could spare me a little nourishment."

But she moved back from him, her nostrils dilating slightly and her expression unfavourable. "I'd be glad to give you all you want to eat," she said coldly, "but I think you'd better sign the pledge first."

"Ma'am?" said Tuttle in plaintive astonishment.

"I think you've been drinking."

"No, lady! No!"

"I'm sure you have. I don't believe in doing anything for people that drink; it doesn't do them any good."

"Lady——" Tuttle began, and he was about to continue his protest to her, when her husband interfered.

"Run along!" he said, and tossed the applicant for nourishment a dime.

Tuttle looked sadly at the little round disk of silver as it lay shining in his asphalt coloured palm; then he looked at the donor and murmured: "I ast fer bread—and they give me a stone!"

"Go along!" said the man.

Tuttle went slowly, seeming to be bowed in thoughtful melancholy; he went the more reluctantly because there was a hint of fried chicken on the air; and before he reached the pavement a buxom fair woman, readily guessed to be of Scandinavian descent, appeared in the dorway. "Dinner's served, Mrs. Pinney," she called briskly.

Tuttle turned and looked at Mrs. Pinney with eloquence, but she shook her head disapprovingly. "You ought to sign the pledge!" she said.

"Yes, lady," he said, and abruptly turned away. He walked out into the street, where a trolley car at that moment happened to stop for another passenger, jumped on the step, waved his hand cordially, and continued to wave it as the car went down the street.

"Well of *all!*" Mrs. Pinney exclaimed, dumfounded, but her husband laughed aloud.

"That's a good one!" he said. "Begged for 'nourishment' and when I gave him a dime went off for a street-car ride! Come on in to dinner, ma; I guess he's passed out of our lives!"

Nothing was further from Mr. Tuttle's purpose, however; and Mr. and Mrs. Pinney had not finished their dinner, half an hour later, when he pushed the bell-button in their small vestibule, and the buxom woman opened the door, but not invitingly, for she made the aperture a narrow one when she saw who stood before her.

"Howdydo," he said affably. "Ole lady still here, isn't she?"

"What you want?" the woman inquired.

"Jest ast her to look this over," he said, and proffered a small paper-bound Bible, open, with a card between the leaves. "I'll wait here," he added serenely, as she closed the door.

She took the Bible to the dining-room, and handed it to Mrs. Pinney, remarking, "That tramp's back. He says to give you this. He's waitin'."

The Bible was marked with a rubber stamp: "Presented by Door of Hope Rescue Mission 337 South Maryland Street," and the card was a solemn oath and pledge to refrain from intoxicants, thenceforth and forever. It was dated that day, and signed, in ink still almost wet, "Arthur T. De Morris."

Mrs. Pinney stared at the pledge, at first frowningly, then with a tendency toward a slight emotion; and without speaking she passed it to her husband for inspection, whereupon he became incredulous enough to laugh.

"That's about the suddenest conversion on record, I guess!" he said. "Used the dime to get down to the Door of Hope and back before our dinner was over. It beats all!"

"You don't think it could be genuine, Henry?"

"Well, no; not in twenty minutes."

"It *could* be—just possibly," she said gently. "We never know when the right word *may* touch some poor fellow's heart."

"Now, ma," he remonstrated, "don't you go and get one of your spells of religious vanity. That was about as tough an old soak as I ever saw, and I'm afraid it'll take more than one of your 'right words' to convert him."

"Still——" she said, and a gentle pride showed in her expression. "We can't tell. It seems a little quick, of course, but he may have been just at the spiritual point for the right word to reach him. Anyhow, he did go right away and get a pledge and sign it—and got a Bible, too. It might be—I don't say it probably is, but it just might be the beginning of a new life for him, and it wouldn't be right to discourage him. Besides he must really be hungry; he's proved that, anyhow." She turned to the woman in waiting. "Give him back the Bible and his card, Tilly," she said, "and take him out in the kitchen and let him have all he wants to eat. Tell him to wait when he gets through; and you let me know; I'll come and talk to him. His name's Mr. De Morris, Tilly, when you speak to him."

Tilly's expression was not enthusiastic, but she obeyed the order, conducted the convert to the kitchen and set excellent food before him in great plenty; whereupon Mr. Tuttle, being not without gallantry, put his hat on the floor beside his chair, and thanked her warmly before he sat down. His appetite was now vigorous, and at first he gave all his attention to the fried chicken, but before long he began to glance appreciatively, now and then, at the handmaiden who had served him. She was a well-shaped blonde person of thirty-five or so, tall, comely, reliable looking, visibly energetic, and, like her kitchen, incredibly clean. His glances failed to interest her, if she took note of them; and presently she made evident her sense of a social gulf. She prepared a plate for herself, placed it upon a table across the room from him and sat there, with her profile toward him, apparently unconscious of his presence.

"Plenty room at my table," he suggested hospitably. "*I* jest as soon you eat over here."

"No," she said discouragingly.

Not abashed, but diplomatic, he was silent for a time, then he inquired casually, "Do all the work here?"

"Yep."

"Well, well," he said. "You look too young fer sech a rough job. Don't they have nobody 'tend the furnace and cut the grass?"

"Did," said Tilly. "Died last week."

"Well, ain't that too bad! Nice pleasant feller was he?"

"Coloured man," said Tilly.

"You Swedish?" Tuttle inquired.

"No. My folks was."

"Well sir, that's funny," Tuttle said genially, "I knowed they was *some*p'n Swedish about you, because I always did like Swedish people. I don't know why, but I always did taken a kind o' likin' to Swedish people, and Swedish people always taken kind of a likin' to me. My ways always seem to suit Swedish people—after we git well acquainted I mean. The better Swedish people git acquainted with me the more they always seem to taken a likin' to me. I ast a Swedish man oncet why it was he taken sech a likin' to me and he says it was my ways. 'It's jest your ways, George,' he says. 'It's because Swedish people like them ways you got, George,' he says." Here Tuttle laughed deprecatingly and added, "I guess he must 'a' be'n right, though."

Tilly made no response; she did not even glance at him, but continued gravely to eat her dinner. Then, presently, she said, without any emphasis: "I thought your name was Arthur."

"What?"

"That pledge you signed," Tilly said, still not looking at him, but going on with her dinner;—"ain't it signed Arthur T. De Morris?"

For the moment Mr. Tuttle was a little demoralized, but he recovered himself, coughed, and explained. "Yes, that's my *name*," he said. "But you take the name George, now, it's more kind of a nickname I have when anybody gits real well acquainted with me like this Swedish man I was tellin' you about; and besides that, it was up in *Dee*-troit. Most everybody I knowed up in *Dee*-troit, they most always called me George fer a nickname like. You know anybody in *Dee*-troit?"

"No."

"Married?" Tuttle inquired.

"No."

"Never be'n?" he said.

"No."

"Well, now, that's too bad," he said sympathetically. "It ain't the right way to live. I'm a widower myself, and I ain't never be'n the same man since I lost my first wife. She was an Irish lady from Chicago." He sighed; finished the slice of lemon pie Tilly had given him, and drank what has left of his large cup of coffee, holding the protruding spoon between two fingers to keep it out of his eye. He set the cup down, gazed upon it with melancholy, then looked again at the unresponsive Tilly.

She had charm for him; and his expression, not wholly lacking a kind of wistfulness, left no doubt of it. No doubt, too, there fluttered a wing of fancy somewhere in his head: some picture of what might-have-been trembled across his mind's-eye's field of vision. For an instant he may have imagined a fireside, with such a competent fair creature upon one side of it, himself on the other, and merry children on the hearth-rug between. Certainly he had a moment of sentiment and sweet longing.

"You ever think about gettin' married again?" he said, rather unfortunately.

"I told you I ain't been married."

"Excuse *me!*" he hastened to say. "I was thinkin' about myself. I mean when I says 'again' I was thinkin' about myself. I mean I was astin' you: You think about gittin' married at all?"

"No."

"I s'pose not," he assented regretfully; and added in a gentle tone: "Well, you're a mighty fine-lookin' woman; I never see no better build than what you got on you."

Tilly went out and came back with Mrs. Pinney, who mystified him with her first words. "Well, De Morris?" she said.

"What?" he returned blankly, then luckily remembered, and said, "Oh, yes, ma'am?"

"I *hope* you meant it when you signed that pledge, De Morris."

"Why, lady, of course I did," he assured her warmly. "If the truth must be told, I don't never drink hardly at all, anyways. Now we got prohibition you take a poor

man out o' work, why where's *he* goin' to git any liquor,
lady? It's only rich people that's usually able to git any
good stew on, these days, if I'm allowable to used the expression, so to speak. But that's the unfairness of it, and
it makes poor people ready to break out most anytime.
Not that it concerns me, because I put all that behind me
when I signed the pledge like you told me to. If the truth
must be told, I was goin' to sign the pledge some time
back, but I kep' kind o' puttin' it off. Well, lady, it's done
now, and I'm thankful fer it."

"I do hope so, I'm sure," Mrs. Pinney said earnestly.
"And I want to help you; I'll be glad to. You said you
wanted some work."

"Yes'm," he said promptly, and if apprehension rose
within him he kept it from appearing upon the surface.
Behind Mrs. Pinney stood Tilly, looking straight at him
with a frigid skepticism of which he was fully conscious.
"Yes'm. Any honest work I can turn my hand to, that's
all I ast of anybody. I'd be glad to help wash the dishes
if it's what you had in your mind, lady."

"No. But if you'll come back to-morrow moning about
nine or ten o'clock, I'll give you two dollars for cutting
the grass. It isn't a *very* large yard, and you can get
through by evening."

"I ain't got no lawn-mower, lady."

"We have one in the cellar," said Mrs. Pinney. "If you
come back, Tilly'll have it on the back porch for you.
That's all to-day, De Morris."

"All right, lady. I thank you for your hospitillity and
I'll be back in the morning," he said, and as he turned
toward the door he glanced aside at Tilly and saw that
her mouth quivered into the shape of a slight smile—a
knowing smile. "I will!" he said defiantly. "I'll be back
here at ten o'clock to-morrow morning. You'll see!"

But when the door closed behind him, Tilly laughed
aloud—and was at once reproved by her mistress. "We
always ought to have faith that the better side of people
will conquer, Tilly. I really think he'll come."

"Yes'm, like that last one 't said he was comin' back,

and stole the knife and fork he ate with," said Tilly, laughing again.

"But this one didn't steal anything."

"No'm, but he'll never come back, to *work*," said Tilly. "He said 'You'll see,' and you will, but you won't see *him!*"

They had a mild argument upon the point, and then Mrs. Pinney returned to her husband, who was waiting for her to put on her Sunday wrap and hat, and go with him to spend their weekly afternoon among the babies at their son's house. She found her husband to be strongly of Tilly's opinion, and when they came home that evening, she renewed the argument with both of them; so that this mild and orderly little household was slightly disturbed (a most uncommon thing in its even life) over the question of the vagrant's return. Thus, Mrs. Pinney prepared a little triumph for herself;—at ten o'clock the next morning Tuttle opened the door of Tilly's bright kitchen and inquired:

"Where's that lawn-mower?"

He was there. He had defeated the skeptic and proved himself a worthy man, but at a price; for again he was far from well, and every movement he made increased well-founded inward doubts of his constitution. Unfortunately, he had taken his flask of White Mule to bed with him in his limousine, and in that comfortable security moderation had seemed useless to the verge of absurdity. The point of knowing when to say no rests in the "when"; and when a man is already at home and safe in bed, "Why, my Glory!" he had reasoned it, "Why, if they ever *is* a time to say yes, it must be then!" So he had said "Yes," to the White Mule and in the morning awoke feeling most perishable. Even then, as in the night, from time to time he had vagrant thoughts of Tilly and her noble build, of the white and shining kitchen, and of those disbelieving cool blue eyes that seemed to triumph over him and indict him, accusing him of things she appeared to think he would do if he had the chance. There was something in her look that provoked him, as if she would stir his conscience, and though his conscience disturbed him no more than a baby's disturbs a baby, he was indeed somewhat disquieted by that cold look of hers. And so, when he had collected his mind a little, upon waking, he muttered feebly. "I'll show her!" Something strange and forgotten worked faintly within him, fluttered a little; and so, walking carefully, he kept his word and came to her door.

She looked at him in a startled way. Unquestionably he caused her to feel something like an emotion, and she said not a word, but went straightway and brought him the lawn-mower. He looked in her eyes as he took it from her hand.

"You thought I wouldn't come," he said.

"Yes," she admitted gravely.

"Well," he said, and smiled affably, "you certainly got a fine build on you!" And with that, pushing the lawn-mower before him, he went out to his work, leaving her visibly not offended.

"You showed her!" he said to himself.

In the yard he looked thoughtfully upon the grass, which was rather long and had not been cut since the spring had enlivened it to a new growing. The lot seemed longer than it had the day before; he saw that it must be two hundred feet from the street on which it fronted to the alley in the rear; it was a hundred feet wide, at least, and except for the area occupied by the house, which was of modest proportions, all of this was grass. He sighed profoundly: "Oh, Gosh!" he mourned. But he meant to do the work, and began it manfully.

With the mower rolling before him, reversed, the knives upward, he went to the extreme front of the lot, turned the machine over, and, surveying the prospect, decided to attack the lawn with long straight swathes, running from the front clear through to the alley—though, even before he began, the alley seemed far, far away. However, he turned up the sleeves of his ancient coat an inch or two, and went at his task with a good heart. That is to say, he started with a good heart, but the lawn-mower was neither new nor sharp; the grass was tough, the sun hot, and his sense of unwellness formidable. When he had gone ten feet, he paused, wiped his forehead with a sleeve, and leaned upon the handle of the mower in an attitude not devoid of pathos. But he was yet determined; he thought of the blue eyes in the kitchen and resolved that they should not grow scornful again. Once more he set the mower in motion.

Mrs. Pinney heard the sound of it in her room upstairs, looked from the window, and with earnest pleasure beheld the workman at his toil. Her heart rejoiced her to have been the cause of a reformation, and presently she went down to the kitchen to gloat gently over a defeated antagonist in argument.

"Yes'm," Tilly admitted meekly. "He fooled me."

"You see I was right, Tilly. We always ought to have faith that the best part of our natures will conquer."

"Yes'm; it looks so."

"Have we some buttermilk in the refrigerator, Tilly?"

"Yes'm."

"Then I think you might have some ready for him, if he gets too hot. I don't think he looks very well and you might ask him if he'd like some. You might ask him now, Tilly."

"Now?" Tilly asked, and coloured a little. "You mean right now, Mrs. Pinney?"

"Yes. It might do him good and help keep him strong for his work."

"All right," Tilly said, and turned toward the ice-box; but at a thought she paused. "I don't hear the lawnmower," she said. "It seems to me I ain't heard it since we began talking."

"Perhaps he's resting," Mrs. Pinney suggested, but her voice trembled a little with foreboding. "We might just go out and see."

They went out and saw. Down the full length of the yard, from the street to the alley, there was one long swathe of mowed grass; and but one, though it was perfect. Particularly as the trail of a fugitive it was perfect, and led straight to the alley, which, being paved with brick, offered to the searchers the complete bafflement of a creek to the bloodhound. A brick alley shows no trace of a reversed lawn-mower hurrying over it—yet nothing was clearer than that such a hurrying must have taken place. For Arthur T. De Morris was gone, and so was the lawn-mower.

"Mr. Pinney'll laugh at me I guess, too!" Mrs. Pinney said, swallowing, as she stood with Tilly, staring at the complete vacancy of the brick alley.

"Yes'm, he will," said Tilly, and laughed again, a little harshly.

.   .   .   .

The fugitive, already some blocks distant, propelled the ravished mower before him, and went so openly through the streets in the likeness of an honest toiler seeking lawns to mow that he had to pause and decline several offers, on his hurried way. He took note of these opportunities, however, remembering the friend he was on his way to see, and, after some difficulty, finding him in a negro pool-room, proffered him the lawn-mower in exchange for five dollars, spot cash.

"I ain' got it,' replied Bojus, flaccid upon a bench. "I ain' feelin' like cuttin' nobody's grass to-day, nohow, an' besides I'm goin' stay right here till coas' clear. Mamie ain' foun' out who make all her trouble, 'cause I clim' out the window whiles she was engage' kickin' on cellah do'; but neighbours say she mighty s'picious who 'twas. I don' need no lawn-mo' in a pool-room."

"Well, you ain't goin' to stay in no pool-room forever; you got to git out and earn your livin' some time," Tuttle urged him. "Every man that's got the gumption of a man, he's got to do that!" And upon Bojus's lifeless admission of the truth of this statement, the bargaining began. It ended with Bojus's becoming the proprietor of the lawn-mower and Tuttle's leaving the pool-room after taking possession of everything in the world that Bojus owned except a hat, a coat, a pair of trousers, a shirt, two old shoes and four safety-pins. The spoil consisted of seventy-eight cents in money, half of a package of bent cigarettes, a pair of dice, a "mouth-organ" and the peculiar diamond ring.

This latter Mr. Tuttle placed upon his little finger, and as he walked along he regarded it with some pleasure; but he decided to part with it, and carried it to a pawn-shop he knew, having had some acquaintance with the proprietor in happier days.

He entered the place with a polite air, removing his hat and bowing, for the shop was a prosperous one.

"Golly!" said the proprietor, who happened to be behind a counter, instructing a new clerk. "I believe it's old George the hackman."

"That's who, Mr. Breitman," Tuttle responded. "Many's the cold night I yousta drive you all over town and——"

"Never mind, George," the pawnbroker interrupted crisply. "You payin' me just a social call, or you got some business you want to do?"

"Business," said Tuttle. "If the truth must be told, Mr. Breitman, I got a diamon' ring worth somewheres along about five or six thousand dollars, I don't know which."

Breitman laughed, "Oh, you got a ring worth either five or six thousand, you don't know which, and you come in to ask me to settle it. Is that it?"

"Yes. I don't want to hock her; I jest want to git a notion if I ever do decide to sell her." He set the ring upon the glass counter before Breitman. "Ain't she a beauty?"

Breitman glanced at the ring and laughed, upon which the owner hastily protested: "Oh, I know the ring part ain't gold: you needn't think I don't know that much! It's the diamon' I'm talkin' about. Jest set your eye on her."

The pawnbroker set his eye on her—that is, he put on a pair of spectacles, picked up the ring and looked at it carelessly, but after his first glance his expression became more attentive. "So you say I needn't think you don't know the 'ring part' ain't gold, George? So you knew it was platinum, did you?"

"Of course, I knowed it was plapmun," Tuttle said promptly, rising to the occasion, though he had never before heard of this metal. "I reckon I know plapmun when I see it."

"I think it's worth about ten or twelve dollars," Breitman said. "I'll give you twelve if you want to sell it."

Eager acceptance rushed to Tuttle's lips, but hung there unspoken as caution checked him. He drew a deep breath and said huskily, "Why, you can't fool me on this here ring, Mr. Breitman. I ain't worryin' about what I can git fer the plapmun part; all I want to know is how much I ought ast fer the diamon'. I ain't fixin' to sell it to you; I'm fixin' to sell it to somebody else."

"Oh, so that's it," said Breitman, still looking at the ring. "Where'd you get it?"

Tuttle laughed ingratiatingly. "It's kind of funny," he said, "how I got that ring. Yet it's all open and above-board, too. If the truth must be told, it belonged to a lady-cousin o' mine in Auburndale, Wisconsin, and her aunt-by-marriage left it to her. Well, this here lady-cousin o' mine, I was visitin' her last summer, and she found I had a good claim on the house and lot she was livin' in, account of my never havin' knowed that my grandfather—he was her grandfather, too—well, he never left no will, and this house and lot come down to her, but I never made no claim on it because I thought it had be'n willed to her till I found out it hadn't, when I went up there. Well, the long and short of it come out like this: the house and lot's worth about nine or ten thousand dollars, but she didn't have no money, so she handed me over this ring to settle my claim. Name's Mrs. Moscoe, Mrs. Wilbur N. Moscoe, three-thirty-two South Liberty Street, Auburndale, Wisconsin."

"I see," Breitman said absently. "Just wait here a minute, George; I ain't going to steal it." And, taking the ring with him, he went into a room behind the shop, remaining there closeted long enough for Tuttle to grow a little uneasy.

"Hay!" he called. "You ain't tryin' to eat that plapmun ring are you, Mr. Breitman?"

Breitman appeared in the doorway. There was a glow in his eyes, and although he concealed all other traces of a considerable excitement, somehow Tuttle caught a vibration out of the air, and began to feel the presence of Fortune. "Step in here and sit down, George," the pawnbroker said. "I wanted to look at this stone a little closer, and of course I had to go over my lists and see if it was on any of 'em."

"What lists?" Tuttle asked as he took a chair.

"From the police. Stolen goods."

"Looky here! I told you how that ring come to me. My cousin ain't no crook. Her name's Mrs. Wilbur N. Moscoe, South Liberty Street, Auburnd——"

"Never mind," Breitman interrupted. "*I* ain't sayin' it ain't so. Anyway, this ring ain't on any of the lists and——"

"I should say it ain't!"

"Well, don't get excited. Now look here, George"—— Breitman seated himself close to his client and spoke in a confidential tone—"George, you know I always took a kind of interest in you, and I want to tell you what you need. You ought to go get yourself all fixed up. You ought to go to a barber's and get your hair cut and your whiskers trimmed. Don't go to no cheap barber's; go to a good one, and tell 'em to fix your whiskers so's you'll have a Van Dyke——"

"A what?"

"A Van Dyke beard. It's swell," said Breitman. "Then you go get you a fine pearl-gray Fedora hat, with a black band around it, and a light overcoat, and some gray gloves with black stitching, and a nice cane and a nobby suit o' clo'es and some fancy top shoes——"

"Listen here!" Tuttle said hoarsely, and he set a shaking hand on the other's knee, "how much you willin' to bid on my plapmun ring?"

"Don't go so fast!" Breitman said, but his eyes were becoming more and more luminous. He had the hope of a great bargain; yet feared that Tuttle might have a fairly accurate idea of the value of the diamond. "Hold your hosses a little, George! You don't need so awful much to go and get yourself fixed up like I'm tellin' you, and you'll have a lot o' money left to go around and see high life with. I'll send right over to the bank and let you have it in cash, too, if you meet my views."

"How much?" Tuttle gasped. "How much?"

Breitman looked at him shrewdly. "Well, I'm takin' chances: the market on stones is awful down these days, George. Your cousin must have fooled you *bad* when she talked about four or five thousand dollars! That's ridiculous!"

"How *much?*"

"Well, I'll say!—I'll say seven hundred and fifty dollars."

Tuttle's head swam. "Yes!" he gasped.

.   .   .   .

No doubt as he began that greatest period in his whole career, half an hour later, he thought seriously of a pair of blue eyes in a white kitchen;—seven hundred and fifty dollars, with a competent Swedish wife to take care of it and perhaps set up a little shop that would keep her husband out of mischief and busy—— But there the thought stopped short and his expression became one of disillusion: the idea of orderliness and energy and profit was not appetizing. He had seven hundred and fifty dollars in his pocket; and Tuttle knew what romance could come to him instantly at the bidding of this illimitable cash: he knew where the big crap games were; he knew where the gay flats and lively ladies were; he knew where the fine liquor gurgled—not White Mule; he knew how to find the lights, the lights and the music!

Forthwith he approached that imperial orgy of one heaped and glorious week, all of high-lights, that summit of his life to be remembered with never-failing pride when he went back, after it was all over, to his limousine and the shavings.

It was glorious straight through to the end, and the end was its perfect climax: the most dazzling memory of all. He forgave automobiles, on that last day, and in the afternoon he hired a splendid, red new open car, with a curly-haired chauffeur to drive it. Then driving to a large hardware store he spent eighteen dollars, out of his final fifty, upon the best lawn-mower the store could offer him. He had it placed in the car and drove away, smoking a long cigar in a long holder. Such was his remarkable whim; and it marks him as an extraordinary man.

That nothing might be lacking, his destiny arranged that Mrs. Pinney was superintending Tilly in the elimination of dandelions from the front yard when the glittering equipage, to their suprise, stopped at the gate. Seated beside the lawn-mower in the tonneau they beheld a superb stranger, portly and of notable presence. His pearl-gray hat sat amiably upon his head; the sleeves of his fawn-coloured overcoat ran pleasantly down to pearl gloves; his Van Dyke beard, a little grizzled, conveyed an impression of distinction not contradicted by a bagginess of the eyelids; for it is strangely true that dissipation sometimes even adds distinction to certain types of faces. All in all, here was a man who might have recalled to a student of courts some aroma of the entourage of the late King Edward at Hombourg. There was just that about him.

He alighted slowly—he might well have been credited with the gout—and entering the yard, approached with a courteous air, being followed by the chauffeur, who brought the lawn-mower.

"Good afternoon, lady and Tilly," he said, in a voice unfortunately hoarse; and he removed his pearl-gray hat with a dignified gesture.

They stared incredulously, not believing their eyes.

"I had a little trouble with your lawn-mower, so I up and got it fixed," he said. "It's the same one. I took and got it painted up some."

"Oh, me!" Tilly said, in a whisper. "Oh, me!" And she put her hand to her heart.

He perceived that he dazzled her; that she felt deeply; and almost he wished, just for this moment, to be sober. He was not—profoundly not—yet he maintained his dignity and his balance throughout the interview. "I thought you might need it again some day," he said.

"Mis-ter De *Mor*-ris!" Mrs. Pinney cried, in awed recognition. "Why, what on earth——"

"Nothin'," he returned lightly. "Nothin' at all." He waved his hand to the car. "One o' my little automobiles," he said.

With that he turned, and, preceded by the chauffeur, walked down the path to the gate. Putting his whole mind upon it, he contrived to walk without wavering; and at the gate, he paused and looked wistfully back at Tilly. "You certainly got a good build on you," he said.

Then beautifully and romantically he concluded this magnificent gesture—this unsolvable mystery story that the Pinneys' very grandchildren were to tell in after years, and that kept Tilly a maiden for many months in the hope of the miraculous stranger's return—at least to tell her who and what he was!

He climbed into the car, placed the long holder of the long cigar in his mouth, and, as the silent wheels began to turn, he took off his hat again and waved it to them graciously.

"I kept the pledge!" he said.

Frank Sullivan

THE VANDERBILT CONVENTION

UNDOUBTEDLY, the Vanderbilts constitute one of the most interesting families this country has produced. Intertwined as they are with the industrial development of the country they have, in addition, a romantic interest that intrigues the great mass of their newspaper-reading countrymen.

Some Vanderbilt, somewhere, is always doing something that arouses the curiosity of his fellow-Americans. One roams the oceans in search of rare specimens of deep-sea fauna. Another drives an old-fashioned coach and four at Newport. One is at the Rota, in Rome, pleading for an annulment of her marriage. One flouts tradition to enter trade as a newspaper-publisher. But whatever the Vanderbilts do, they are, as a newspaper chap I know would put it, "good copy."

There is one difficulty. The descendants of the doughty old Commodore have grown to be almost as numerous as the proverbial sands of the sea. Indeed, he who attempts to explain which Vanderbilt is which is tackling a man-sized problem. Who married whom? When were they divorced and who got the custody of what? How many Willie K.'s are there? Is it Cornelia or Muriel who rides horseback astride? Is Harold married? When did Mrs. Belmont cease being Mrs. Vanderbilt? They are, in truth, a complicated group.

What follows here is an attempt to explain the Vanderbilt family tree simply and briefly. I shall not go into the more remote branches; that would indeed be a Herculean task. My aim, rather, will be to explain and identify the various Vanderbilts who have figured, more or less, in the public eye.

The Commodore, the original Cornelius Vanderbilt, married, first, Sophia Johnson, and second, Frances

Crawford. His son, William Henry Vanderbilt, inheritor
of the bulk of the doughty Commodore's fortune, married Maria Louisa Kissam. They had issue as follows:
four sons, Cornelius, Frederick, William Kissam, and
George, and four daughters, who became Mrs. Elliot
Shepard, Mrs. Henry White, Mrs. Hamilton McKay
Twombly, and Mrs. William Seward Webb.

William Kissam married, first, an Alabama girl from
an old family named Smith. She later married O. H. P.
Belmont. William Kissam then married Mrs. Anne
Rutherford Harriman Sands. No. Mrs. Anne Sands Harriman Rutherford. No, that's not right either; let's get
this straight. He married, secondly, Mrs. *Anne Harriman
Sands Rutherford*. She then became, by a process of
elimination, Mrs. Anne Harriman Sands Rutherford Vanderbilt.

Cornelius Vanderbilt married Alice Gwynne. That is,
not the *first* Cornelius. The first Cornelius was the Commodore and he married, first, Frances Crawford, and,
second, Sophia Johnson. No, it's the other way round;
he married, first, Sophia Johnson, and, second, Frances
Crawford. And his grandson, William Kissam, married
Anne Harriman Sands Rutherford.

Now then. The Cornelius Vanderbilt who married Alice
Gwynne was not the Cornelius whose yacht recently blew
up in the East River. No. The Cornelius whose yacht
blew up in the East River is the Cornelius who married
Grace Wilson, and they had issue as follows: Cornelius
Vanderbilt, Jr., and Grace Vanderbilt (Mrs. Henry Gassaway Davis III). Cornelius Vanderbilt, Jr., son of the
Cornelius whose yacht blew up, is the Cornelius whose
newspapers blew up. His grandfather, Cornelius Vanderbilt, is the Cornelius who married Alice Gwynne. There is
no record of anything belonging to this Cornelius ever
having blown up.

Now then. Cornelius and Alice Gwynne Vanderbilt
had issue as follows: Cornelius, Alfred Gwynne (named
after his mother), Reginald, Gertrude, and Gladys.

Gertrude married a Hungarian nobleman, Count

Lâszló Széchényi. No, it couldn't have been Gertrude who married the Count. Gertrude is the sculptor, isn't she? Well then, if she's the sculptor, she's the one who married Payne Whitney, because that one is the one who's the sculptor. I remember distinctly reading *that*. No, that's not right, either. It wasn't Payne Whitney that Gladys—I mean Gertrude—married; it was *Harry* Payne Whitney. You see, *Payne* Whitney and *Harry* Payne Whitney—well, maybe it would be better to clear up the Vanderbilts today and leave the Whitneys for some other day.

Now then. It was Birdie Vanderbilt who married the Hungarian Count. No, Birdie is the sculptor. No, it's Gladys who's the sculptor; what am I thinking of! Her statue blew up. No, it was her yacht that blew up.

No, it was Cornelius' yacht that blew up. Birdie married William K. Not the William K. that married, first, Mrs. O. H. P. Belmont, *née* Smith, and, second, Mrs. Anne Harriman Sands Rutherford. Not that one. Birdie married the William K. who married, first, Virginia Fair. Cathleen is their daughter. No, Cathleen is Reginald's daughter. Reginald married, first, Ellen French, and, second, Margaret Emerson McKim Mead and White. No, that wasn't Reginald.

Suppose we start *all* over again and get this thing straight. Let's begin once more with the doughty old Commodore. He married, first, Sophia Johnson, and second, Frances Crawford. William Henry Vanderbilt was their son. Not the William Henry Vanderbilt who gives all the clambakes; the other one, the one who married Maria Louisa Kissam.

Now, if William Henry and Maria Louisa Kissam, after getting married, had let it go at that, things wouldn't have become so complicated. But they didn't. They had issue: eight children. These eight children had children and these children in turn had children, so that in the due course of time there came to be so many Vanderbilts that the family became known as the Vanderbilt

Convention. And the doughty old Commodore had started practically on a shoestring!

Now then. What I am trying to do here is simply to give an explanation of which Vanderbilt is which, so that the reader who is interested may be able to distinguish them.

Damn it all, why the hell should people want to distinguish the Vanderbilts, anyhow? This country is supposed to be a democracy, isn't it? When our forefathers gathered at Boston—no, it wasn't Boston. It was Philadelphia. Well, it was either New York or Philadelphia. I don't *care* which one it was. It was on some Sub-Treasury steps, and our forefathers, when they gathered to free the Vanderbilts from the tyranny of George II—no, George III—stipulated, didn't they, that each person in the new nation should be conceived in liberty and dedicated to the proposition that all men are entitled to the pursuit of life, liberty, and the pursuit of happiness.

All right then, why harry the poor Vanderbilts this way? Why not let them alone once in a while? Whose business is it which of them is which? The trouble with this country is that there are a lot of morons in this country who can't mind their own business. They have to be always reading intimate details about the lives of other people. They want everything explained to them. What business is it of theirs which Vanderbilt is which? It's the sensational tabloids, and these physical-culture magazines, that encourage all this morbid curiosity. Why can't the Vanderbilts come and go in peace, same as any other citizen? Who do they think they are, anyhow? Why, for that matter, the old man, the doughty old Commodore, who married Sophia Johnson, first, and Frances Crawford, second, was in trade. He ran a ferry between Staten Island and Manhattan!

His son was William Henry Vanderbilt, who married William Kissam—no, Louisa Maria Kissam, and they had issue (eight children) and then somewhere down the line someone of them married Count Lâszló Széchényi. They have five children and he fought a duel. But Reginald

Vanderbilt married Cathleen Neilson and their daughter, Cathleen, married Henry Gassaway Davis III.

No. It wasn't Cathleen who married Henry Gassaway Davis III. Cathleen married Harry C. Cushing III. It was Grace, daughter of the Cornelius whose yacht blew up, who married Henry Gassaway Cushing III.

If only each Vanderbilt would arrange to have something of his, some little bit of personal property, easily distinguishable, blown up, it would be so much easier to tell them apart. "Ah, there goes Phyllis Vanderbilt. Which one is she, you ask? Why, she's the one whose first husband blew up."

It seems to me that somewhere, some time, some Vanderbilt married Irving Berlin III. On second thought, I guess not. I guess I'm thinking either of Cornelia, daughter of Mrs. George W. Vanderbilt (Mrs. Peter Goelet Gerry) who married the Hon. John Francis Amherst Cecil, or of Mary Cadogan, who married the Marquis of Blandford, son of the Duchess of Marlborough who was Consuelo Vanderbilt (Mrs. Jacques Balsan), daughter of the William Kissam Vanderbilt who married Mrs. O. H. P. Belmont and, later, Mrs. Anne Harriman Sands Rutherford Vanderbilt.

Consuelo, erstwhile Duchess of Marlborough (Mrs. Jacques Balsan), would therefore be the aunt of the Consuelo who married Earl E. T. Smith.

Now, there was a time when the Smiths outnumbered the Vanderbilts by two to one, but that era is passing. The Vanderbilts are beginning to absorb the Smiths, although as yet no Vanderbilt has overtly married a Jones. Still, you never can tell. The descendants of the doughty old Commodore are an impulsive and passionate race and if one of them ever chanced upon an unusually comely Jones (*olav hasholem!*) there is no telling what might ensue.

I trust I have made everything clear.

Dorothy Parker

THE GARTER

THERE it goes! That would be. That would happen to me.
I haven't got enough trouble. Here I am, a poor, lone
orphan, stuck for the evening at this foul party where I
don't know a soul. And now my garter has to go and
break. That's the kind of thing they think up to do to
me. Let's see, what shall we have happen to her now? Well,
suppose we make her garter break; of course, it's an old
gag, but it's always pretty sure-fire. A lot they've got to
do, raking up grammar-school jokes to play on a poor,
heartsick orphan, alone in the midst of a crowd. That's
the bitterest kind of loneliness there is, too. Anybody'll
tell you that. Anybody that wouldn't tell you that is a
rotten egg.

This couldn't have happened to me in the perfumed
sanctity of my boudoir. Or even in the comparative privacy of the taxi. Oh, no. That would have been too good.
It must wait until I'm cornered, like a frightened rat, in
a room full of strangers. And the dressing-room forty
yards away—it might as well be Sheridan. I would get
that kind of break. Break, break, break, on thy cold gray
stones, O sea, and I would that my tongue could utter the
thoughts that arise in me. Boy, do I would that it could!
I'd have this room emptied in thirty seconds, flat.

Thank God I was sitting down when the crash came.
There's a commentary on existence for you. There's a
glimpse of the depths to which a human being can sink.
All I have to be thankful for in this world is that I was
sitting down when my garter busted. Count your blessings
over, name them one by one, and it will surprise you
what the Lord hath done. Yeah. I see.

What is a person supposed to do in a case like this?
What would Napoleon have done? I've got to keep a cool
head on my shoulders. I've got to be practical. I've got

to make plans. The thing to do is to avert a panic at all costs. Tell the orchestra for God's sake to keep on playing. Dance, you jazz-mad puppets of fate, and pay no attention to me. I'm all right. Wounded? Nay, sire, I'm healthy. Oh, I'm great.

The only course I see open is to sit here and hold on to it, so my stocking won't come slithering down around my ankle. Just sit here and sit here and sit here. There's a rosy future. Summer will come, and bright, bitter Autumn, and jolly old King Winter. And here I'll be, hanging on to this damned thing. Love and fame will pass me by, and I shall never know the sacred, awful joy of holding a tiny, warm body in my grateful arms. I may not set down imperishable words for posterity to marvel over; there will be for me nor travel nor riches nor wise, new friends, nor glittering adventure, nor the sweet fruition of my gracious womanhood. Ah, hell.

Won't it be nice for my lucky hosts, when everybody else goes home, and I'm still sitting here? I wonder if I'll ever get to know them well enough to hang my blushing head and whisper my little secret to them. I suppose we'll have to get pretty much used to one another. I'll probably live a long time; there won't be much wear on my system, sitting here, year in, year out, holding my stocking up. Maybe they could find a use for me, after a while. They could hang hats on me, or use my lap for an ash-tray. I wonder if their lease is up, the first of October. No, no, no, now I won't hear a word of it, you all go right ahead and move, and leave me here for the new tenants. Maybe the landlord will do me over for them. I expect my clothes will turn yellow, like Miss Havisham's, in "Great Expectations," by Charles Dickens, an English novelist, 1812–1870. Miss Havisham had a broken heart, and I've got a broken garter. The Frustration Girls. The Frustration Girls on an Island, The Frustration Girls at the World's Fair, The Frustration Girls and Their Ice-Boat, The Frustration Girls at the House of All Nations. That's enough of that. I don't want to play that any more.

To think of a promising young life blocked, halted,

shattered by a garter! In happier times, I might have
been able to use the word "garter" in a sentence. Nearer,
my garter thee, nearer to thee. It doesn't matter; my life's
over, anyway. I wonder how they'll be able to tell when
I'm dead. It will be a very thin line of distinction between
me sitting here holding my stocking, and just a regulation dead body. A demd, damp, moist, unpleasant body.
That's from "Nicholas Nickleby." What am I having,
anyway—An Evening with Dickens? Well, it's the best
I'll get, from now on.

If I had my life to live over again, I'd wear corsets;
corsets with lots of firm, true, tough, loyal-hearted gar-
ters attached to them all the way around. You'd be safe
with them; they wouldn't let you down. I wouldn't trust
a round garter again as far as I could see it. I or anybody else. Never trust a round garter or a Wall Street
man. That's what life has taught me. That's what I've got
out of all this living. If I could have just one more chance,
I'd wear corsets. Or else I'd go without stockings, and
play I was the eternal Summer girl. Once they wouldn't
let me in the Casino at Monte Carlo because I didn't have
any stockings on. So I went and found my stockings, and
then came back and lost my shirt. Dottie's Travel Diary:
or Highways and Byways in Picturesque Monaco, by One
of Them. I wish I were in Monte Carlo right this minute.
I wish I were in Carcassonne. Hell, it would look like a
million dollars to be on St. Helena.

I certainly must be cutting a wide swath through this
party. I'm making my personality felt. Creeping into
every heart, that's what I'm doing. Oh, have you met
Dorothy Parker? What's she like? Oh, she's terrible. God,
she's poisonous. Sits in a corner and sulks all evening—
never opens her yap. Dumbest woman you ever saw in
your life. You know, they say she doesn't write a word of
her stuff. They say she pays this poor little guy, that lives
in some tenement on the lower East Side, ten dollars a
week to write it and she just signs her name to it. He has
to do it, the poor devil, to help support a crippled mother

and five brothers and sisters; he makes buttonholes in the daytime. Oh, she's terrible.

Little do they know, the blind fools, that I'm all full of tenderness and affection, and just aching to give and give and give. All they can see is this unfortunate exterior. There's a man looking at it now. All right, baby, go on and look your head off. Funny, isn't it? Look pretty silly, don't I, sitting here holding my knee? Yes, and I'm the only one that's going to hold it, too. What do you think of that, sweetheart?

Heaven send that no one comes over here and tries to make friends with me. That's the first time I ever wished that, in all my life. What shall I do if anyone comes over? Suppose they try to shake hands with me. Suppose somebody asks me to dance. I'll just have to rock my head and say, "No spik Inglese," that's all. Can this be me, praying that nobody will come near me? And when I was getting dressed, I thought, "Maybe this will be the night that romance will come into my life." Oh, if I only had the use of both my hands, I'd just cover my face and cry my heart out.

That man, that man who was looking! He's coming over! Oh, now what? I can't say, "Sir, I have not the dubious pleasure of your acquaintance." I'm rotten at that sort of thing. I can't answer him in perfect French. Lord knows I can't get up and walk haughtily away. I wonder how he'd take it if I told him all. He looks a little too Brooks Brothers to be really understanding. The better they look, the more they think you are trying to get new with them, if you talk of Real Things, Things That Matter. Maybe he'd think I was just eccentric. Maybe he's got a humane streak, somewhere underneath. Maybe he's got a sister or a mother or something. Maybe he'll turn out to be one of Nature's noblemen.

How do you do? Listen, what would you do if you were I, and . . . ?

Christopher Morley

OFF THE DEEP END

SHE's what yachtsmen call one of the 12's; which means, I think, that she measures twelve meters on the water-line. But I won't be too sure about that, for the lingo of scientific yachting is full of conventional and arbitrary terms. As education for a philosopher I recommend a deepwater voyage in a racing craft on her maiden trip. For here is a beautiful plaything, a perfect theory, an algebraic equation of stresses (or guesses) and strains, existing previously in blue-prints only, suddenly put out to earn her first offing in the dirty weather of the Nova Scotia coast. It is Jonathan Edwards embarking on life in some gay abstraction about the Fall of Man. Do you wonder that when you go to sea in a paradox, an hypothesis, and she weathers it all, comes through, you love her? I am not skilful enough to conjure up all the fabulous essence of that voyage; but if you'll be patient I'll tell about it as it comes to me. I see her again, a white fancy in the opal shine of noon, as the tug *Togo* cast us off in the fog of Halifax bay. New, untried, with stiff gear and 1952 square feet of canvas and all her pretty little brass winches still unverdigrised by salt. A doctrine, an ecstasy, a theory going out with a letter of introduction to Fact. Yes, the right place for a philosopher!

So I won't be sure about her water-line, but her long beautiful overhang, almost identical forward and aft, gives her 69½ feet over-all. If you lie on deck looking overstern (in a gentle weather) and see how smoothly she slips through water, you'll perceive that she's more than mere theory. Afloat in calm, with her white canvas up, she looks like a figure drifted from the pages of Euclid. Perhaps the idea is to make these racing craft as near an isosceles triangle as possible. Her tall mast (incredibly, terrifyingly tall to one accustomed only to knockabout craft: 80 feet above deck, 8 feet below) is stepped nearly amidship; and with Marconi rig (a triangular mainsail, no gaff) and a boom that does not project outboard you can imagine her an almost perfect segment of a huge circle. Her fore and back stays are the radii, her white hull the curve of the arc. To one all ignorant of racing boats everything about her in rig and gear was an astonishment. But certainly the internationalist finds her a good omen, for she was planned by a famous New York designer, built in Germany, her canvas is signed by Ratsey of Cowes and she was delivered in Halifax. *Iris*, her name, and I expect you'll see her picture in the rotogravures, leaning flat over in some gusty racing weather on Long Island Sound. The Commodore will be at the tiller and the New York Yacht Club pennant aloft. I hope it'll be the same pennant and not a new one: the little flag that whipped away four inches of its length in that wind we had off Cape Sable.

I shall always associate the adventure, in a left-handed way, with Edmond de Goncourt; who would, incidentally, have been a good man to record it. He would have felt all its suggestions to the full, but how he would have hated it. The lover of Parisian cafés and salons, the endless gossiper upon æsthetic niceties, devotee of the lamplit foolscap and the leisurely phrase, how delightfully ill he would have been and how unhappy in oilskins. As I write this, I get out my Halifax oilies again, to smell them and try to imagine what de Goncourt would have thought of that fascinating horrid whiff. To get it at its best, of course, you must be prodded up at 3 A.M. to go out for the dawn watch—the lobster trick as newspaper men used to call it. Gaping, sodden, stupefied, heavy in half a dozen layers of clothing, propped against the bulkhead of a reeling cabin, colder than the eye of Calvin Coolidge (such was the irreverent phrase we invented to describe the gray water of New Scotland) you stumble into those clammy crinkly gelatinous yellow overalls. And you will never do it without an ironic thought of their trade name. BANKER'S IDEAL is the phrase stamped on them; and you think of various merry bankers of your acquaintance, warm in their beds to looard of Park Avenue. Of course it's a different kind of banker that the oilskin merchant has in mind: the fisherman of the Grand and lesser banks. But thereafter, if ever you're inclined to complain of the heat, you can summon up that smell, and see the patient Commodore (a great contemner of sleep) outlined against a speckle of stars waiting to be relieved at the helm. De Goncourt, I believe, would not have been at his best. There is no reason for my bringing him into the picture, except that his Journal (a copy of which I had just found at Mendoza's) was the book I took along to read on board the *Nerissa*, the comfortable Red Cross ship that took us to Halifax. But in the *Iris* de Goncourt remained on the shelf unread. I used to see him there and think how unhappy he would have been. He was too sensitive. He describes how once, travelling in a railway train, he saw seven Englishmen wind their watches simultaneously, in a sort of automatic unison. The symbolic horror of this made him feel quite ill, so much so that he moved to another compartment.

It was in the *Nerissa*, during the two-day run to Halifax, that my spirit, always a lively foreboder, became aware of the fact that there is a great deal of water between Long Island Sound and Nova Scotia. Yet one did not brood this excessively, for as one shipmate remarked, when the voyage was first discussed, "the bar opens as soon as she gets to City Island." And let it be affirmed here that if there should be in this narrative any reference to gentlemanly potations, all were strictly legal. For aboard the *Nerissa* (why is not the Red Cross Line more advertised?) you are in a British steamship; and in Halifax, though it is a dry town, there is an admirable government warehouse, the Vendors' Stores, where with perfect legality Ships' Medical Supplies may be taken on for the comfort of the crew of seagoing vessels of over 26 tons. Duly signed on as Able Seamen in the consul's office, the Commodore's associates were justified in expecting fortification in case of emergency. Only a madman, it is

my conviction, goes to sea without some Jamaica rum in
his locker. And equally, only a madman drinks other than
medicinally while actually navigating. The sea is not kind
to tipplers.

The efficacy of this adventure, as education is philosophy, lay partly in its complete contradiction of the student's customary way of life. The Commodore and the
Personal Representative (this latter so-called because an
associate of the boat's designer) were lifelong yachtsmen.
Even the Younger Generation, so to identify the junior
member of the outfit, was a man of some experience in the
humours of racing sloops. But for the chronicler, though
not unfamiliar with salt water, this was all a transposi-
tion into quite a different key; so much so that it operated
as an Aristotelian catharsis. Even the libations were different. Yachtsmen, I can affirm, drink Martinis and
champagne, two fluids that are not often on my menu.
The admirable *Nerissa* is an ocean liner in miniature. If
the *Olympic* were to calve (or yean) in mid-sea, *Nerissa*
or her sister *Sylvia* would be the offspring. It's a girl! So
there was an odd feeling in being surrounded by every
evidence of ocean voyage, yet with the knowledge that we
were never, by steam reckoning, very far from land. Also
there was a large deck-load of cabbages on their way to
St. Johns, a reassuringly earthly sight. On the other
hand, there were the familiar bathtubs and lavatories of
Shanks and Co., Barrhead, one's favourite maritime
plumbers. So everything agreed to instil that sensation
of unreality, of incredulity, which is the healthiest tonic
for too docile servants of routine. And in spite of
Nerissa's well-chilled champagne there was a queer sentiment of inversion in so luxuriously traversing those long
rollers of gray sea, those white nowheres of fog, which we
were to revisit within a few days under our own canvas
and our own wit. The PR, whose cabin I shared, had a
great roll of blue-prints which purported to give every
possible cross-section of *Iris's* comely person; he had a
long inventory of her gear, from anchors down to napkins
and silver. Comminuted realist in matters that concern

safety at sea, I could not help reflecting that we had no blue-print nor inventory of the next week's weather. In the snug smokeroom of the *Nerissa* is a painting of Cabot Discovering Newfoundland, in a vessel somewhat slenderly rigged. One overtook oneself in a comic feeling of kinship with the hardy mariner, who was obviously glad to see land. For the object of this expedition was to make testimony, not testament.

Nerissa is a little floating island of Britain, as British ships always so sturdily are. From the bread-sauce that accompanied the roast chicken, to the after-dinner parade of the junior officers doing a marching foursome up and down the deck, not without an eye to see how any lady passengers were taking it, she is British to an extent that only an American can savour. I don't quite know why, but I shall long remember a little episode of the smokeroom. Together with those who were going to sail *Iris's* sister, *Tycoon*, we had spent a long evening in palaver. Bill, the orator of *Tycoon's* crew, was in notable form, and had held the floor to the great pleasure of all hands. His soliloquy, enriched by a bottle of champagne which was propped among the cushions of the settee to avert accident, had touched upon stage reminiscence, horse racing, the textile industry, and a lengthy anecdote dealing with a crisis in the life of the New York Credit Men's Association. During all this an elderly Scot, sitting near, had lent an attentive silence. For perhaps two hours he sat, following Bill's humours with an appreciative but solemn eye. Finally, a pause arriving, he spoke, and there was something charmingly random in his inquiry. "What would you do," he said, leaning forward gravely, "if you were in a community where 250 men had sworn to take your life?"

"I'd get out of it," said Bill.

Iris, when we first saw her, together with *Tycoon* and several other German-built craft, was on the deck of the freighter *Lorain* which had arrived from Bremen only a few hours earlier. Securely frapped in cradles they had made the voyage without mishap, but the hoisting them off by the big floating crane *Lord Kitchener* was an anxious business. That day it rained in a way that surprised even Halifax, a connoisseur of moisture. We stood about for hours in the downpour watching while the complicated job of unlashing and lifting the hulls was cleverly done. There was a curious eagerness in those two graceful shapes as the wire hawsers were gradually unbound. *Tycoon's* blue body, *Iris's* white, like pinioned gulls. They rose slowly, hung suspended from the crane, and were lowered overside. It was strange to see them come alive then. As *Tycoon*, unloaded first, was towed away, there was a sharp crack of thunder, almost like a salute.

By the time *Iris* was unloaded, after we had had a stout freighter's lunch of pea soup and corned beef and cabbage aboard the *Lorain*, the weather had cleared. *Iris* took the water without mishap. Riding a little high, without the weight of her big stick still to come, she dipped and swung gracefully. She knew her element. Now she was more than a blue-print.

If there were any ladies in the Halifax Hotel who wanted to do any writing that evening, they had to do it elsewhere than in the Ladies' Writing Room. For in that chamber the crews of both *Iris* and *Tycoon* dined privately in honour of their ships. That night they were captains bold in Halifax. That was the end of ease. The oilskins had been bought, and work was to begin.

Central Wharf in Halifax is a pleasant place for idling. I shall always think of it with affection as the scene of one of the best loafing days I ever enjoyed. There was plenty to be done, our little fleet of six boats were an apiary of business, but the thousand minutiæ of rigging those craft for sea was a specialized affair for experts in which I had no hand. To go to the Vendors' Stores and help select the liquor for the voyage was almost the only task I was entrusted.

After previous days of deluge this was a clearing weather, at first hazy, then warm and bright. There is something magical, as many have learned, in Nova Scotia air. It is far enough north to have in it the whiff of ever-

green balsam and great untainted woodlands, the birth-
right of the Canadian nostril. There is the cleanness of
salt-washed rocks, the iodine of seaweed, the douce vapour
of not far distant fog, and (in Halifax, at least) a delicious almost European fragrance of bitumen, the soft-
coal exhalation of breakfast chimneys. And in this diapa-
son of fragrance one sitting at ease on the stringpiece of
the wharf could discern small savoury grace-notes and
minors: the woody tang of new packing-cases burst open,
new creaky cordage, spar-varnish, rusty anchors, fish, the
strong soupy gush from the galley of the rusty old
Andalusia, a Swedish tramp just in from Jamaica. With
it all was mingled the memory of two other sunny days
when I had visited Halifax—once in 1910 when a boy
who seems now almost unrecognizable was pleased by
flower-boxes in her windows (they seem to have given that
up) and once in 1927 when the *Caronia* tarried there for
Sunday luncheon and the hotel waitress was shocked by
our asking for a bottle of beer. But let me add that
though beer is not available (except as Ships' Stores)
there is a sparkling Nova Scotia cider that is as good as
champagne.

So one loitered and watched our little tribe of argonauts make ready for sea. There were six in the flotilla:
three 12's (*Iris, Tycoon, Isolde*), two 8's (*Whippet* and
Margaret F. IV), and one very tiny cockleshell, the
Robin. Robin's curator was a Russian skipper, a charming fellow who had enchanted me on the voyage up by
tales of his hardships in the Revolution. He looked a little solemn as he went about the job of fledging his small
bird for voyage; and indeed I think no troubles of his
homeland can have been more dangerous for him than
setting out in that graceful toy. But man is always at his
most winning when preparing for argument with Posei-
don, who accepts no excuses. A convention of clergymen
assembled in synod of eucharistic congress could not have
been graver in legislating the inscrutable than our
yachtsmen as they tallied rigging and stores. Not quite
believing, the observer watched the tall masts of the 12's

hoisted by the derrick, lowered into place. This was a day when all ligatures were cut. Nothing to do but fill one's pipe and light it, to study pensively all these oddments of gear and to think that on this or that much might depend. Friendly Mr. Warren, the Halifax shipping agent, whose approval puts the whole town at your service, took the idler members of *Iris's* crew to lunch at a peaceful old clubhouse. Here YG was first introduced to British condiments, such as pickled walnuts, which brought tears to his eyes.

The angled bastions of the Citadel make a good polygon for afternoon stroll. The fortress seemed almost deserted, as fortresses ought to be on fine days. We peered into the deep moat, considered that its cool strong cellars would make admirable vaultage for wine, and were pleased by the sparrows that nest in niches of the masonry. It is worth while to build great strongholds if in after years they afford good lodging for sparrows, green slopes for rolling children, starry ceiling for summer love. Certainly that broad hill is excellent for flying kites. And far below in the harbour the masts of the three 12's reminded us that all this was mere interlude. At this very moment the adjuster was calculating *Iris's* compass deviation. It was a good time for considering one's own deviations. Sunny air was round us like crystal. An afternoon of pure nothingness, cast off from familiar duty, new routine not yet begun. Surely there should have been some valued thought to deduce from this. Some analogy that the whole of life itself will some day have to be so regarded, as the mere flutter of a sparrow's wing in and out of a hole in the wall? YG and I felt about in our minds for an idea and found only a large torpor. We abandoned philosophy and went to buy fleece underwear and rubber boots. That was better than philosophy, it was wisdom.

The quiet Halifax Hotel seemed specially solid and gratifying that evening. With a secretly testamentary tenderness we wrote some post-cards; we laid out and reckoned our provision of lumbermen's socks, woollen mitts and sweaters and oilskins. It amuses me to recall that we grumbled a little because the bedroom was warm, for Halifax keeps its steam going well into June. PR, who has a taste for bedtime gossip, kept me awake by telling me news about these racing sloops that he had not mentioned before. Of these 80-foot masts he remarked that they were hollow, built in longitudinal sections and glued together. Glued together! a merry thought in a moist climate, I reflected. I fell asleep hoping that the German industry in adhesives was an honest one.

Tycoon had the outside berth, so we couldn't cast off until she did. *Iris* was ready; we had borrowed *Tycoon's* nail-clipper and all hands had trimmed their fingers, always the amateur's final gesture to civilization; not mere delicacy I assure you, but preparation for dealings with tough canvas. But still we must linger (to tell you the truth) because *Tycoon's* case of beer was late. So we lost those early airs from NW. It was towards noon before we got off. The weather was a warm hazy calm. We had to beg a tow from the tug *Togo*, to start us down the harbour. "Light Sly air" was the first entry in the log. "Sly" meant Southerly, but it might also have meant what it said. There was gentle insinuation in that weather and in the low barometer. Through milk-white banks of fog the *Togo* hauled us rapidly. She cast us off north of Neverfail Shoal. Our canvas was up. Now we were alone, we two, and could look at each other. Pearly haze thinned and thickened about us. We could see *Tycoon's* blue hull, with white waterline stripe and green underbody, leaping like a mackerel in the long swell. The high spires of canvas leaned amazingly upward; when the mist thickened we could not see the top. Running side by side we took stock of ourselves, tightened shrouds, compared chronometers. *Tycoon*, a tilting phantom of beauty, crumbled swiftly over the gray slopes. By her we could judge our own profile. Breeze came fresh from SW. *Iris* set a course for Halifax Light Vessel, a dozen miles out. *Tycoon* turned westerly along the coast. They did not see each other again until Long Island Sound.

So with magical swiftness we were on our own. A tug, in a hurry to get back to another appointment, had rushed us down the harbour and cast us off—it seemed a little heartless—into a blanket of fog. Land was almost instantly out of sight, and our consort also. A long belly-wabbling sea came rolling under our bronze bottom. The chime of the Neverfail bellbuoy sounded like a summons to lunch, and from the cockpit one kept an eye on the swingtable in the main cabin. I had watched the stores going aboard. There, I said to myself, a large and frolic meal will be set out, such as yachtsmen enjoy. This was not like old days in the ketch *Narcissus* where I myself had to do the cooking. There was a steward, seasoned by years at sea, to ration us. I thought (though a little dubiously) of the lobsters I had seen going aboard. But the corner of the table, visible from the cockpit, remained bare. No one said anything about food. I was much on my good behaviour. This was my first experience of real yachting. But, in the odd way one divines things, I felt that to say anything about food would (somehow) be amiss. I kept to looard of the Commodore, for I was taught young that one does not go to windward of the skipper. But his pipe (which, waking, he is never seen without) was very strong. Until about 2 o'clock I feared that perhaps there was not going to be any lunch. After that time my apprehension was different. I began to fear that perhaps there was. But about half past four (meanwhile nothing having been said) YG appeared with some slices of raisin bread. Then the truth came out. Our steward, the hardened seaman, was ill.—We did not see him for four days.

So, without disaster, the first corner was rounded. The Commodore, of course, nothing can touch; he has the entrails of Gibraltar. But the rest of us, if we had had to face a generous meal, might have been troubled. As it was, only the captain (another lifelong salt) and the steward were ill. But I noticed, in my own secret reckonings with myself, that tobacco seemed to have lost its charm that afternoon.

Fog came down thick, and there was a steamer whistling not far away. She was inward bound round the lightship, we supposed; but the sound of her blast might have come from anywhere in an arc of nearly ninety degrees. A small fisherman's horn, pumped by hand, seems inadequate answer to that deep thuttering groan of a high-pressure steampipe. You get a very different sense of proportion when you hear a big ship's foghorn not from her own deck but from a small craft plunging from sea to sea. Suddenly the water seems very wrinkled and gray. Those waves are slate colour, even when broken they are not white but granite; they roll you in wet wastes of fog to teach you the blessings of being warm and steady. Put your foot down now, wherever you are, and verify the good sensation of firm solidity beneath you! Such are the thoughts of the first evening, when you put from snug harbour into wind and fog and low barometer. Soon you adapt yourself; after a day or so the tumbling that bothered you becomes the perfection of all rhythms, the joyous composition of all movement. But you are not sentimental the first day out.

The surprised faces of the lightship crew, as we passed close by them, might have suggested some surprise in our own minds. Our rig was evidently uncanny to them, and I was a little grim to remember how I had last seen that vessel, from the warm forward deck of the good old *Caronia* a level August morning. For now we were bundled up in all the half dozen layers of wool and oilskin, and chilly even so—always excepting the Commodore, exempt from all human weakness. And my testimony of the rest of that afternoon, as we zig-zagged (roughly speaking) SW and NW, must be, if honest, mostly of sleep. Such drowsiness as I have never known came down upon me. I fell loglike into a bunk and lay as one drugged and shanghaied. It was the miracle and quintessence of slumber, for one was dimly self-aware and knew how much one was enjoying it, yet too far gone for any shame or desire. One was as passive as a participle. If the voyage of the *Iris* had granted me even nothing else than that first period of swooning I

should be sufficiently grateful. It was an experience. There
are some of us who, in civil life, sometimes have difficulty
in getting to sleep. I found myself, in this sea-stupor,
chuckling at the notion of a sailor ever complaining of
insomnia. There was no instant, in the first two days,
when I could not have immediately gone Rip Van Winkle
by just closing my eyes. Along about dusk that evening,
the weather being dubious, the Commodore decided to
take down the mainsail and put a trysail on her for the
night; a very reasonable precaution with a new and untried vessel on a bad coast. I believe I made some meagre
pretence of activity when all hands were called on deck,
but whatever I did was done in pure hypnotism. I feel
the less embarrassment in this confession because I noted
in the long-salted PR signs of the same delicious lethargy.
His bright eye, an orb as clear and humorous as a hen's,
closed its lid as nesciently as any other's. Not food nor
drink nor any lure of life had the faintest appeal. One
did not even unbutton an oilskin nor remove a hat. One
collapsed where one was. Only the sailor, I conclude,
knows how to take sleep seriously.

There is a bathtub that has a window just over it;
through which, in the exhilaration of the morning sluice,
when everything seems for a few moments fairly simple,
one looks into the green depth and shading of a Long
Island glade. Marvelling at those gradations of colour,
the movement of boughs and leaves, the savoury stability
of earth underneath, the good hairy grass, the cheerful
esperanto of many birds, one is tempted to confess privately that land is much more beautiful than sea. It is a
silly thought, for beauty is not a matter for comparisons;
but it is safe to say that most praises of marine life, by
whomever written, were composed after the observer was
safe ashore. The sea writers I love best have always had a
very handsome terror of it. Conrad, whose *Mirror* is bible
and prayer-book to those who have sea-humility in their
souls, tells in one magnificent chapter how he was first
initiated into an awareness of its cruelty. There are essays
in that book that are in the exact mood and tender humour

of Charles Lamb, a parallel that may surprise you. But some of his memories commit him to a very different feeling. "And I looked upon the true sea—the sea that plays with men till their hearts are broken. Nothing can touch the brooding bitterness of its heart. To love it is not well."

So you commit yourself to the deep in a mood of piety. And the humour of the situation is that some of the realest hardships of the sea, so I suspect, are endured not by shellbacks in windjammers, but by yachtsmen who put out in dainty craft scarcely provided against cold and wet. At least the old windjammer had a good pot-bellied stove in the focsle. One's half waking visions, in the neighbourhood of Cape Sable, were imaginings of red-hot stoves. For our steward, as I told you, was prostrate, and those who, tempted by thoughts of grub, ventured to the galley to light the gas cooker, took one breath of rich meats and returned to the cockpit to study the sky. The chronicler, usually a lover of kitcheneering sport, went privily to the icebox, intending to prepare a meal for his companions. He opened the door and studied the Commodore's generous larder. There was a royal exhalation of pork, cheese, bacon, butter, cream, and fish. He came again topside and said nothing of his impulse. But man is always perverse. Even the entire unwillingness to prepare it for himself does not prevent his dreaming of food. Was it that night—the second night out—that I had the curious hallucination of the pork chop? I think it was. Our watch was on duty from 9 until midnight. An afternoon of fog had cleared away towards sunset. The moon, nearly full, was very bright. The great white triangle of *Iris's* mainsail slanted up against the Dipper. We were making about 6 knots, on a course W. by N., there was a pleasant shearing hiss under her bow, the decks glistened silverly. There was the soft glow of the compass, set in the flooring of the cockpit; faint red and green shine where the running lights were set; a crack of cheerful brightness through the forward companion where the Commodore and YG slept a well-earned watch below. PR was at the helm, and the chronicler, attempting to persuade himself that all these charming light effects counterbalanced the cold, passed into a small stupor. He was wearing canvas gloves and over these two pairs of large woollen mitts. In his trance he dreamed of a large hot well-browned pork chop. He actually felt it in his hand, tasted its good savour, brought it to his jaws in realization; and woke to find a couple of inches of cold wet wool crammed into his mouth.

Honour to whom honour! It was YG who kept the ship alive with coffee, and (after some 48 hours) broke out two cans of Campbell—one of soup and one of beans. On the third day, Cape Sable having been passed and a bottle of *Ne Plus Ultra* broached, the first health of the voyage was drunk, to the Canner of Camden. The greatest man who ever lived in Camden was not necessarily Walt Whitman. I give you Mr. Campbell of the Soups.

It was 7.30 on the morning of the first of June, so the notebook tells me, when we made Cape Sable abeam. A tall pharos dimly seen across miles of tumbling gray; as the ads used to say, a small thing to look for, a big thing to find. The log said 212.5 miles and we reckoned the first leg of our cruise well accomplished. But only two hours later we found the mainsail parting from the little brass slides that hold it to the mast. The lashings of twine were evidently not strong enough to carry so big a canvas in a wind. The kind of zipper gear used on the masts of racing craft was quite new to me, and I confess I had my doubts about it. So the mainsail was got down, and the trysail hoisted instead, while the skipper and Charley set about lashing the slides to the eyelets with wire. We then discovered that our patent log had somehow chafed through and gone adrift. Thereafter the Commodore reckoned our speed by throwing an empty matchbox overboard at the bow and timing it to the stern with a stop-watch. Our rate of progress was not much to brag about, for with the trysail we could not get very close to the wind, and there was a heavy bumpy sea.

The starbo'lins had by this time come to consider themselves the lucky watch, probably because the Commodore

usually granted them a little extra sleep. At any rate it
was they who had what they will probably remember as
the greatest single episode of the voyage. The three of
them were yarning in the cockpit. With their usual love
of ease, they were gratified that the Commodore had decided to keep her under trysail for the night. Making a
course NW, she was throwing up fine showers of spray
which were tinged pink by the sunset. The PR and Captain Barr were gossiping about whales; the chronicler
propped at his favourite post in the companion-way where
one's legs at least are warm. Suddenly the PR cried out
with amazement in his voice, "By God, there he is now!"
Then his sea manners came to his rescue and he repeated
more formally, "Whale ho, on the starboard beam."

I was looking off to windward, meditating that that
sunset looked a windy one. I turned just in time. The
other two were gaping like lunatics. Right alongside of
us, certainly not more than fifty feet away, a huge dark
back showed above the water. I could see the pale oily
film that seeped off his skin and tinged the water. He
looked as big as a submarine. We had to luff up into the
wind to avoid hitting him, as he was proceeding gently
right across our bow. The great slope of his chine sank
quietly, and we waited half expecting to feel the *Iris*
lifted beneath us. He must have passed exactly under us,
for a minute or so later he came up on the other side
and spouted a fountain that shone faintly in the pink
twilight. He seemed very much at his ease, loitering
easily in that cold dusky water; the sound of his blowing
something between a hiss and a sigh. We saw him spout
several times, at increasing distances, as he departed with
his own proper dignity. It was all too incredible for very
sharp observation. Moby Dick himself! We were silent for
some time. What abysses of chill, fading from green to
immortal black, does he visit in his going? What expression does he wear in his unblemished eye? We had met
him in his own honourable realm; sliding, so to speak, on
his cellar door. We had heard the very sound of his breathing, and had offended him not nor paid him ought but

respect. Who shall say anything new of Moby Dick? Not I.

"I'm glad we didn't hit him," said the PR as after long astounded gazing we remembered the compass and resumed our course. "To be kicked to death by a whale would be undignified."

That night there were mares' tails in the sky, long skeins and streamers of cloud brightened by the moon. By 6.30 A.M. sea and wind were rising merrily. There was no talk now of putting on the mainsail. Even on the trysail the lashings of the slides were beginning to go, she was taken down and reefed. There came pouring rain and strong SW gale. The jib also we took down. Now, unless we ran with a bare pole, this was all that could be done. The glass hovered between 29.50 and 29.55.

When you speak to me of the Bay of Fundy, that is the day I shall remember. When one was below, the morale was not too good. This was now the fourth day, and what with one thing and another the cabin had not had a cleaning since we sailed. The sea had been rough and those not on actual duty had no ambition for anything but sleep. The patent German ash-tray, come from Bremen, had capsized first of all and spilled matches and tobacco everywhere. Water coming liberally through the skylights had moistened everything to a paste. *Iris*, leaping merrily among hills and valleys, was easing herself to the strain, but her chorus of creaks and groans was anxious to those below. Large consignments of ocean came upon her with the heavy solidity of an automobile smash. How wet were those brown blankets! I admit that the chronicler and YG, brooding below and watching cracks widen in the bulkheads and panellings, had a vague notion that she might dissolve about them. I remembered the German glue industry. The Commodore, coming down to examine the chart, was entertained to find his underlings suggesting it would be a good thing to seek shelter somewhere. He was quite right, of course; we were best where we were.

But above, when one's eye grew accustomed to the size of that sea and the way she handled herself, there was real thrill. How big were the waves, people always ask? It cannot be answered because in a heavy sea the hills are too broad to allow the eye any fair scale of measurement. But you see them with a different eye from that of the passenger in a big liner. On a big ship you look down on the water and its colour seems darker. From *Iris* we looked closely into these long ridges that loomed above; we could see how coldly green and translucent they were. Every once in so often there was some particularly big comber one could mark from far away: it came striding, breaking in a crest a hundred yards long, with a definite menace written all over it. There was something unpleasantly personal about those waves. "I'll get you if I can," seemed to be their autograph. They would rise, perhaps thirty feet above us, leaving us momently in a dull green twilight, far down the hollow. Then with the soar of a rising gull, she would ride up as the great shoulder lifted her. A swirl of cream about her nose as the comber spilled a few buckets along her deck, and we gazed triumphant from the summit along leagues of water laced and wrinkled with foam. For nine or ten hours we were practically hove to, riding switchback on these big ones. Wind sang in our rigging, rafts of fog swathed us in. It was a specially big sea coming through the skylight late in the afternoon that really brought us round the corner. Several gallons of cold water soused on the Commodore's head as he lay asleep. He sat up promptly, looked about at the foul mess in his pretty cabin, and remarked only, "Well, boys, let's clean up." Somewhat gingerly, creeping about in that frolicking hull, we did so. The sea began to moderate. Charley, our able seaman, after a long trick at the helm, could endure starvation no longer. When relieved, he dug out a side of pork from the icebox and began hacking it into chops. The sound and smell of frying began to mitigate our chills. The PR had remarked that in these voyages you fill the refrigerator at Halifax, and when you get to New York you find there's more ice than you started with. But after our first real meal in four days we felt different. There were pork chops and onions and potatoes and

canned fruit. So was my vision of the pork chop fulfilled.
The weather cleared enough to make an attempt at a sunset observation. Emboldened by pork chops we shook out
the reef in the trysail and put up the jib. I think it was
then that the Commodore was justified in making his
favourite remark—"Well, boys, things are looking up."

Somewhere in those waters, perhaps still faintly perfumed by the Commodore's pipe, there is an invisible
longitude, a Shadow Line, where the Bay of Fundy becomes the Gulf of Maine. For when the Commodore roused
his starboard watch at 4.15—having given them an hour
and a quarter as lagniappe—there was that good feeling
of having turned a corner unawares, some unseen facet
of space and time. There was quite a new theology in the
air. Which was natural enough: it was Sunday morning.
The first thought that circulated in the chronicler's system was, "Spring's coming." For in the WNW breeze was
a nostrilsome savour of pines and balsam. It smelt like
graduating from Bowdoin College. This dim sea, rubri-
cated by a full red setting moon, could not be identified
by any instrument more accurate than the nose, for we
had had no reasonable observations since Cape Sable. But
the chronicler's nose perceived the State of Maine and
vouched for it. About sun-up, still reckoning by the nostril and the matchbox log, we felt that we had more than
enough northing; we tacked and made a course SW by S.

Now, with gales and chilblains left astern, was time to
resume the famous mainsail. At 6.15 we took down the
trysail and were ready to raise our full-page spread. I
particularize the episode because it is a parable of the
uses of indolence. The chronicler, always evasive of toil,
was wont to give an apparent demonstration of zeal, to
justify himself in the Commodore's eye. When great
weights of canvas were to be handled or hoisted he could
cry *hoick* (or however you prefer to spell that rhythmical
groan) with the loudest, but it was mostly subterfuge.
And now, while Captain Barr and Charley and the PR
were lustily tailing onto halliards and winch, the chronicler was standing by (keeping that big mast between him

and the Commodore) and sojering. He was pretending to be doing something. I don't know just what, but in reality he was surveying all that intricate gear with his usual questioning amazement. So it was he who observed that the bronze gooseneck, which holds the boom to the mast, was cracked almost through. The metal had gone a sort of roquefort cheese colour and was radiated with fissures. Obviously the thing was unsafe. In that pleasant breeze and with so gross a canvas the thing would most likely snap, there would be a big boom thrashing loose and all sorts of devilment.

With reluctant hearts the company abandoned the proud mainsail for good and all. The boom was unshipped and lashed on deck. Up again went old stand-by, the trysail. And the mainsail was stowed in the Commodore's cabin where it filled all the space and where that uncomplaining commander crept in and out of his bunk like a chipmunk in a tangle of underbrush.

This was a two-hour job. Now, in the first clear sunshine and fair breeze of the voyage, we must go soberly along under storm gear. *C. G. 24*, a smart destroyerish lady in naval gray, passed near us and evidently took note of our cautious demeanour. We had, to sea eyes, much the look of a man who attended a smart wedding in cutaway garb and a golf cap. But there is one great etiquette among ships: you know there is a valid reason for everything, and don't ask rude questions. Our progress was lenient, but these royalties of sunshine were making up arrears of comfort and we were well cheered. Some half-cooked porridge was discovered, abandoned by the steward days before in the crisis of his malady. This was warmed up by YG and we felt reintroduced to civilization and food.

That sunny forenoon was notable first for a series of sextant observations. The Commodore and PR, after calculations enduring nearly two hours, announced preliminary theories. By one of these we were somewhere SE of Portland. By another, we were on a latitude with the Isles of Shoals. This reminded YG and the chronicler of Mr. Edmund Pearson's excellent murder story, "Murder at Smuttynose" (Smuttynose is one of those islets) and in the sunny calm that fell towards noon our favourite crime yarns were discussed. From this, in the Commodore's legal mind, it was a logical transition to the theme of shaving. We did so, and there was a general renovation. Wet clothes and blankets were brought up to air. The emaciated steward was excavated from his berth in the focsle and propped up in the cockpit to air. At high noon, after a final flurry of sun-shooting, the two navigators gave out statements to the Press-box. (The Press was represented by YG and the chronicler, both concerned with journalism. YG, incidentally, confided to me that he is writing a book about Eccentrics; we agreed that this voyage should be fertile in material.) Our position was authoritatively stated as 42° 54′ N., 60° 47′ W. You can look it up on the map and see how near it tallied with nasal prognostics.

This reckoning was entered in the log as our position at Wedding Time. For it so happened that this date was the marriage anniversary of one of the company. *C. G. 24* was no longer in sight, and anyhow we were not yet in territorial waters. The sound of splitting wood was heard from the main cabin, where we had been barking our shins on those cases for four days. The other three, hearing the Commodore hatcheting down below, looked at each other with a sweet surmise. The shy trafficker, as Matthew Arnold says, undid his corded bales. An empty box came flying up through the companionway and fell with an agreeable thump onto the calm ripple that slid softly by. Honourable men know how to solemnize a date of sentiment. Need I insist what was the stencil on those floating jetsams? Mumm's the word.

I mark the crossing of 43 Latitude and 70 Longitude, and adjacent undulations, with the triple stars of Baedeker and other magi. By matchbox log we were making some 3½ knots. The scenery was level; the barometer reapproaching 30; the steward himself again. What a meal; and afterward to loaf about the deck, fed and warm. *Iris*, we told the Commodore, looked like Cleopatra's barge that afternoon. The trysail indeed had a Levantine look, and Nile itself could not have been calmer than the sunny drowse into which that day had blossomed. Cushions of cramoisie were strewn about—the sodden mattresses of our cabin settees. A sensual scene with so abandoned an array of socks, slippers, sweaters, oilskins, mittens, blankets, trousers. The Commodore's windbreaker jacket, yellow wool turned outward, hung spread-eagled on a line forward of the mast, like the golden fleece. Now there was time for these Argonauts, these grave Tyrian traders, "frightened with amber grapes and Chian wine," to look at one another and praise the discomforts they had known. Was Matthew Arnold ever a yachtsman? There are so many delightful lines of his that suggest a sea passion. I don't know why it is, but I always think of The Scholar Gipsy when becalmed in a boat. A volume of Arnold should be in every sea library against such afternoons. We had "day and night held on indignantly," and now, as that soft weather lapsed around us to golden shimmer we lived like commas in a perfect poem. It pleases me to remember that at one time that afternoon we spoke affectionately of C. E. Montague—probably reminded by Arnold, of whom Montague had lately written in the *Saturday Review*. We spoke of his exquisitely witty writing, of the great gusto of his lifelong campaign for all liberal and generous causes, of his *Disenchantment*, surely one of the noblest and fieriest books of our time. Several times during this voyage C. E. M. had come into our thoughts and conversations. The first news I learned on getting home was of his death, the very day we had arrived in Halifax.

I have spoken of the *Robin*, the smallest of our little fleet that assembled at Central Wharf. Anxiety as to her welfare was pretty frequent in our thoughts. I should like here to write into the log a copy of a letter to Starling Burgess (our designer) from the undaunted Captain

Shadrin, her Russian skipper. This fine sailorly document deserves applause:

I arrived at Gloucester on the 19th day of June at 11 A.M. from Halifax. I was going to leave Halifax on Sunday, the third day of June, with three other boats. While they were going away from the wharf Yacht *Whippet* broke my lower spreader, so I had to remain at the wharf until that was fixed. The 4th day of June was the King's birthday and a local holiday, so I had to wait until Thursday and at 3 o'clock that day I left Halifax. Made Sambro Light at 5:30; at sunset I was becalmed until the 6th day of June at 6:30; made about 10½ miles to Pearl Island. Barometer dropping, wind southeast, breezing up, following a heavy rain. The *Robin* was making good passage about 9½ knots per hour. Began to dip astern and took heavy sea, almost filling up cockpit. At 1 A.M., the 7th day of June, I arrived at Liverpool and anchored; blowing a gale; staying at anchor for 30 hours, and left on June 8th at 8 A.M. proceeding westward. With fair breeze and fair weather, but towards sunset under heavy northwest squalls arrived at Shelbourne at 9 P.M. Yacht *Whippet* going out of the harbour under power and I spoke her. Almost calm with heavy southwest swell running outside. That is the last I saw of the *Whippet*.

On the 9th day of June at 6 P.M. left anchorage and reached Cape Rosevay and returned back to anchorage. That night gale was blowing southwesterly with heavy rainsqualls all night until morning; many vessels arrived at Shelbourne for shelter. By the way I was sorry for my friends in yachts who happened to be out that night. Monday, June 11th, left at 5 P.M. under heavy head swell, choppy sea, and strong tide, making poor headway; anchored at Cape Negro Island on the cove for the night at 8 P.M.

Tuesday, June 12th, left Cape Negro at 7 P.M., wind northerly; made Cape Sable at noon; shifting wind, westerly, increasing sea and heavy tide rips, decided to go into Pubnico; arriving at anchor at 5 P.M. that day, weather threatening, barometer dropping, no show to proceed until the 16th day of June. Captain Red Peter was at Pubnico until the 12th day of June on the yacht *Isolde,* and left there that morning. Then I heard that he went to Tusket Island, from the Customs officer, and stayed there until the 15th of June. All well. I can't say if this report is correct.

I left Pubnico on the 16th day of June, Saturday, at 6 A.M. Fair and clear, barometer 30.15, wind north. Decided to head across the bay. Under various adverse westerly winds I was beating across the Bay of Fundy for three days and nights without any sleep, and with much discomfort. Made Cape Elizabeth Light on the 19th of June at 1.30 A.M. and arrived at Gloucester. All well and secure. Reported and went to rest.

Throughout the entire passage I never had a chance to get on a fair slant and most of time by the wind. Made seven tacks across the Bay. Quality of *Robin* is excellent and she is very reliable and at times I fell in love with her, and can stand up in very rough weather on beam seas almost as good as any schooner; the only objection I have that she is dipping stern in rough following sea. Slight alterations on the cockpit would overcome this weakness.

I am very sorry that I did not report to you beforehand from the ports of anchorage and beg your pardon for anxiety in my behalf. I have enough experience to handle my end to the best advantage under any conditions to a satisfactory end to all concerned.

NICHOLAS L. SHADRIN.

"At times I fell in love with her." There speaks the true seaman.

We drifted W by N into a warm sunset. Still perhaps unduly doubtful of our reckonings, we drew lots as to what part of the coast we would pick up. At 6.56 P.M. we sighted Cape Ann on the port bow. But we were quite helpless in that delicious calm. We swam idly with the tide. In the dusk we sighted a small power schooner lying enigmatically offshore. With foghorn and flashlight we halloed her, thinking perhaps she would give us a tow to Rockport; but she paid no heed to our signals. When we drifted alongside she replied to our hail with inhospitable monosyllables. Captain Barr at last—perhaps unguardedly—remarked, "What you fellows doin', fishin'?" After that there was complete silence. Probably she was indeed one of Matthew Arnold's shy traffickers. It would have been fun to pop a cork at her in the dark.

We had tiptoed almost into Rockport harbour by midnight, when the tide turned and carried us out again. The Commodore was pleased, as it had always been his intention to make Marblehead anyhow. I have given you no picture of the Commodore at all unless you see him as one who likes to accomplish what he sets out for.

Marblehead, the font and chrism of New England yachtsmen, was an old story to those others; but all new to the simple chronicler. He rose through the hatch, about six o'clock of that blithe airy morning, and found *Iris* rippling through a strait of bouldered coves. One with several good hours of oblivion behind him looks dispassionately on the vigils of others, so he forbore to chaff the Commodore on the amount of tobacco ashes sprinkled along the cockpit coaming, spoor of the commander's all-night watch. The PR was making himself so busy and helpful about the deck that one suspected he also had gone shut-eye and was but newly revived. "You can take the jib in," were the Commodore's exact words at 6.18, in a tone worthy of Cabot. There was more than just the due severity of great commanders in this long vigil of his. I think he had wished to spare his new ship the embarrassment of publicly arriving in so tony a harbour under jury rig. As Emily Post, if her stocking should choose to run, so (I divine) would *Iris* have felt to appear under trysail opposite the verandah of the Eastern Yacht Club. So, in the morning hush, while even the lobsters destined for Marblehead's luncheon were hardly alert, we stole in among many handsome craft and let go our hook. 4 days

19 hours 35 minutes we reckoned our passage. It was duly logged, with a small private ceremonial. The Commodore, pipe still in mouth, crawled in under the folds of canvas that filled his bunk and was off soundings at once. The others, in the imperative instinct of family men, went ashore to telephone. The stern and rockbound coast undulated gently beneath them. Bells rang in far away Long Island and all was reported O.K. Tobacco and newspapers were then sought. Teetering a little on the floor of a rustic pharmacy they read that a Miss Earhart had just flown from Boston to Halifax in five hours.

In the differential calculus of such beachcombers, family and tobacco were obviously the primary items; but these verified, next came a strong hankering for a bath. There was plenty of water handy, but it looked (and felt) unbearably chill. Across the harbour lay the luxurious quarters of the Eastern Yacht Club. Thither, with the *lavabo* cry of the psalmiest, aspired the hearts of PR and the chronicler. YG, who had been up all night, asked nothing better than to be left asleep where he had fallen, in a dinghy pulled up on the public dock. But we prodded him up, assuring him that it was not well to sleep in a full beam of sun. For without him we had no clear title to the desiderated tub. The Commodore, a member of the Club, might not be disturbed. But YG, affiliated to our commander, might rank as a member-in-law. To him we clung; kept vigorously nudging him awake in the soft drowsy air of June, and so made good our course into the very bathroom of the clubhouse. The Messrs. Shanks themselves, in Barrhead's deepest porcelain, never had happier ablution.

One must not melodramatize what were, after all, only very small adventures; but still the happenings of a man's mind are his own and subject to no alien supervision. In that Monday forenoon stillness, a James Russell Lowell sort of morning, in the very tissue and entity of seemly Massachusetts, we had the broad club verandah to ourselves. How green and trim was the lawn, where some sail were bleaching; how polished the brass cannon above the

landing stage. On the club beach some baby brahmins,
well supervised by excellent nursemaids, played with a
docility rarely found in the rude urchins of Paumanok.
They were making sand patties, but only to pass away
the time until old enough to go to Harvard or Wellesley.
The big framed chart of members' burgees, including that
of the King of Spain, reminded us that for the moment
we were not just sunburned casuals, we were Yachtsmen.
Life seemed to be solved. Where were those cold yeasts of
sea, those glimmering slopes of jade and crystal with
darkness written on them? Across far water there was
pointed out the blue horizon of what is called (I believe)
the North Shore, home of the great mandarins of Massachusetts. There were yachts with surprising newfangled
gear, such as a kind of propped-up mast; there were
motor boats with evident Rolls Royce blood in them, with
glass windshields and double rudders. There was a great
glass case of silverware, racing prizes. The world rode at
anchor and the sea said nothing. We made comfortable
arcs in rocking chairs and watched our tall white *Iris*
where the Commodore lay sleeping in his canvas niche.

Our consort the *Duenna*, a stout and sea-kindly power
boat, met us at Marblehead. The wind was light and contrary, so she took us in tow. There were still three days,
but they were of a quite different psychology and require
no special exegesis. Except when the *Duenna* (admirably
named, for she chaperoned us as though *Iris's* virtue were
of the frailest) left us to dart into various ports for fuel,
we made the rest of the voyage at the end of a line; and a
ship in tow is a mere somnambulist. This is not to say
there were not many pleasures to ponder. It would be a
breach of manners not to pay tribute to the dinner prepared by the resuscitated steward after we had got
through the Cape Cod Canal. That night Lazarus laughed
indeed. The Commodore, after a long sleep as we towed
down toward the Cape, roused about 6, lit his pipe, and
stated that things were looking up. He then made a further pronouncement, in regard to evening mess, that im-
bedded in the minds of his Able Seamen and shone there

like a jewel. Hours went by, and these latter began to
wonder whether this utterance had been forgotten. Perhaps it had been only a sleepy ejaculation, the syllables
of a mind still half in dream. To inquire or remind would
obviously have been unseemly; yet as time went on and
we approached the fragrant Canal, sweet in the twilight
with aromas of sea-grasses, weedy rocks, tidal mud, sand
and pine-gum and all juniper and huckleberry relishes,
the younger set looked at each other anxiously. To show
how ardently the mind may occupy itself with small matters, I admit that as the Commodore stood cheerfully on
the after deck I kept my left ear (which hears better than
the right) turned toward him, not to miss the faintest al-
lusion to The Topic. With my left ear I heard him say
something; and when YG asked me anxiously "D'you
suppose he's forgotten?" I was able to report that he had
not.

The Cape Cod Canal, by the way, now run by Uncle
Sam, seems one of the rare instances of fewer formalities
when a Public Work is taken over by the federal government. In the old days of private ownership there was
much more detail, fees to pay and whatnot. Now they
simply ask you the length of the ship and that's all.

It was getting on towards 9 o'clock, but the Commodore hadn't forgotten. By the time we anchored off Monument Beach for the night—a quiet rainy night, perfect
for sleep—we had sent fresh broiled mackerel and straw-
berry shortcake to their manifest destiny. We sat and ate
and palavered in a tranquil glow that was not just the
light of our lantern. I shall not be excessive on this topic,
but the last two days were very largely concerned with
grub. We had four or five empty days to catch up with.
Now that there was little navigating to consider, almost
at any moment some member of the company could be
found eating. The PR discovered some marmalade among
the stores, and remained at table long after all others. "I
haven't been eating enough marmalade in the last three
or four years" was his excuse.

So with the agile *Duenna* running ahead of us like a

cottontail rabbit, kicking up a plume of spray and exhaust, we came swift along. We picked up the familiar landmarks of the Sound one by one, including the two desolate masts in Fisher's Island Sound. They testify tragedy where some shipmaster missed the channel by only some 50 yards. Inland waters give one plenteous parable. The habituated landsman thinks of large bodies of sea water as a liquid subject to embarrassing up-and-down movement, but fairly stable on its base. But—as the Bay of Fundy or Long Island Sound itself will promptly tutor you—these vast masses are excessively fluid and move to and fro in the most surprising fashion. A little study of Current Tables and Tide Diagrams is highly illuminating; or a glimpse of the tide boiling through the Race, between New London and New Haven. And why, I've often wondered, does the Department of Commerce get so little acclaim for its quiet, faithful and endless work in keeping buoys, beacons and bells in constant A1 service? Consider the lives and property daily and nightly confided unquestioning to these safeguards we all take for granted as we do the phenomena of stars and weather. An occasional halloo of gratitude would not be amiss. So we thought as we saw one of the Sound lightships—the *Cornfield,* I think it was—under tow, on her way back to replace her substitute, after some refitting I suppose. It was an odd sight, and (in the very expressive habit of ships) she had a rather surprised and shamefaced air, like a respectable matron being escorted home after a spree.

It was late in our last afternoon, our eighth day from Central Wharf. The sun came out warm and handsome, and as good commuters should we made the home waters about 6 P.M. As we entered Cold Spring Harbour we came into summer. Like stepping into a greenhouse we sailed into the warm spice of Long Island June. An astonishment of rich velvety scent, so palpable we exclaimed in surprise. There was mown grass in the air, rhododendron, lilac, arbutus, moist oak woods. We were too Saxon perhaps to say much about it, but I think a sort of Long

Island patriotism took hold of us. This was something we understood and had, for a few days, almost forgotten. This was not the hard beauty of those northern granites, nor even the demure propriety of Massachusetts. The rocks were not so cold a gray; the trees not so austerely evergreen; the sands of Lloyd's Neck were warm and yellow. In the harbour the dainty little fleet of many coloured sailboats hovered like butterflies. As we came ashore we heard the twitter of birds. "Gosh," said the PR, bursting into a perspiration, "before we eat, the Commodore will have to let me get out of this Halifax underwear."

Stephen Vincent Benét

AMERICAN NAMES

I HAVE fallen in love with American names,
The sharp names that never get fat,
The snakeskin-titles of mining-claims,
The plumed war-bonnet of Medicine Hat,
Tucson and Deadwood and Lost Mule Flat.

Seine and Piave are silver spoons,
But the spoonbowl-metal is thin and worn,
There are English counties like hunting-tunes
Played on the keys of a postboy's horn,
But I will remember where I was born.

I will remember Carquinez Straits,
Little French Lick and Lundy's Lane,
The Yankee ships and the Yankee dates
And the bullet-towns of Calamity Jane.
I will remember Skunktown Plain.

I will fall in love with a Salem tree
And a rawhide quirt from Santa Cruz,
I will get me a bottle of Boston sea
And a blue-gum nigger to sing me blues.
I am tired of loving a foreign muse.

Rue des Martyrs and Bleeding-Heart-Yard,
Senlis, Pisa, and Blindman's Oast,
It is a magic ghost you guard
But I am sick for a newer ghost,
Harrisburg, Spartanburg, Painted Post.

Henry and John were never so
And Henry and John were always right?
Granted, but when it was time to go

And the tea and the laurels had stood all night,
Did they never watch for Nantucket Light?

I shall not rest quiet in Montparnasse.
I shall not lie easy at Winchelsea.
You may bury my body in Sussex grass,
You may bury my tongue at Champmédy.
I shall not be there. I shall rise and pass.
Bury my heart at Wounded Knee.

T. S. Stribling

MATING OF POMPALONE

SUN YET LEE, the copra exporter, told me this story one evening as we strolled around the savanna in Port of Spain. We were passing an Italian villa, done in Barbados chalk, when a servant opened a huge gate, and a man and a woman on splendid black horses galloped out and drummed off down the driveway. What made me turn and watch them until they were lost in the veil of the moon was the manner in which the man rode. The woman, clearly, was the bouncing product of a riding-school, but the man, I thought, must have spent much of his life in the saddle in one of three places on earth, Cossack Russia, the North American cattle ranches, or the South American pampas. I was about to ask a question when Sun Yet Lee forestalled it.

"That is the Magnificent Pompalone and his wife, the Lady Bettina," he said. "He came here some years ago from the Llanos of the Orinoco. I knew him as well as any one gets to know a *llanero* and a Venezuelan. Those were the days when society here in Port of Spain rather shunned him, because it was understood that he got his fortune by some rather lucky murders and robberies."

"That," I said, "is supposed to form a certain bar, is it?"

"For a period it does, in this white world of the West," agreed my companion with a certain expression on his face; "but over here, time softens such informalities, time and a thoughtful handling of the fortune." He continued looking after the riders down the huge oval of the savanna, and after the hoof-beats died away he added rather acridly, "Although I was his first friend, you observed, I suppose, that they did not recognize me at all."

I was surprised at the remark. "Why, it's moonlight,

Sun Lee!" I said rather blankly. "How could you expect them to recognize you in the moonlight?"

"Naturally I do not," returned my companion. "If they fail to see me when I pass them face to face at high noon under a Trinidad sun, then, as you say, how could I expect them to recognize me in the moonlight?"

Sun Lee's tones were impregnated with that subcutaneous rancour which I believe all Chinese feel when talking to or of a white man. I felt inclined to laugh, but something in Lee's manner kept me quiet. Presently he continued in the same vein.

"You see, they have risen somewhat in society since then, the Magnificent Pompalone and the Lady Bettina. I understand the Governor had them at his last ball, which is something—since the Governor grants pardons. And so"—Sun Yet Lee made a little gesture—"why should he recognize me any more?"

I murmured something about friends.

"Friends? Surely you have observed, sir, that a white man measures his social progress much as a mariner determines his nautical speed; the one heaves over his log, the other heaves over his friends. Naturally, the faster he goes, the swifter he——" Sun Yet Lee broke off to lift a hand and waggle delicate fingers in the direction the Magnificent Pompalone had taken.

The Chinaman's opinion of my race and, I could but suppose, by inclusion, of me, left a little gap in our conversation which I found difficult to bridge. I stood looking rather emptily at the pale villa with its nine black windows of the second story just seen above the high wall. Presently I made the unnecessary observation:

"So you knew them?"

"When the Magnificent Pompalone was married," said Sun Yet Lee, "I stood up with him as best man. He came to me and asked it out of friendship. 'Sun Lee,' he said, 'every white acquaintance I have in Port of Spain has excused himself from standing up with me in my marriage ceremony. Now, for the very reason that they will not come, out of the memory of Najalka, I ask for your kind offices.'

"So I went. At the wedding, there were just two other men: the bride's father, who was a newly rich distiller by the name of Sherbrooke, and a threadbare nonconformist minister whom they dug up somewhere in town and induced to perform the ceremony. I remember how he kept bowing and smiling in the huge empty room as if everything were all right."

My companion stood in the moonlight, looking at the villa and indulging in a private and mirthless smile at the lonely wedding he had attended. He stood so long in silence, leaning against the iron rails that enclose the savanna, that I thought I had heard the last of the matter, when he took it up again at quite a different point.

As I say [my companion resumed], we were friends, and I had served the Magnificent Pompalone on one or two occasions; so when a coolie boy picked his way into my shop on Tragarette Road and handed me a note, I was not surprised to see the huge envelope and the coat of arms showing a tiger rampant embossed on the flap, which told me it was from the Magnificent Pompalone. The message, in his usual harsh handwriting, said:

Find out all the details of Betty Sherbrooke's intimate life and come to my villa for four o'clock tea.

I was getting in a fair amount of copra that afternoon, but I make it a rule always to deal light-heartedly with my business, so I closed my door straight in the face of a string of carts loaded with at least thirty fanegas of copra, and set off to find out what I could about Betty Sherbrooke.

I went to my friend Wong Lu, who runs a laundry on Richmond Street. As I had thought, my friend Wong did the Sherbrooke laundry, and so for a long while I sat on the edge of his ironing table, talking to him and watching his iron smooth out cuffs and shirts and pajamas.

At six o'clock I came up this pitch walk and entered the little postern gate you see there where the bougainvillea leans over the top of the wall.

I found Pompalone in the breakfast room, on the second floor, giving on a back view from the villa. If Pompalone had not been seated at the table, this breakfast room would have been rather an extraordinary affair, with black ebony window frames and between the windows murals of life-sized tigers. The damask on his table was not white but was embroidered in bars of black and gold reminiscent of the tiger's colouring. It would have been an extraordinary setting, I say, if the man at the table had not subdued it and brought it into tone, with his jet-black hair, sallow skin, wide nostrils and smouldering quartz-coloured eyes. The rank indifference with which he picked his big white teeth with a pen-knife reduced the murals to mere murals inconspicuous, conventional.

As I entered between black and yellow portières, he waved me abruptly to a chair on the opposite side of the table, and began in his usual brusque fashion:

"What did you find out about the girl?"

"The Sherbrooke family," I said, "has lately acquired wealth."

"How did you learn?"

"The mother and father still wear cotton hosiery, and their children, a daughter and son, wear silk."

Pompalone gave an impatient jerk of his head. "And the girl, Betty, what of her personal habits?"

"She has just taken up horseback riding. She has a completely new riding habit from boots to cap and crop. That only happens once, at the beginning of the fad."

"Is she strong?"

"She is framed on ample lines," said I. "Her handkerchiefs show that she uses little powder and no paint at all, so her complexion, whatever it may be, is natural."

The Magnificent Pompalone nodded. "That is the animal side of this Betty Sherbrooke. What about the girl herself, her spirit? Is she ambitious, full of fire? You must realize, Sun Yet Lee, that I want to marry a woman who will beget great children." In his rising vehemence the *llanero* set down his cup on the embroidered spread with such force as to break the vessel. "We men are handicapped there, for after all our children depend mainly on our wives. There is where we fail!"

Pompalone arose, and in his gestures had shaken the great purpleheart table, pulled the heavy cloth this way and that, upsetting half the vessels.

"Wait, wait a moment," I begged him. "This girl Betty Sherbrooke is not what you suggest. I noticed an interesting point in her laundry. On her underwear she had embroidered a design for a coat of arms, trying it in different colours to see which would look best. Without doubt, she has employed some antiquary to trace back her lineage to the English nobility, with an idea of assuming a crest. Or perhaps she may hope that her father will be knighted."

Pompalone nodded. "Well, that is something—her tracing back her lineage. I personally would regret to rest my claim to greatness on my ancestors. I start my lineage. I am the first Pompalone. That is my shield carved over my door a tiger rampant. Nobody gave it to me. The men who crossed my path—suggested it.

"Still, after all, a woman is a derivative creature, and one could hardly expect her to originate an escutcheon. If this comely wench, Betty, is thinking of escutcheons at all, that is something. All right, all right, we will have to try her out and see if she can bear super-children, for after all a man must chance it with some one. He can't be everything."

He made a gesture. "And she likes horses. She is learning to ride. Very well, we will have her a horse and a stable. There are too many garages, Sun Yet Lee, and too few stables. Nobody but a poltroon would exchange a horse for a machine. You can't spur a machine to death!" He stood frowning a moment, then his face cleared. "We must have horses for this jade who embroiders escutcheons on her underwear. I'll have a stable built right against that wall." He pointed toward a very high yellow wall which delimited his ground on the west side at the back of his villa. "We must please this hussy. Do you drop in from time to time, Sun Lee, to see how it looks." And with a gesture he dismissed me.

Well, the Magnificent Pompalone flung a great body of men to work on his stables, and the new building arose just as ornate as his villa. It was of the same style of architecture; it was a minor villa for his horses—creatures he could spur to death.

At about the same time William Sherbrooke, the distiller, began erecting that mansion whose turrets you can see yonder rising above that banyan tree.

[I looked, caught a glimmer of the tower in the moonlight, and nodded.]

That mansion is a replica of some old English castle. You know how newly-rich colonials run to castles. Well, this construction swelled Pompalone's enthusiasm for the English girl. It showed her flair, the pulse in her blood, so he thought.

Betty Sherbrooke was often at the villa; she took a possessive interest in the stables her fiancé was building. And as I watched her and the Magnificent Pompalone together, I was forced to admit that she made a mate for him. She was quite as tall as he, finely moulded, and was one of those cool blondes with glinting hair, sea-coloured eyes, and lips as red as the comb of a laying hen, which, of course (Sun Yet Lee made a gesture), was as it should be.

She had the persistent vivacity of a girl who was going out on an adventuresome lark and had made up her mind to go through with it, and—enjoy it. She was a foil to the Magnificent Pompalone, who regarded her with eyes that smouldered in his swarthy face, and was preparing to receive her into a villa ornamented with tigers.

Under the hands of imported masons the stables grew upward in white blocks, round by round. I was in the grounds one evening when the top of the rising masonry had almost reached the level of the high yellow wall. Miss Betty had climbed up and was looking about her, when I heard her call: "Oh, Pompalone! Just come up and look what a garden our neighbour has. What a lovely thing!"

I glanced up, and the blonde girl in the brilliant sunshine on the white stone-work was rather a breath-taking sight. Pompalone went hurrying up the ladder, and, out of curiosity, I followed.

Miss Betty was pointing. "Why, that is a little Buddhist temple, that thing with the gilded dome, and a little lake with water lilies and rushes and stepping-stones to gather them. Pompalone, I never saw anything so lovely!"

By that time I was at the top of the wall myself. All three of us stood admiring it silently. Naturally, where their crude Caucasian eyes saw the obvious accents, I observed the nuances of the garden, the harmony of colour under the gilded dome and its reflection among the pink water lilies in the pool, the massing of flowers and grass, and the effect of the mango tree in the corner, which strewed shadows through the sunshine and qualified it. Well, such a jewel-box really left our side of the wall, with its villa and stable, a pale, washed-out affair; but then naturally no Occidental can approach the colour sense of the East.

"How I wish that were mine!" breathed Miss Betty, after a long stare with her covetous Northern eyes.

"Sun Lee," said Pompalone, "find out who owns that garden."

"Why, a Hindu, naturally, Pompalone," said I, for I saw it lacked the delicacy of a Chinese garden.

The Magnificent Pompalone gave me a look and said dryly, "Find out the name of the Hindu, and the price of the garden."

"Pompalone," said I, "that garden hasn't the look of a garden that's for sale."

"True! True!" exclaimed Pompalone. "It's a low thing to go about asking the price of beauty—to dicker for loveliness! God's lightning! No wonder beauty escapes this race of English hucksters in Trinidad. A beautiful thing, like a beautiful woman, should be seized, Sun Lee!" He struck his fist on the wall. "You shame a man to ask

him the price of his garden! You shame a woman to ask
her hand in marriage! Abduction and robbery, Sun Lee,
are the highest forms of esthetics. Caramba! There can be
no doubt that a man admires your handiwork if he will
slit your throat for it, or that he loves a woman if she
maddens him!"

Miss Betty had both fingers in her ears. "Pompalone!
Pompalone! How often have I asked you not to talk like
that!"

"Not talk like that!" echoed Pompalone. "And yet you
yourself are trying to trace back your ancestry to the
English barons, men who had blood in their veins and
took what pleased them, man, woman or thing. No wonder you honour them!"

"That was a long time ago, Pompalone," said Miss
Betty, a little shakily.

"Yes, nowadays the slogan seems to be, 'Let your grandfather do the robbery.' At any rate, it is impractical for
me to climb down into this little garden and take it, so,
Sun Lee, I will have to ask you to find out who owns it,
and offer him his price."

The next day I went to my friend Wong Lu and
watched him roll cuffs through his mangle. His place
smelled pleasantly of steam and fresh clothes; for the smell
of a laundry among odours is much as the taste of chop
suey among foods. We talked of this and that, and presently I said: "Wong Lu, who is this wealthy Hindu who
continually sends you to launder silk robes of solid colours, yellow, purple, red, the *kapra* of men and the *ouranee*
for women?"

Wong Lu pondered a moment. "You must be speaking
either of Dookie Ran or Rhamba Singh."

"Which has children?"

"Dookie Ran."

"Then I mean Rhamba Singh. Let me see, he is the old
coolie who buys cacao beans down on Victoria Street."

"That's the old man, skinnier than I am, and the colour
of nutmeg."

I left the laundry and walked on down to Victoria
Street. Rhamba Singh had a little hole in the wall which
led back to an old stable yard. Rhamba Singh had covered
a part of this yard with pieces of tarpaulin and tin and
stray planks, and so had rigged up a shelter for his stock.
Under this were bags of cacao beans in rows, and the whole
place was heavy with the sweetish odour of cacao, with a
hint in it of curry, which came no doubt from the old
coolie's preparing his own noon lunch.

The old Hindu himself was working like a porter among
his beanbags. He wore a breech clout, a single shirt flap-
ping about his loins, and a turban. Then I realized I was
in the presence of a philosopher as well as an esthete, and
if I meant to buy the garden I must act with consideration.

After I had priced some beans and bargained for three
sacks, I sat down on the pile, drew a cigarette out of
my bamboo case, lighted it and breathed in the smoke. As
I talked the smoke floated out of my mouth and nostrils.

"Rhamba Singh," I observed, "it requires a man of wisdom, like you, really to enjoy anything, a fine horse, a private temple, a garden——"

The old coolie looked up at me without a trace of comprehension in his cinnamon face, and grunted.

"I say," I repeated, "it takes a wise man to enjoy a
garden. Look, for example, at these wealthy Englishmen
in Port of Spain: their homes are palaces, their business
houses are mansions, and their clubs châteaux. They go
between these places in luxurious motors, with never a
break from year to year; and yet they never understand
why they grow weary of existence, like children with their
bellies full of sweets."

Rhamba Singh looked at me blankly with his wrinkled
old face like dried mace, and grunted, "Want more
beans?"

I inhaled again and considered. "Four more sacks. And
their women, Rhamba Singh. What an absurdity, running
about the streets with their faces naked for any one to

see! They heap their wives together at dances and banquets half naked, as if they were determined to cloy even desire by a prodigious surfeiting and lose love in the gray ashes of their days."

Old Rhamba Singh nodded. "That is true, Sun Lee. Desire is in the eyes and the thoughts. Only a fool eats the songbird in his garden."

"That which you say, Rhamba Singh, is the second thought of wisdom, not the first thought of youth."

"That is true, Sun Lee; the first thought of my youth was quite different. It was one night in Mangalore in Ghats when I saw a nautch girl dancing. Had it not been for that girl, Sun Lee, I would still be a Sudra in Bengal. I can remember her anklets and armlets and castanets and the plates of burnished brass over her breasts. They were gold in my eyes, Sun Lee. I pushed my way through the crowd and got to the man who beat the drum, and gave him a copper *pie* to tell me her name. It was Najalka. I asked what she was worth. The drummer spat.

" 'You spent your last *pie* to buy her name, and now you ask what she is worth—take care, you dog of a Sudra, lest your shadow fall on my foot.'

"I stood aside so the light fell on me in a different way, but still I had her name, and as I stood drinking her through my ears and eyes, I thought, 'What if Najalka were dancing for me alone in some garden by a temple?' and, Sun Lee, my bowels melted within me and I went away.

"The next month, white men from the West came to Mangalore to indenture labour, and I put my fingers on a pen while they wrote. Then they put me in a barracoon with six hundred and twelve Sudras and pariahs, all mixed without order except such as we could keep in the barracoon where we ate and slept. We stayed there three months waiting for a ship to come and take us to the West. Some of us died and were never carried to the Tower of Silence, but were thrown into the bay there at Mangalore. But I lived on, Sun Lee, because somewhere ahead of me down the gardens of the years, I could see a nautch girl dancing.

"At last I sailed with four hundred others, and we stopped at the Fijis, at Samoa, at this and that point; finally my papers were given to an Englishman here in Trinidad.

"I worked for him ten years, when my indenture was finished and I might stay here or go back to India. I stayed here and wrote to Bengal, and after a year I received a letter saying that Najalka was dead, but that she had left a little daughter, a little Najalka, a pretty creature who danced and who was worth eight hundred rupees.

"But I did not have the eight hundred rupees, so I picked up sticks in the jungle and burned them and sold charcoal here in Port of Spain; I bought mangoes on the estates and sold them in the streets; I helped lade the ships at the wharf. But by the time I had eight hundred rupees, Sun Lee, I was old enough to realize I must have other rupees to keep Najalka's daughter. One does not bed a fawn in a sty. But when I had more rupees, came another letter from Mangalore telling me that the daughter of Najalka had died in childbed and that a little daughter, another Najalka, was in her stead.

"So I sent them my eight hundred rupees, and told them to teach her to sing and dance until she was worth these rupees and then to send her to me. And so I came at last with Najalka, the daughter of Najalka, the daughter of Najalka. She is very like, Sun Lee, and when I gaze upon her a long time, I see the mother of her mother dancing in the torchlight at Mangalore; the same steps, the same songs, and my heart beats; and yet, after all, Sun Lee, no man can unroll the years."

After such a tale, a white man might well have been stolid enough to offer Rhamba Singh money for his garden, but we Chinese have had the benefit of training and courtesy; our parents before us were Chinese. So I crossed my hands on my chest and bowed to Rhamba Singh and walked backward out of his door and wished him more years and greater wisdom.

I was no sooner in my own shop than a boy came flying in, shrilling: "Sun Lee! Sun Lee! I have been looking everywhere. The Magnificent Pompalone is storming for you. He has sent runners to Wong Lu's, to the chop suey place, to the fan tan dive——" By this time we were both hurrying toward the villa.

I found the Magnificent Pompalone in his ballroom on the second story, where you see the nine windows set down the front in three groups of three windows each.

He was tramping up and down the polished *syp* floor, which shone so that it looked as if two Pompalones tramped the ballroom, one inverted and one erect. He was flinging away his black cigars as quickly as he lighted them. I entered as quietly as I could, and I said, with a placating gesture, "So you have seen the girl with the purple *ouranee* and the gold bangles."

He turned on me with a furious gesture. "Sun Yet Lee! Have you allowed me to waste my time on that moon-faced wench when such a dream, such a madness—just beyond my wall——"

"My dear Pompalone!" I hurried, for he seemed coming to pull me down. "I had no idea there was such a girl——"

"What! What! And you standing there describing her dress and her bangles! Don't trifle with me, Sun Lee!"

"Really! Really!" I cried, for he was advancing on me. "I deduced her costume from the garden, the colour of the garden. I—I knew what it had to be, Pompalone, you understand."

"How did you know there was any girl at all!"

"Oh!" I waved my hands. "The garden."

The Magnificent Pompalone glared at me a moment longer, then made a gesture. "Well, that's neither here nor there. I climbed up to look at my garden this morning, and she was there, bathing in the pool among the water lilies. God's lightning, Sun Lee, but I was seized with madness! I put my hands on the top of the wall to vault inside when I realized that a forty-foot drop might injure even me. I started to go and climb down by the mango tree, but that first hesitation, that single forethought, brought on a troop of others. I thought if I were down I could not escape with her at once. I could not climb back up with her and lock her in the villa. Besides, the villa was not safe. Port of Spain was not safe. This damnable government of the English!

"I knew I dare not look a moment longer, or I would fling myself down and lose her. And yet, Sun Lee, I have found all my life long, the man who hesitates at a woman or a crime, loses both. So listen, this must be done! In the morning be you hid in the garden when she bathes. Have gags and bonds ready——"

"But, Pompalone," I interrupted, "would you not prefer to have her consent?"

Pompalone stopped in his pacing to stare at me. "Her consent! I, Pompalone, stand pleading with a slip of delight, *may* I take her, *will* she do me the honour to come to me! Ah-h-h! Sun Yet Lee, you sound as sickly as these Trinidadian English!"

"But look!" I pressed the point. "You have been wooing this Betty Sherbrooke very patiently for days and weeks——"

The Magnificent Pompalone looked at me and made an enigmatic reply. "Miss Sherbrooke inspires patience."

"Still, we would best not go at this thing helter-skelter, Pompalone," I counseled. "The Hindus have a festival of Hosein only two days off, and on that day old Rhamba Singh will surely be in the processional with the others. If you could find patience till day after to-morrow, that would be the surest."

He began tramping again, the two images of Pompalone, the one above, the other below the *syp* floor. Finally he turned and waved a hand at me. "God's lightning! Go, man, and arrange it so. I get the girl on the festival of Hosein, and, Sun Yet Lee, do not mention her to me until that day."

The festival of Hosein is a mighty day with the coolies

here in Trinidad, and in the two days preceding I fell to work gathering the things I would need to kidnap a woman; a thin rope ladder, a delicate pair of handcuffs, some silk bands to tie her ankles and knees and wrists and elbows, and a tiny little gourd for a gag, a small pretty one I found down at the native market with yellow and green stripes. I smiled to think how the vendor would look if he knew what I wanted with it. For the silk bands I chose orange and scented it with frangipani. I would have liked silver handcuffs for the capture, something carved like bangles.

Here Sun Yet Lee paused for several moments, musing over the point, and finally asked me if I had ever arranged to kidnap a woman. I was a little shocked and told him I had not.

My companion nodded, and looked up at the moon. "It is no dull enterprise, I assure you. Since that day I have often thought that civilization made a great backward step when men ceased to acquire wives by capture. That surely made the world duller both for men and women."

"But, Sun Lee," I cried, "a man's moral nature forbids such a thing! In every gentleman there is an innate courtesy, a chivalry which prevents——"

My Chinese companion lifted a hand. "Have you ever laid out little handcuffs and a tiny gag and perfumed silks to capture a beautiful woman——"

"No!" I cried. "Certainly not!"

"Then you are in no position to say what you would feel or how you would act."

"Well, confound all this moralizing!" I cried, with a beating heart. "I know I wouldn't do such a dastardly thing; but—tell me what happened in the garden!"

On the night following the day I had this interview with Pompalone (Sun Lee continued), that is, the second night before the festival of Hosein, I thought I would best go to Rhamba Singh's garden and see precisely how it lay, so that I could work out the finer details of the capture.

There was a full moon that night, and this long pitch walk, the banyans over it, the white villa and the towers of that mansion yonder all lay precisely as they look now. The only difference was, the stables of the Magnificent Pompalone, which you cannot see from here, were unfinished.

I came in quietly through that side gate and did not go up to the villa at all, because Pompalone had given me strict orders not to mention Najalka until I had her bound and ready to deliver to his arms. I went in through that side gate, followed the shadow of the fence around to the stables in the rear and so to the top of Rhamba Singh's garden wall.

I got over into the shadow of the mango tree, hooked my rope ladder between the bricks, slid over the top, and a moment later was down on the inside. It was like dropping into a bath of perfumed air. The night was filled with the smell of orchids and lilies, and down in the pool, beneath my lily pads, I could see the gleam of the little gilded temple. It was a sweet and delicate garden, but as I stood in it, the thought came of old Rhamba Singh living in the filth of barracoons, journeying in the foul holds of labour ships, and working for ten years for his freedom, all for this garden and this girl, and then for me, a Chinese gentleman, to come and disturb his nest. That was no happy thought. "Ah, Sun Yet Lee!" I mused. "Your ancestors who are looking down on you to-night, what are they thinking about you?"

I was standing in the shadow of the mango with the pity of the moon light and the flowers in my heart, when there came the whisper of a step on the grass and a voice like a little bell said in Hindustani, "Sahib, how came you here!"

I turned with a little start, and saw the girl standing quite near me. The moonlight falling in splashes over her brought a catch to my throat, but I managed to say soberly enough, as if I addressed such a creature every day:

"Down this rope ladder, Najalka."

She stood looking at me with eyes that were utterly

black from the moonlight. "Are you a friend of Rhamba Singh?"

I was tempted to lie, but I said, "A rope ladder is the friend only of the man who uses it, Najalka."

"Then why did you come here, sahib—to steal? There are only flowers in this garden."

My pulse was growing in my neck and I answered a little unsteadily, "That is why I came here, Najalka—to steal a flower."

"To steal a flower! Why, sahib, I will give you one!" And she reached up and broke a sweet spray from a vine.

When she offered it, she was so fair, and her face was so like a lotus petal,—she and her mother and her mother's mother had been dancing girls trained and tutored to please men until with them it was like breathing. When I touched her hands, my voice broke and I knelt and pressed both her palms to my face and I trembled.

"Oh, Najalka! These are the flowers I meant, and without them, I will die."

The girl stood quite still for a moment, and then she gave a laugh like a little bell very softly rung. She took away one of her hands and pushed it through my hair.

"So it is I—I, Najalka, you have come for at last."

I peered up into her face and drew in my breath. "Can it be you were looking for me, Najalka?"

"I was looking for some one, sahib, I did not know whom. Every dawn since I was brought here, I have looked out at the pool and flowers and thought: 'Surely some one will come and steal me away to-day from this eternal moping in old Rhamba Singh's garden."

My arms glided up about her in amazement. "But, Najalka," I whispered, "you sweet, dark flower! Does Rhamba Singh only keep you like a bee orchid in his garden?"

"He eats me with his eyes," she whispered impishly. "Ah, the devouring eyes of old men! How they eat—eat—eat girls and gardens, diamonds and temples and lily ponds! They eat us all up, sahib, and we get swallowed down into the old man's purse. His purse! Ugh, his purse!"

"His purse!" I repeated blankly, for Najalka's fancy was too airy even for me.

She shook a little perfumed finger in my face. "Oh, yes, right down into his purse!" She laughed, like a soft ringing of little bells. "Because that is the only place an old man can hold a girl."

A sound frightened us. Najalka heard it first. It was a slow step in the house at the other end of the garden. A lump leaped in my throat, but before I ran up my rope ladder, I caught her to me and pressed my lips against the flower of her mouth.

"To-morrow—to-morrow night," I whispered, almost choking, "at this hour, and we will fly, and now——"

She pressed her lips passionately to mine. "Every— every night, oh, my sweet love. Now hurry—hurry, he is coming!"

I went up the rope ladder like a chinchilla, whipped it up after me and walked away on the first story of the stables with a beating heart. When I got to the ground a voice said in my ear:

"Ah, is that you, Sun Yet Lee?"

My throat jumped tight. I stood staring and speechless at the Magnificent Pompalone. I swallowed, and then I answered, I think in a composed voice, "I was looking over the ground, Pompalone."

"I see you were," said Pompalone.

"I didn't mention it to you, Pompalone, because you asked me not to refer to the topic again until I was ready to—to act."

The Magnificent Pompalone looked at me. "That was very thoughtful of you, Sun Yet Lee."

"I try to act for my friends," said I, "exactly as if I were acting for myself."

"Gratitude will bankrupt me," said Pompalone. "And now, Sun Lee, come with me into the villa. We will spend the night there together. We have preparations to make to-morrow, our last day before the festival of Hosein. We

must get a racing launch to carry us into the delta of the
Orinoco; we must hire negro watermen who can fight as
well as sail, and who stick at nothing. Come ahead, don't
hang back. Decidedly, you would best sleep with me tonight, so that we may start together early in the morning."

A weakness came over me. I looked at the snow-white
villa in the moonlight, and suddenly it seemed to me to be
a huge white tomb, and the nine windows in three groups
seemed to be a name carved upon the tomb, the name "Sun
Yet Lee." With this evil fancy sticking in my throat I
followed Pompalone inside.

It seemed to me the aura of Najalka clung about me as
visibly as my own clothes. A lingering perfume of her condemned me. It seemed impossible for Pompalone to glance
at me and not know that I had just come from her. . . .

He directed me into his great bedroom where he had two
huge ebony beds, with tiger heads of yellow *poui* carved
in high relief and inset into the headboards. It was a dis-
maying bedroom. The silken covers were striped in black
and orange. He directed me to one, then threw himself on
the other, with boots, hat, coat and everything on, and
immediately became silent. Whether he slept or not I did
not know, and I did not dare to lift my head and see.

Whether I myself slept or not, I cannot say, for when
a man is anxious and miserable for a girl, day dreams and
night dreams so run in his head he cannot say which is
which.

At dawn, Pompalone arose as casually and started
about his plans as directly as if he had simply sat a moment on the bed and had arisen immediately to go about
his affair.

He commended my light rope ladder and took it from
me with the words, "If I had had this yesterday morning,
Sun Lee, my life might have been different."

We worked all day at hiring the boat and the boatmen,
a racing motor to run from the villa to the wharf. When
we were back that evening, I offered to go out and get

provisions for our voyage at the market, but he said that had been attended to by a ship chandler. I suggested that I go to a drug store for ether to give the girl so we could carry her to the boat unconscious. He said he never used ether in kidnaping women.

I grew more and more nervous. At last I turned to him earnestly as we sat for a second time on the huge ebony beds under the yellow tigers' heads.

"Pompalone," I said, "why are you going to take this girl, Najalka? You know she is not the type to beget children and found a great family. She is a wisp, a fragrance, a fruitless flower. Now, Betty Sherbrooke has in her veins the conquering blood of England; her castle tower shines through the window——"

Pompalone made a gesture. "What you say is true, Sun Yet Lee; Betty Sherbrooke would mean a great family —but what is a great family? A family, Sun Lee, is a man's reaching out for some desire which he himself never did attain. The passion for a family is a man's resignation of himself, and a hope that his sons may fare on toward some unknown goal. But this Najalka, Sun Lee"—he swung his head toward the garden—"is the goal itself. In her, Life curls and breaks and flows back down the beach into the sea again. She is Life's aristocratic moment. Up to her leads the past; she embodies the present; and as for the future, Life regurgitates and sets once more about lifting a passion flower from the muck. It is quite within a strong man's power, Sun Lee, to decide whether he will be the bloom or the stem which conveys the ascending sap."

I knew there was no need of talking further with the Magnificent Pompalone. For there was a certain truth in what he said. All men, this world over, no matter how staid and conventional they may appear, in reality are waiting for some woman. That is why all men, young or old, wistfully interrogate every woman's face, asking: "Is this she, with whom I may bloom and die? Or am I still to tread the round of life through my children?" That is what the Hindus really mean by Nirvana.

Sun Yet Lee broke off his discourse and stood looking away through the moonlight. And in my own heart came half-remembered wistfulness and bootless quests.

And what does a man hope for in his son, in that strange vicarious immortality of a son? We hope our sons will be more fortunate than we. Not in wealth, not in honour, not in fame, for these are footling things, but we hope that Life will deal more kindly with the son than with the sire, and there we let it rest, with our real disappointment unuttered in our hearts.

At daybreak (began Sun Yet Lee) we heard the drums of the festival of Hosein.

The Magnificent Pompalone arose from the black and gold bed, as if he had lain down in passing, and went to the window.

"They begin early," he said.

"Then you have never seen it before?"

"No, this is my first year in Port of Spain."

"Your first year and your last day, Pompalone."

He nodded.

A distant drum was throbbing in my ears like a pulse. Somehow it reminded me of Najalka, and I wondered what she would think of my bringing the terrible *llanero* to our tryst.

I looked out of another window, and saw the van of the coolies come into view around the pitch walk under the banyans. The wail of reed instruments rode up to me on the rumour of the drum. A scattering of children came running ahead of the procession, and the marchers came into plain view carrying a great paper tower. Eight coolies bore it on a litter, a high paper tower that was quite as high as the second-story windows in which we leaned. On top of the tower was the bloody head of a slaughtered goat. A stick in its neck held the head upright, and we could see its eyes behind the down curve of its horns. It was a sacrifice to some coolie god, and they would carry the tower and the goat head down to the wharf and fling them in the river; such was their custom.

The procession was grotesque. Some of the men wore only a breech clout, others a shirt, others a *kapra* of muslin wrapped about their bodies; some were in English clothes, some wore turbans and *alpagartas*. And their songs rose in a strange melancholy that harked back to the cruelties and mysteries of India. At intervals among the marchers moved men with censers, and as they waved their silver baskets, the air was filled with the frail odour of sacrifice.

In the procession, Pompalone pointed out a figure in a robe and a turban.

"Look, Sun Lee, there is old Rhamba Singh."

I looked and recognized the old man, who, oddly, was looking up at me.

Pompalone drew inside and came and laid a hand on my shoulder. "Now," he said, "we can go."

I took a last look at old Rhamba Singh in the procession of Hosein, and my bowels melted within me. My legs grew so weak that I could hardly walk. I turned and followed Pompalone below.

The *llanero* made not the slightest effort at concealment, although there was indeed no cause for any. As he climbed up the ladders of his half-built stable, his nostrils expanded and I saw the veins lift in his neck. And in my own ears a pulse began to murmur, for it is impossible, sir, to set about abducting a woman casually, as if she were a doe. My heart beat, and I went scrambling up the ladder behind Pompalone. And I whispered, "Perhaps I would better go first, Pompalone, to keep from frightening her."

I suppose he did not hear me. He went down first. The garden was empty. The gilded dome of the little temple gleamed down beneath the lily pads. And the thought of my last moment here with Najalka, on this very spot, swept over me like a great grief. I followed after Pompalone, toward the house, with a dead heart. "When she sees me," I thought, "what will she think of Sun Yet Lee? Oh, Sun Yet Lee, what do the shades of your ancestors think now? For it is one thing to steal love for yourself, but it is a surpassing treason to betray that love to another." And I wiped my eyes covertly on my sleeve and over and over in my head whispered: "What will she think of you? What do your ancestors think? Oh, Sun Yet Lee!"

The Magnificent Pompalone strode on straight toward the house, and I after him. I passed the door of the little temple with the gilt dome. And out of the corner of my eye, I caught a glint of gold and crimson inside.

I stopped, I stood in my tracks. My eyes started from their seats and my chest grew so heavy I scarcely could breathe.

I heard my name called, but I could not answer. My tongue was as dry as a parrot's and in my head a voice whispered, "To-day, Sun Yet Lee, is the day of your death, though you live to be as old as K'ung-fu-tse."

Pompalone was shaking my arm. "What is it?" he growled. "Are you dumb, Sun Yet Lee? Has your rabbit heart——" And then he saw what I saw. . . .

All of her bangles and anklets and *napools* and *caras* bedecked her, and the delicate plates of gold curved about her little breasts as she lay before the image of Buddha, with her hands together so that her thumbs and forefingers touched, just as did those of the Buddha.

She might have been asleep, save that her face had been gilded, after the custom of the Hindu dead; thus, she looked very like the image which brooded above her with thumbs and forefingers together.

I cannot say what the Magnificent Pompalone thought, but my own heart was filled with a strange tragedy not common among men. Of a man who walks among women looking wistfully into this face and that, querying: "Is it she? Is it she?"

And when he sees the face—it is past.

Outside, on the entrance of the temple, old Rhamba Singh had written with the last of his gilt paint:

"Najalka, the daughter of Najalka, the daughter of Najalka."